THE RECORD SOCIETY OF LANCASHIRE AND CHESHIRE

FOUNDED TO TRANSCRIBE AND PUBLISH
ORIGINAL DOCUMENTS RELATING TO THE TWO COUNTIES

VOLUME CXLV

The Society wishes to acknowledge with gratitude the support given towards
publication by

Lancashire County Council

ISBN 978 0 902593 80 0

Printed in Great Britain by 4word Ltd, Bristol

THE CHALLENGE OF CHOLERA: PROCEEDINGS OF THE MANCHESTER SPECIAL BOARD OF HEALTH 1831–1833

Edited by Alan Kidd and Terry Wyke

PRINTED FOR THE SOCIETY
2010

FOR THE SUBSCRIPTION YEAR 2008

COUNCIL AND OFFICERS FOR THE YEAR 2008

President

J.R.H. Pepler, M.A., D.A.A., c/o Cheshire Record Office, Duke Street, Chester CH1 1RL

Hon. Council Secretary

Dorothy J. Clayton, M.A., Ph.D., A.L.A., F.R.Hist.S., c/o John Rylands University Library of Manchester, Oxford Road, Manchester M13 9PP

Hon. Membership Secretary

J.C. Sutton, M.A., F.R.I.C.S., 5 Beechwood Drive, Alsager, Cheshire, ST7 2HG

Hon. Treasurer and Publications Secretary

Fiona Pogson, B.A., Ph.D., c/o Department of History, Liverpool Hope University, Hope Park, Liverpool L16 9JD

Hon. General Editor

Peter McNiven, M.A., Ph.D., F.R.Hist.S., 105 Homegower House, St Helens Road, Swansea SA1 4DN

Other Members of the Council

P.H.W. Booth, M.A., F.R.Hist.S.
Diana E.S. Dunn, B.A., D.Ar.Studies
M.R.V. Heale, B.A., M.Phil., Ph.D.
B. Jackson, M.A., D.A.A.

C.B. Phillips, B.A., Ph.D.
B.W. Quintrell, M.A., Ph.D., F.R.Hist.S.
D. Szechi, B.A., D.Phil., F.R.Hist.S.
T.J. Thornton, M.A., D.Phil.

CONTENTS

PREFACE

The Proceedings of the Manchester Special Board of Health are deposited in Manchester Local Studies and Archives, Manchester Central Library. They consist of two volumes: the first volume (M9/36/1) covers the period 10 November 1831-15 August 1832, the second volume (M9/36/2) covers the period 16 August 1832-31 October 1833. The latter includes instructions and correspondence with the Central Board of Health, a correspondence that can also be followed in the letter books of the Central Board in the National Archives (PC1/93-97; PC1/99-100; PC1/102-103; HO31/17).

The local board of health was the principal agency by which the State looked to meet the threat of cholera in 1831. Local boards were ad hoc bodies with limited powers, operating for the duration of the crisis. Over 800 local boards were established in England and Wales in 1831-32. The administrative records of the majority of these have not survived. Where they have done so, they mainly cover smaller communities. In the Manchester region, for example, the minute books of the boards of Heaton Norris (Stockport Archives, B/CC/6/16) and Bacup (Manchester Local Studies and Archives L102/7/1) are in the public archives. Fortunately, the Proceedings of the Manchester Special Board – so named to distinguish it from the existing Manchester Board of Health – are part of the city's municipal archive. They are one of the few sets of minutes of a local board of health of a major town to have survived. Even though the minutes of the board's various sub-committees are lost, the proceedings present a remarkable record of how one urban community prepared itself for the onset of Asiatic Cholera, and then responded to this frightening disease once it arrived in the town.

In preparing the Proceedings for publication we have been helped by many people. Even in the 'publish or perish' culture of the modern university most books take longer to complete than their authors estimate. This volume has had a long gestation period and we would like to thank the Council of the Record Society of Lancashire and Cheshire for their patience in awaiting its arrival. We are especially grateful to Peter McNiven, the society's general editor, who has provided encouragement and excellent advice in preparing the final text for publication.

We are extremely grateful to Kevin Bolton, Principal Archivist in the Archives and Local Studies Department of Manchester Central Library, for permission to reproduce the volumes and for his assistance in accessing them for transcription and checking. We are also indebted to Richard Bond and his staff in the Local Studies Library for facilitating our research into the 1832 epidemic. We have also benefited from the assistance of Michael Powell and his staff in Chetham's Library.

We are most grateful to Nigel Rudyard who typed the original manuscript with an expertise that went far beyond that of a mere typist. More recently, Bob Mather transcribed the sextons' registers of the Collegiate Church for the months covering the epidemic. Stephen Yates of the Visual Resources Centre, Manchester Metropolitan University, prepared the illustrations included in this volume. The map of the township of Manchester was drawn by Ian Reid of Information and Communication Technology Services, Manchester Metropolitan University.

Anti-medical sentiment 1832: Henry Heath's lithograph caricatures members of the Central Board of Health as taunting prospective patients with a skeletal dummy representing cholera. (Courtesy of Wellcome Images).

INTRODUCTION*

Cholera remains a significant disease in third world countries today, where its association with poverty, impure water supplies and inadequate sanitation can sometimes be compounded by the failures of governments, as the epidemics in Zaire in 1994 and Zimbabwe in 2008–09 demonstrated.[1] In spite of the availability of cheap and easily administered oral re-hydration therapy since the 1970s,[2] epidemics with high case fatality rates continue to challenge national and international medical authorities. Surveillance of high-risk areas and co-ordinating responses to outbreaks are priorities for the World Health Organization's Global Task Force on Cholera Control, set up in the wake of the 1991 Peru epidemic.[3] By contrast, for Western industrialised societies cholera has become one of the conquered diseases, testimony to the effective implementation of scientific public health policies since the nineteenth century. However, before these advances cholera epidemics repeatedly swept across the newly industrialising world. There were five cholera pandemics between 1817 and 1896.[4]

Britain's first epidemic of what was known as 'Asiatic Cholera', to distinguish it from the endemic 'English Cholera' or 'summer diarrhoea',[5] was in 1831–32, part of the second pandemic. Cholera returned in 1848–49, 1853–54 and 1866. Recorded deaths in all these epidemics totalled 140,000, although in an age without reliable national mortality data this probably underestimated the real figure. The epidemic of 1831–33 alone left a trail of over 51,000 deaths across the British

---

*   Sections of this introduction draw on A. Kidd and T. Wyke, 'The Cholera Epidemic in Manchester 1831–2', *Bulletin of the John Rylands University Library of Manchester*, 87 (2005), pp. 43–56 and A. Kidd, 'Constructing a Moral Pathology of the Industrial Town: Manchester and the Cholera Epidemic of 1831–1832' in A. Fahrmeir and E. Rembold, eds., *Representation of British Cities: the Transformation of Urban Space 1700–2000* (Berlin, Philo, 2003), pp. 73–89.

1   'Public Health Impact of the Rwandan Refugee Crisis: What Happened in Goma, Zaire in July, 1994?', *The Lancet*, vol. 345, issue 8946, 11 February 1995, pp. 339–44; 'Zimbabwe's Humanitarian Crisis Worsens', *The Lancet*, vol. 373, issue 9662, 7 February 2009, p. 447.

2   J.N. Ruxin, 'Magic Bullet: The History of Oral Rehydration Therapy', *Medical History*, 38 (1994), pp. 363–97.

3   Marcos Cueto, 'Stigma and Blame During an Epidemic. Cholera in Peru, 1991' in Diego Armus, ed., *Disease in the History of Modern Latin America: From Malaria to AIDS* (Durham, North Carolina, Duke University Press, 2003).

4   Debate continues over the precise dating of the pandemics but the generally agreed dates are: 1817–23, 1829–51, 1852–59, 1863–79, 1881–96. R. Pollitzer, *Cholera* (Geneva, World Health Organization, 1959); D. Barua and W.B. Greenhough III, eds., *Cholera* (New York, Plenum, 1992), pp. 7–14.

5   The symptoms and treatment of English cholera were discussed before 1832 in popular medical manuals such as William Buchan's *Domestic Medicine*. On the local usage of cholera to describe bowel complaints see S. Chapman, ed., *The Autobiography of David Whitehead of Rawtenstall (1790–1865) Cotton Spinner and Merchant* (Helmshore Local History Society, 2001), pp. 151–2.

Isles.[6] This was a significant death toll, but as an epidemic disease causing death and debility, cholera was surpassed by typhoid, scarlet fever, smallpox and measles. Neither did it rank in the serious mortality crises identified by Wrigley and Schofield in their classic reconstruction of population in England from the sixteenth to the nineteenth century.[7] Nonetheless it was the Asiatic Cholera that became embedded in the national consciousness. This was in no small part due to the fact that it can be one of the most rapidly fatal illnesses to affect humans, for which, in 1831, there was no effective remedy and for which public prayer and fasting were official policies.[8] The incubation period during which the enteroxin producing strains of the bacterium *vibrio cholerae* infected the intestines could be anything between a few hours and five days. After this the predominant symptoms were dramatic: severe and watery diarrhoea (rice-water stools), vomiting, and massive loss of fluids and electrolytes (as much as 20 litres), resulting in dehydration and damage to the internal organs. An infected person would become cold with their skin bluish in colour: their body literally beginning to shrivel. Death could occur within a few hours of the initial onset. For those who came into direct contact with cholera, the sickness, the stench and the detritus fixed themselves firmly in the mind. The 'blue vomit', as cholera was graphically named, struck fear into the soul.

Cholera crossed from Asia to Europe and reached Britain in 1831, the first cases being confirmed in Sunderland in October.[9] It subsequently spread to other main centres of population, carried via popular transport routes (rivers, canals, turnpikes), infecting such places as Newcastle, Hull, Liverpool, Leeds, Sheffield, Nottingham, Bristol, Plymouth, Exeter and London. The decentralised nature of

6   The most important general accounts of the first epidemic in Britain are R.J. Morris, *Cholera 1832: the Social Response to an Epidemic* (London, Croom Helm, 1976) and M.J. Durey, *The Return of the Plague, British Society and the Cholera, 1831–2* (Dublin, Gill and Macmillan, 1979). Margaret Pelling, *Cholera, Fever and English Medicine 1825–1865* (Oxford, Oxford University Press, 1978) is indispensable for understanding the competing theories of disease transmission. Asa Briggs' pioneering essay, 'Cholera and Society in the Nineteenth Century', *Past & Present*, 19(1) (1961), pp. 76–96 remains essential reading. There are also a considerable number of published and unpublished local studies of the 1831–32 epidemic. For the epidemic in Manchester there is useful material in two unpublished dissertations: T. Jones, 'The Cholera in Manchester', University of Manchester, B.A. dissertation, 1948; M. Clifford, 'Medicine, Politics and Society: Manchester's 1832 Cholera Epidemic', University of California at Berkeley, B.A. dissertation, 1979.

7   E.A. Wrigley and R.S. Schofield, *The Population History of England 1541–1871* (Cambridge, Cambridge University Press, 1981), pp. 335–6.

8   R.J. Janet, 'Providence, Prayer and Cholera: the English General Fast of 1832', *Historical Magazine of the Protestant Episcopal Church*, 56 (1987), pp. 297–317. Working-class radicals poured scorn on this policy. The First Salford Cooperative Society resolved to hold a feast on the day of the General Fast, it being their opinion that it was want of proper food that made the poor vulnerable to the disease. *Poor Man's Guardian*, 25 February 1832. As in other communities the local clergy explained the meaning of this divine visitation to their congregations; see, for instance, Charles Burton, *Discourses Suited to these Eventful and Critical Times* (London, Holdsworth and Ball, 1832).

9   Accounts of the Sunderland outbreak began to be reported in the Manchester press in mid-November; see *Manchester Guardian*, 12 November 1831.

state power in nineteenth-century Britain left the local communities in these towns and cities largely responsible for their own measures in response to the epidemic. Each could set up a special board of health with the advice and guidance of a Central Board of Health, established in London in June 1831, but the work of prevention and medical care had to be managed locally and funded locally, by charitable monies or by local taxation.[10]

Although Manchester was one of the main epidemic centres in England, there were proportionately fewer deaths than in several other large centres of population such as Liverpool or Leeds. The official number of deaths for Manchester and Salford was 706 and 216 respectively.[11] Nonetheless the cholera in Manchester has attracted historical interest beyond the morphology of disease. This is chiefly because of the publication in 1832 of James Phillips Kay's pamphlet *The Moral and Physical Condition of the Working Classes Employed in the Cotton Manufacture in Manchester*. Kay was a member of the Special Board of Health, and the first edition of the pamphlet, written before cholera had appeared in the town, drew upon the findings of the Special Board of Health to provide a detailed and alarming quantitative and qualitative account of the living conditions of those who worked in Manchester, both inside and outside of the town's iconic cotton spinning mills.[12] An enlarged second edition was published in the autumn. Kay, however, chose not to discuss the epidemic in detail but instead to elaborate further on the moral and political questions facing urban industrial society.[13] Kay's pamphlet suggested that a programme of interventionist social action could remedy physical and moral ills that were seen chiefly to lie in the realm of personal behaviour and responsibility rather than being a result of the factory system, which he stoutly defended. It is no surprise that such a defence of industrialism should come from Manchester.

Manchester

Manchester had pioneered the application of steam power to factory production at the crucial point when the industrial revolution became an urban revolution. Steam powered cotton mills arose in profusion from the 1790s onwards and the urban environment was reshaped in the image of the burgeoning factory system. Manchester was the archetypal industrial town.[14] Steam-powered mills, along with

10   The correspondence between the Central Board of Health and the local boards can be followed in the out-letters and in-letters books of the Central Board, The National Archives PC1/93–97; PC1/99–100; PC1/102–103; HO31/17.
11   C. Creighton, *A History of Epidemics in Britain* (London, Frank Cass, 1965 ed.), p. 826.
12   The first edition was published in April 1832. A pre-publication advertisement announced the title as 'Observations on the prevalence of causes tending to depress the health of the working classes employed in the cotton manufacture of Manchester, with remedial suggestions'. *Manchester Guardian,* 24 March 1832.
13   The second edition, reprinted by a number of publishers in the 1960s and 1970s, is the one most cited by historians.
14   R. McNeil, 'Manchester: Symbol and Model for the World' in R. McNeil and D. George, eds., *Manchester: Archetype City of the Industrial Revolution* (Manchester, GMAU, 2002).

warehouses and workshops, clustered around the network of canals and canal arms that penetrated to the heart of the town. Row upon row of terraced housing built to accommodate the industrial workforce aggregated into entirely new factory districts, such as Ancoats, comprised almost exclusively of steam-powered mills, factories and workers' housing.[15] By the time of the cholera epidemic a generation had grown up inured to the rhythm of the steam engine. Manchester had become the first and the largest industrial city of the modern age and the centre of the world's market in cotton goods. Moreover, during industrialisation it had become a centre of innovation in the application of transport technologies, first canals and then, in 1830, railways. Together with the factory system these transformed the urban environment.[16] By 1831 the novelty and enormity of what was happening in Manchester was becoming apparent. One of the most striking and potentially alarming features of the process was the seemingly inexorable growth of the town's population.

The population census of 1831 revealed Manchester to be the country's largest and newest urban centre outside London. The full *Abstract of Population Returns of the Census of Great Britain, 1831* was not published until 1833 and thus was not available at the time of the cholera epidemic. But the first indication that the town's growth had been exceptional came in June 1831 when preliminary returns indicating a massive increase in Manchester's population were reported in the local press.[17] These reports were confirmed in October 1831 (the month prior to the convening of the Special Board of Health in Manchester) by the publication of the *Comparative Account of the Population of Great Britain, 1801, 1811, 1821 and 1831*. In this the population figures for Manchester were combined with those for Salford and for the town's immediate suburbs. According to the *Comparative Account*, whilst between 1801 and 1831 the population of London had increased from 0.9m to 1.5m, Manchester's population had multiplied more than two and a half times over the same thirty year period: from 95,000 to 238,000.[18] In a table especially designed to reveal the extent of urban growth over the previous thirty years, Manchester appeared as the largest urban centre outside London, having almost 100,000 more inhabitants than Birmingham and nearly 50,000 more than Liverpool. Only Glasgow had grown as fast but the Scottish city had 35,000 fewer inhabitants. Moreover, the census

15   See A. Kidd and T. Wyke, '"More than an Example": Ancoats in Historical Perspective', *Manchester Region History Review*, 7 (1993), pp. 2–14.
16   A. Kidd, *Manchester: a History* (Lancaster, Carnegie, 2006); R. Lloyd-Jones & M. J. Lewis, *Manchester and the Age of the Factory* (London, Croom Helm, 1988); D. Farnie, *The English Cotton Industry and the World Market 1815–1896* (Oxford University Press, 1979); I. Miller & C. Wild, *A & G Murray and the Cotton Mills of Ancoats* (Lancaster, Oxford Archaeology North, 2007); D. Brumhead & T. Wyke, eds., *Moving Manchester: Aspects of the History of Transport in the City and Region Since 1700* (Manchester, Lancashire and Cheshire Antiquarian Society, 2004); P. Maw, T. Wyke & A. Kidd, 'Warehouses, Wharves and Transport Infrastructure in Manchester During the Industrial Revolution: the Rochdale Canal Company's Piccadilly Basin, 1792–1856', *Industrial Archaeology Review*, 31 (2009), pp. 20–33.
17   *Manchester Guardian*, 11 June 1831.
18   PP 1831 (348), p. 13.

made it clear that the rate of growth was accelerating. Whilst Manchester's population had risen by 22 per cent between 1801 and 1811, it had more than doubled in the next twenty years. Between 1821 and 1831 alone Manchester had acquired over 76,000 new inhabitants; more new residents than the entire populations of towns and cities like Aberdeen, Newcastle-upon-Tyne, Nottingham, Hull, Plymouth or Leeds.

Urban growth can be measured by means other than aggregate population figures. Between 1773 and 1831 the total number of houses in the township of Manchester had risen from 3,446 to 22,445. If to this figure is added the number of dwellings in neighbouring Salford and the surrounding suburbs then the true extent of the urban sprawl is revealed. Beginning in the later decades of the eighteenth century, the town experienced a 70-year 'building boom', which was physically to construct the first industrial city. Whole districts grew up beyond the cluster of short and winding streets that had surrounded the Collegiate Church since medieval times. These might be middle-class residential districts with their distinctive patterns of broad streets and squares. More commonly, they were solidly working-class districts like Ancoats and New Town, both to the north, astride the roads to Oldham and to Rochdale. Virtually undeveloped in the 1790s, these two districts housed over 57,000 people according to the census of 1831.

This 'galloping urbanization' caused Manchester to break through its ancient township boundaries. Contiguous townships such as Ardwick, Chorlton on Medlock and Hulme began sprouting houses and industrial works. It was on this southern side of Manchester in particular that the first generation of middle-class suburbs was under construction. Chorlton's population numbered 20,569 in 1831, an increase of 12,360 over the previous census. Importantly, these were administratively separate districts which would be expected to make their own preparations for the cholera, establish their own Boards of Health and decide on fundamental questions such as whether to treat the diseased at home or remove them to hospitals.

Beneath this generalized picture were important diversities. Population densities varied enormously between the police districts into which Manchester had been divided for administrative purposes in 1792. Competing demands for land in the centre, combined with changing attitudes towards living in the town, were establishing new residential patterns. Thus whilst population density was increasing overall, it was evident that in parts of the centre of the township (Police Districts 5, 6, 12) population was declining in absolute terms whilst in other districts (Police Districts 1, 3, 11, 13) the population, through migration and natural growth, was increasing at a rate far in excess of the average for the township, and one that placed pressures on infrastructure and, in turn, highlighted limitations in the existing system of local government.

Managing this instance of urban expansion, hitherto unprecedented in human history, was a system of local government comprising four separate but overlapping agencies: Court Leet, parish vestry, police commissioners and the quarter sessions of the Salford Hundred. The powers of the Court Leet (chief officials of which were the boroughreeve and the constables) were receding, whilst those of

Table 1: Manchester Township, Population Density, 1821–1831[19]

Police District	Area (acres)	1821 (persons per acre)	1831 (persons per acre)
1 New Cross	404	52.4	78.2
2 St Michael's	500	40.0	51.2
3 Collegiate Church	42.5	244.7	269.0
4 St Clement's	131	102.4	118.0
5 St Paul's	53	144.8	137.3
6 Exchange	36	48.5	35.4
7 Minshull	59.5	139.4	164.4
8 St James's	36	76.3	76.2
9 St Ann's	30.0	119.5	110.6
10 Oxford Street	74	11.6	52.5
11 St Peter's	65.5	154.3	208.2
12 St Mary's	15.5	145.3	119.9
13 Old Quay	27	199.9	269.2
14 St John's	80	61.1	85.4

the parish vestry and police commissioners were expanding: the former as poor relief rolls rose, the latter as further responsibilities were added by Acts of Parliament, most recently in 1829. None of these bodies were representative. This was the era before the parliamentary and municipal reforms of the 1830s. The only one to have an electorate in any sense was the police commission established by Act of Parliament in 1792 and reformed by a further Act of Parliament in 1828. In principle all townsmen owning property with an annual rent or value in excess of £30 or occupying such premises could become a commissioner. However, it has been estimated that this enfranchised only 8.3 per cent of the town's population. Moreover, in reality the reins of power were firmly in the hands of a small coterie of individuals. The police commissioners included the warden and fellows of Christ Church and the boroughreeve and constables as ex officio members. Thus the various arms of local government were integrated with the same personnel at the helm. Moreover, they shared the same political allegiance. The boroughreeve and constables, parish officers (churchwardens and sidesmen) and the leading police commissioners were all part of a closely-knit, Tory-Anglican, oligarchy that ran the town. The stranglehold of this group was not to be superseded until a Liberal-Nonconformist 'offensive' in the 1820s and 1830s culminated in the successful incorporation of the borough in 1838 by Richard Cobden and others. It was against this backdrop of rapid expansion in industry and population coupled with a concentration of political power in the hands of a small

---

19 Calculated from population figures in J. Wheeler, *Manchester: Its Political, Social and Commercial History, Ancient and Modern* (London, Whittaker, 1836), pp. 247–50.

group[20] that the Manchester Special Board of Health was established to prepare the town for the onset of cholera. The title, Special Board, was necessary because Manchester already had a Board of Health. Established since 1795, its main concern was the running of the fever hospital, one of the town's first specialist medical institutions, which occupied premises close to the Manchester Royal Infirmary in Aytoun Street.[21]

Special Board Membership

The minute book of the Special Board of Health begins with a meeting on 10 November 1831 in the boardroom of the House of Recovery, Aytoun Street. Subsequent board meetings were held in the more spacious premises of the Town Hall, King Street. The Board's composition, proposed at this first meeting, was later confirmed by a public meeting of leypayers on 17 November. The Board was to consist of the officials, physicians and surgeons of the town's medical institutions (the Manchester Royal Infirmary, the House of Recovery and the Ancoats Dispensary) plus the local political establishment: the boroughreeve and constables of the Township, the churchwardens and sidesmen of the Collegiate Church, members of the Paving and Scavenging Committees under the Police Act of 1828, and the magistrates of the division. The Board had the power to add to its number. The boroughreeve, Benjamin Braidley, calico manufacturer, temperance advocate and supporter of the town's largest Sunday school, was elected chairman.

Some 112 persons appear as present at one or more of the Board's 192 meetings (this figure includes preliminary meetings prior to Privy Council approval of membership and the legal creation of the Special Board of Health). However, as with most committees a smaller core of members did the bulk of the work: a group of around 22 emerges either through a more regular pattern of attendance or through active participation at the more crucial meetings. This group comprised seven medics, four clerics, ten members from business and the professions and a soldier, Lieutenant-Colonel James Shaw. Shaw was the commanding officer for the Manchester district who in 1829 had turned down the offer to become one of the first commissioners of the new Metropolitan Police.[22] The presence on the Special Board of the region's senior military commander indicates an

---

20   A. Redford and I. Russell, *History of Local Government in Manchester* (London, Longmans, Green and Company, 1939), vol. 1; V.A.C. Gatrell, 'Incorporation and the Pursuit of Liberal Hegemony in Manchester 1790–1839', in D. Fraser, ed., *Municipal Reform and the Industrial City* (Leicester, Leicester University Press, 1982); Michael J. Turner, *Reform and Respectability. The Making of a Middle-Class Liberalism in Early Nineteenth-Century Manchester* (Manchester, Chetham Society, 1995).

21   D.S. Sutherland, *The Manchester "House of Recovery" and "Board of Health" 1796–1852. A History of the Manchester Fever Hospital* (Manchester, R. Sage, 1929).

22   Shaw remained commanding officer for the Manchester district until 1836 when he took on the job of organizing the new police in Ireland. G.J. Fulham, 'James Shaw-Kennedy and the Reformation of the Irish Constabulary, 1836–38', *Eire-Ireland*, 16, No.2 (1981), pp. 93–106; entry in the *Oxford Dictionary of National Biography*.

awareness of the potential implications for public order that a cholera epidemic might present. Even without the unrest that cholera might bring in its train, Manchester was a difficult place to govern. Before 1839 the town had two distinct but overlapping police forces; a Day Watch under the control of the Court Leet and a Night Watch answerable to the Police Commissioners. The latter had recently been augmented in 1830 when it was increased in number to 121 watchmen who were provided with a smart uniform of topcoat and gold-laced hat and equipped with staves and rattles.[23] Although this made for a more effective force, it remained inadequate for the task of maintaining law and order in such a large and populous place, which was often the focal point for political and industrial disturbances from across the region. In the absence of effective policing, the county magistrates frequently drew on their powers to call out the military, as they infamously did on the field of Peterloo in 1819 and were to do again in the Plug Plot riots of 1842.

Bearing in mind Manchester's importance as an industrial and commercial centre it is to be expected that Special Board membership would include some significant figures from the town's business community. Several of these were already active in local affairs as elected police commissioners under the 1828 Police Act: these included the textile manufacturers Peter Ewart jnr and Thomas Townend, the manufacturing chemist Frederick Fincham and prominent local Tories, George Faulkner and Hugh Hornby Birley (the latter had commanded the Yeomanry at Peterloo). These were substantial businessmen of middle age. Faulkner and Birley were 51 and 53 respectively in 1831. However, the Special Board membership also drew on the significant numbers of talented younger men attracted to the town. The most youthful of all the Special Board members was the attorney Joseph Heron (22), later to be the first town clerk of the newly incorporated borough of Manchester. Heron acted as Honorary Secretary to the Board.

The medics on the Special Board included established figures such as Samuel Argent Bardsley (aged 68), retired honorary physician to the Infirmary, who as a young doctor had been involved in Manchester's first Board of Health at its inception in 1795;[24] and the surgeon and antiquarian scholar William Robert Whatton (aged 42), who was to be elected to the staff of the Infirmary in 1833. But the ranks of the medical men also included the young James Phillips Kay (28), one of the founders of the Ardwick and Ancoats Dispensary. Further regular attenders included Henry Gaulter (38), physician to the recently opened dispensary in the

---

23   Report of meeting of Police Commissioners, *Manchester Mercury,* 19 October 1830; S.J. Davies, 'Classes and Police in Manchester, 1829–1880', in A. Kidd and K. Roberts, eds., *City, Class and Culture. Studies of Social Policy and Cultural Production in Victorian Manchester* (Manchester, Manchester University Press, 1985), pp. 26–9; Redford & Russell, *History of Local Government,* vol. 1, p. 340, p. 370.

24   E.P. Hennock, 'Urban Sanitary Reform a Generation before Chadwick', *Economic History Review,* 10 (1957–8), pp. 113–19; J.V. Pickstone, *Medicine and Industrial Society. A History of Hospital Development in Manchester and its Region, 1752–1946* (Manchester, Manchester University Press, 1985), p. 25.

suburb of Chorlton on Medlock.[25] Gaulter visited Sunderland at the outbreak of the epidemic and was to lecture on the disease at the Manchester Medical School, and his *The Origin and Progress of the Malignant Cholera in Manchester*, published in 1833, the year of his premature death, was one of the most detailed and significant local studies of the 1832 epidemic.[26] Another regular attender was the physician Edmund Lyon, who held posts at the Infirmary and the Hulme Dispensary, though it should be recognised that the loss of the medical sub-committee minutes means it is impossible to evaluate fully the role of some Board members.

As the inclusion of the churchwardens and sidesmen suggests, the Established Church had a strong nominal presence on the Board. Alongside leading Tory churchmen like Cecil Wray and William Marsden were younger clergy with less remunerative stipends. These included the Welsh-born George Dugard (aged 34), who had been appointed to the recently consecrated St Andrew's, Travis Street, the nearest Anglican church to the great working-class district of Ancoats. Dugard showed an interest in the poor of the parish and was one of the few Anglican clergy to sign the public letter calling on the boroughreeve to consider the live question of working hours in cotton factories.[27] He served in Manchester until 1847 when he left for the parish of Barnard Castle, where his Manchester experience was soon to be called upon in the second cholera epidemic.[28]

Father James Crook, Roman Catholic priest of St Augustine's, Granby Row, was another regular attender. His presence from the outset (he was at the first meeting) indicates the social as well as health concerns of the elite. The 1831 census did not record place of birth, so the size of Manchester's Irish-born population can only be estimated. By 1841 it had reached 30,304 or 12.5 per cent of the total population, and this was before the exodus caused by the Great Famine. But there is no doubt that contemporaries believed that a significant proportion of Manchester's population in 1831 were of Irish origin. Also they were well aware that the Irish lived in some of the poorest quarters of the town.[29] Crook's relatively new parish (founded in 1820) included the poorest of these, the slum known as Little Ireland, off Oxford Road.[30] There were three Roman Catholic chapels in Manchester in 1831 and Crook was well known, having served here since 1824.

25 *Manchester Guardian*, 5 February 1831.

26 Morris, *Cholera 1832*, p. 186.

27 Advertisement in *Manchester Courier*, 3 March 1832. Dugard also filled the position of librarian at Chetham's Library from 1834 to 1837.

28 Information kindly provided by Beverley Pilcher from her unpublished study, 'Barnard Castle and the Cholera Outbreak of 1849' [2004].

29 J.M. Werly, 'The Irish in Manchester, 1832–49', *Irish Historical Studies*, 18 (1973), pp. 345–58; M.A. Busteed & R.I. Hodgson, 'Irish Migrant Responses to Urban Life in Early Nineteenth-Century Manchester, *Geographical Journal*, 162 (1996), pp. 139–53; M. Busteed, 'Little Islands of Erin. Irish Settlement and Identity in Mid-Nineteenth Century Manchester', *Immigrants and Minorities*, 18 (1999), pp. 94–127.

30 M. Busteed, '"The Most Horrible Spot"? The Legend of Manchester's Little Ireland', *Irish Studies Review*, 4 (1995–6), pp. 12–20.

His public roles included filling the office of visitor for the Board of Health.[31] Perhaps his being a Lancastrian by birth may have made him more acceptable to the other members of the newly appointed Special Board than someone like Father Daniel Hearne, Irish-born priest of the overwhelmingly Irish parish of St Patrick's on Livesey Street, Ancoats who has been described by a historian of Manchester Catholicism as a 'ruthless, crusading, barrel orator', an archetype of the Victorian slum priest.[32]

What was the political complexion of the Special Board of Health? Within the middle class in the Manchester of 1831 there were deep religious and political divisions. Whilst the Liberal and dissenting fraction of the middle class contributed much to the town's civil institutions and societies (notably families such as the Philipses, the Gregs, the Heywoods and the Potters) they were excluded from political power by the Tory-Anglican bloc within the middle class. There was no significant aristocratic influence on the town's affairs.[33] It has been implied that leading Liberal figures like John Edward Taylor (founder of the *Manchester Guardian*), the radical newspaper proprietor and editor Archibald Prentice and the merchants Absalom Watkin and Thomas Potter were involved in the work of the Board.[34] But this is a misconception. In reality, only Thomas Potter was a member and he attended very few meetings. It should be no surprise that the composition of the Special Board of Health reflected the Tory-Anglican dominance of Manchester's official bodies. However, the impending crisis does demonstrate the willingness of that Tory oligarchy to draw in a number of moderates from Liberal and Dissenting quarters, whilst excluding the more radical or socially inferior reformers who might challenge the authority of the larger property holders and the Collegiate Church. In this the response of the town's governors to the problems arising from poverty, rapid urban growth and inadequate provision of sanitary arrangements and housing stock represented their desire to educate and inculcate moral and social values. This was a cross-sectional matter. The moral and physical condition of the working classes was the concern of all the great propertied figures in the town regardless of party or creed.

---

31   *Report of the Board of Health in Manchester at the Thirty-Seventh Annual Meeting, June 1 1832* (Manchester, 1832), p. 8.
32   G.P. Connolly, Catholicism in Manchester and Salford 1770–1850, unpublished PhD thesis, University of Manchester, 1980, vol.1 part 2, pp. 408–9; G.P. Connolly, 'Little Brother be at Peace: the Priest as Holy Man in the Nineteenth-Century Ghetto' in W.J. Sheils, ed., *The Church and Healing. Studies in Church History*, vol. 19 (Oxford, Blackwell, 1982).
33   V.A.C. Gatrell, 'Incorporation and the Pursuit of Liberal Hegemony'; A. Briggs, 'Manchester' in *Victorian Cities* (Harmondsworth, Pelican, 1963); A.J. Kidd, 'Introduction: the Middle Class in Nineteenth-Century Manchester' in A.J. Kidd & K.W. Roberts, *City, Class and Culture: Studies of Cultural Production and Social Policy in Victorian Manchester* (Manchester University Press, 1985); M. Turner, *Reform and Respectability: the Making of a Middle Class Liberalism in Early Nineteenth Century Manchester* (Manchester, Chetham Society, 1995); M. Hewitt, *The Emergence of Stability in the Industrial City: Manchester 1832–67* (Aldershot, Scolar Press, 1996).
34   M. Turner, *Reform and Respectability*, p.165.

A related concern was the fear that the epidemic would cause serious disruption to trade. In a commercial town like Manchester this was an understandable anxiety. The Special Board was at pains to ensure that accurate information was available through the press. At the height of the epidemic the Board resolved:

> *That in consequence of there having been several incorrect reports of the state of cholera in Manchester the Board of Health established in that Town fearing that the trade of the Town may suffer from the exaggerated reports made think it necessary to publish a statement of the cases which have occurred.... The Board is also desirous that when reports are in future made the days on which cases occurred should be enumerated and that the preceding Resolution be advertised in the Times, Morning Chronicle, Morning Herald, Courier and standard newspapers with the list of cases.*[35]

The proceedings of the Special Board of Health reflect the limited and constrained nature of its authority. The Central Board in London provided a template for action, but without secure finances (at least at the outset), and lacking powers of coercion, the Special Board could only seek to cooperate with rather than to direct the work of other agencies and individuals. In the main this meant working with the existing instruments of local government, especially the Police and Improvement Commissioners. In particular there was regular contact with the Paving and Scavenging Committee of the Police Commissioners which had responsibilities for the cleansing, paving and sewering of some but not all of the town's streets.[36] In reality, there was a distinct overlap in personnel between the various instruments of local government in the town and the Special Board of Health. But this fact did not necessarily guarantee a smooth path of cooperation between them. In addition to working with local government, the Special Board of Health, and the officers it employed, had dealings with landlords, employers of labour and water carriage companies as well as boards of health from other towns. As well as acting on the financial basis of tax funding from the Manchester leypayers it also managed small amounts of voluntary funds donated to a clothing fund between August 1832 and January 1833. The latter was required because of the policy of burning the clothing and bedding of all those admitted into the hospitals. It employed and paid the salaries of several officials including the resident medical officers at the cholera hospitals. As an 'ad hoc' agency of local public management, it stood separate from central state authority yet it endeavoured to interpret and implement the formulas for dealing with the epidemic devised by the Central Board of Health in London. At the same time, as an independent body, it sought to learn from the experience of other towns and other countries. The Special Board also had responsibility for direct communication with the public; a particularly

35 Special Board, 3 September 1832.
36 Minute Book of Manchester Police Commissioners, 25 August 1828–9 January 1833, Manchester Archives and Local Studies, M9/30/1/6. It should be noted that the second of the four minute books of the Lamp, Scavenging, Fire Engine and Main Sewer Committee has been missing since 1959. It covers the period from March 1831 to November 1833. Manchester Archives and Local Studies, M9/30/4/1–4.

delicate matter in which it was variously accused of creating panic, rousing fears which it should instead have allayed, but conversely of working too secretively, especially of concealing evidence about the progress of the epidemic.[37]

Comprehending the Urban World

One of the key problems for the Special Board was to comprehend the urban structure that had grown up around them. To do this they had to construct a mental map of Manchester; hence the desire to accumulate as much social knowledge as possible through questionnaires and investigations. Their task was assisted by the printing in January 1832 of the first large-scale street map of the town to appear for over thirty years: *Bancks & Co's Plan of Manchester and Salford* based on a survey completed by Richard Thornton in 1831.[38] As a guide to the layout of the towns and suburbs it was without parallel. However, the Special Board of Health was not the first to tread this territory. The Board members could draw upon the experience of the fever wards of the Manchester Royal Infirmary and specifically those medics who had dealt with cases of typhus since the 1790s.[39] The Manchester Board of Health oversaw the Fever Hospital. Although typhus is chiefly transmitted by person-to-person contact and cholera is contracted through infected water supplies there was a correlation between the parts of the town most affected by typhus and the areas with the highest concentration of cholera cases. By investigating typhus cases a number of the Infirmary medics had been brought into contact with some of the poorest quarters of the town. They brought with them their own expertise, their own understanding of fever: 'Poverty and filth, combined with a peculiar state of the atmosphere, are the chief sources of epidemic diseases, and as the two former evils are generally present amongst the indigent, fever is sure to exist in a greater or lesser degree in certain quarters of every large town'.[40]

This had enabled them to construct a medical topography of Manchester such as that published by the physician Edmund Lyon in J. P. Kay's short-lived *North of England Medical and Surgical Journal* of 1830. Prior to the cholera epidemic Lyon had identified the regions of the town that were most subject to the fever. These were precisely the quarters that would be most affected by the cholera. A comparison of Lyon's topography with the epidemiological map of the early cholera cases in Manchester produced by Henry Gaulter reveals a match between fever and cholera 'black spots'. Those areas described by Lyon in 1830 as 'altogether

37   For the former criticism see H. Gaulter, *The Origin and Progress of the Malignant Cholera in Manchester, Considered Chiefly in their Bearing on the Contagiousness and the Secondary Causes of the Disease* (1833), p. 137 and Wheeler, *Manchester* (1836), p. 135; for the latter criticism see the *Manchester Guardian*, 16 June 1832.

38   See introductions to *Historic Maps of Manchester* (Warrington, Digital Archives, 2006) and *Manchester and Salford Ordnance Survey 60 inches 1844–1849* (Warrington, Digital Archives, 2007).

39   J.V. Pickstone, 'Ferriar's Fever to Kay's Cholera: Disease and Social Structure in Cottonopolis', *History of Science*, 22 (1984), pp. 401–19.

40   *Report of the Board of Health in Manchester at theThirty-Seventh Annual Meeting, June 1, 1832* (Manchester, 1832), p. 4.

unsuitable for the habitation of civilized human beings'[41] were precisely those to be made notorious by Kay and later investigators. These were located on low-lying swampy ground along rivers to the south and north of the town. In a curve of the River Medlock surrounded by factories and bordered by the busy thoroughfare of Oxford Road lay the district known as 'Little Ireland'. This largely Irish slum was to figure prominently in assessments of the public health of the town in the 1830s and 1840s. It was to acquire symbolic significance through its treatment in such documents as Kay's *Moral and Physical Condition* of 1832, the *Report of the Select Committee on the Health of Towns* of 1840 and Edwin Chadwick's famous *Report on the Sanitary Condition of the Labouring Population of Great Britain* of 1842. As such, there was a certain inevitability about its inclusion in the young Friedrich Engels' incisive account of the social pathology of Manchester, *The Condition of the Working Class in England in 1844*, although this was not published in English until much later in the century.[42] Other 'fever spots' which were also the focus of the cholera included the labyrinth of passage ways and courts perched precariously on the steep slope between Long Millgate (a narrow thoroughfare but still a major entry point from the north of the town) and the precipitous and polluted banks of the River Irk, the rookeries on the west side of Deansgate, the London Road district, the back streets surrounding Portland Street and the warren of passageways around Shudehill to the north of the town.

Soon after the Special Board of Health first met in 1831 it ordered an investigation into the condition of Little Ireland. A sub-committee, including Edmund Lyon, was appointed to conduct the investigation and subsequently concluded, 'that should cholera visit this neighbourhood a more suitable soil and situation for its malignant development cannot be found than that described and commonly known by the name of Little Ireland.'[43] The Special Board requested that the Scavenging Committee of the town cleanse the unpaved streets that Lyon had noted in 1830 had no scavengers but the dogs and pigs that roamed freely in them.[44] Thus when the Board investigated the medical topography of the town it built upon the knowledge acquired through a generation of fever medicine. An early decision of the Board was that the medical members sat as a separate medical committee and there are several references to the minutes of that committee, which unfortunately have not survived.[45]

41 E. Lyon, 'Sketch of the Medical Topography and Statistics of Manchester, *North of England Medical and Surgical Journal*, August, 1830, pp. 7–25.
42 S. Marcus, *Engels, Manchester and the Working Class* (London, Weidenfeld and Nicolson, 1974), pp. xi–xiii.
43 Special Board, 21 December 1831 sub-committee report.
44 'The number of private, unpaved, and consequently filthy streets is lamentably great in Manchester... the only scavengers that enter them are dogs and swine, allowed to roam at large: and they are useful in their way, by consuming some of the offal which is indiscriminately cast in heaps before the doors.' Lyon, *North of England Medical and Surgical Journal*, August, 1830, p. 17.
45 It was the practice of the Special Board to set up various such sub-committees, some for specific tasks, but others, like the Medical Committee, which met on a more continuous basis. These included committees for the hospitals and placards.

Another of the first actions of the Special Board after it was formally established in November 1831 was to appoint a sub-committee, entrusted with the task
of dividing the town into districts, each with its own district board of health comprised of the resident clergyman, a number of substantial householders and 'one
medical man at least'.[46] The result was fourteen districts (based on the existing
police districts), which were further sub-divided as necessary. At the same time,
a sub-committee comprising all the medical members of the Special Board drew
up two forms of enquiry to be used by the district boards in their investigations.
The first applied to the condition of the streets, the second related to houses. There
were a series of further questions about the tenants themselves: their numbers,
habits, occupations, state of health, quality of household fitments and food, whether
they would assist in cleaning the houses and so on. From the degree of district
organisation involved this was intended to provide a detailed mapping of the state
of the town's environment. Moreover, the in-depth nature of the enquiries penetrated into the very heart of the working-class home. Whilst such action does not
represent the existence of a 'medical policing' of the populace on the Prussian
model, it reflects a presumed right of enquiry about personal habits as well as
environmental conditions in an attempt to contain a communicable disease. As
Kay makes clear, these investigations provided the basis for his conclusions about
the condition of the labouring people. The dual concern about the physical and
moral condition of the town's working-class population, which characterises Kay's
pamphlet, can be found in the investigations conducted by the Special Board of
Health. In addition to the general enquiries conducted by the Special Board, there
were special investigations into conditions and habits in particular districts, such
as that already mentioned into the condition of Little Ireland, and also into particular types of accommodation such as lodging houses.[47]

Following on from its initial investigations the Board concerned itself directly
with ensuring the scavenging of the streets and the cleansing and whitewashing
of houses. It received repeated reports from district board members and others
regarding specific public health nuisances. These were generally passed on to the
Nuisance Committee or the Scavenging Committee of the Police Commissioners.
Mostly the Board drew up lists of streets requiring cleansing and communicated
these to the Scavenging Committee. Until the legal status of the Special Board
was clarified and its finances secured at a meeting of the leypayers in April 1832,
it was powerless to overcome the Scavenging Committee's repeated complaints
of a lack of funds.[48]

Eventually the money was voted for the work, and the accounts of the
Scavenging Committee for 1831 and 1832 respectively reveal a marked increase
in expenditure resulting from preparations for the cholera epidemic.[49] In addition

---

46 Special Board, 21 November 1831.
47 Special Board, 21 April 1832.
48 Special Board, 6 April 1832.
49 Total expenditure increased from £3,178 for June 1830–June 1831 to £4,328 for June 1831–June
    1832. *Manchester Guardian*, 4 September 1831, 4 August 1832.

the Special Board of Health undertook a number of other preventive measures. Money was spent on whitewashing and fumigating houses and upon the cleansing of streets. In addition, they pressured the churchwardens to undertake an inspection of lodging houses and to notify suspicious cases of disease to the Board.[50] They themselves resolved to undertake the almost impossible task of monitoring canal barge and railway traffic coming into the township.[51] The very act of even considering such problems confronted the Board with data that revealed the scale and complexity of their urban world with its myriad human transactions and movements. The minutes for the meeting of 29 February 1832 record that there were at least 267 'pauper lodging houses' in Manchester with a migrant population of unknown proportions. The same meeting discovered the daunting nature of the planned inspection of canal barge crews when it heard that between 600 and 650 bargees worked the London to Manchester route alone.

One of the Special Board of Health's earliest duties was to seek out buildings suitable as cholera hospitals, eventually securing a number of buildings in January 1832. These included the Phoenix or Soho Foundry of Peel, Williams and Peel in Swan Street, Shudehill[52] and a disused factory in Commercial Street, Knott Mill. These were to be the town's cholera hospitals during the epidemic. A factory building on Harrison Street, Ancoats (also referred to in the minutes as the Pollard Street Hospital) was also engaged and later used as a Reception House for the families of cholera cases. The cleansing and equipping of these buildings for the reception of patients was completed by late spring 1832. Meanwhile resident medical officers were appointed for each of the cholera hospitals. Equally important, and again in line with the advice coming from the Central Board of Health in London, preparations were made for the safe and swift burial of the dead. Following an investigation into the existing churchyards, Manchester's cholera graveyard was to be a part of the parish burial ground, near Walkers Croft.[53]

Cholera Arrives

In early 1832, rumours of the spread of the Asiatic Cholera were rife. Local retailers of proprietary stomach pills, chemists with stocks of chloride of lime and businesses such as Whitlaw's medicated vapour baths found the silver lining in this darkening cloud of public anxiety.[54] The epidemic had been regularly reported in London but until the end of March, outside the capital it was largely confined to the eastern seaboard. In April it travelled inland along the Humber

50 Special Board, 28 January 1832 and thereafter.
51 Special Board, 18 February 1832, 17 May 1832.
52 A.E. Musson, 'An Early Engineering Firm. Peel, Williams and Co. of Manchester', *Business History*, 3 (1960), pp. 8–18.
53 Special Board, 5 May 1832.
54 Whitlaw's had premises in Manchester and Salford; advert in *Manchester Times and Gazette*, 26 November 1831. Such advertisements in the local press were a barometer of public anxiety; see N. Howard-Jones, 'Cholera Therapy in the Nineteenth Century', *Journal of the History of Medicine and Allied Sciences*, 27 (1972), pp. 373–92.

estuary and through the Yorkshire towns of Hull, Market Weighton, Goole and Selby. By late April it was in Liverpool and Chester. In spite of Manchester's extensive trading links it was not until 24 May 1832, some six months after the initial outbreak in Sunderland, that the Board heard of the first suspected case of Asiatic Cholera in Manchester, a coach painter, James Palfreyman. The details of the case were systematically recorded by Henry Gaulter along with those of the first two hundred cholera cases in Manchester.[55]

James Palfreyman, Aged 29

Residence, Somerset-street, Dole Field, was removed during his illness to 47, Coronation-street, Salford, where he died.

Employment, a coach painter.

Constitution, a fine stout well-proportioned man.

Natural susceptibility, subject to severe diarrhoea on taking weak acids.

Predisposing cause, had had repeated attacks of painter's cholic, an occasional drunkard, but his general health good: earning a decent livelihood.

Exciting cause, had been drunk on the Tuesday night preceding the attack, had eaten very heartily on Wednesday of lamb's head, liver, lungs and heart, and was never well after.

Locality, crowding, filth, &c. Somerset-street, a cleanish street, three adults and two children in the house, clean in person and house, the street moderately clean and open. The dunghill of Wright's stables nearly opposite, behind a high wall. Palfreyman had often complained of the offensive smell issuing from it.

Dates of Attack and Event, had complained all Thursday the 17th of May of nausea and pain in the bowels, seized with vomiting and purging at 1 a.m. died on Saturday half past 2 p.m.[56]

The cholera was now in Manchester. The Board met on a daily basis during the height of the crisis. At first, the number of cases remained small. 'The Lord be praised!', Benjamin Braidley confided in his diary in late July, 'Hitherto the cholera does not make much progress in Manchester; we have only 108 cases in all since 18th of May; in Liverpool there have been more than two thousand.'[57] August proved to be the most deadly month. As the death toll increased the Manchester Royal Infirmary responded by forbidding in-patients to receive visitors.[58] William Henry, the eminent Manchester chemist, who had been conducting experiments on the effect of heat on disease, provided the Special Board with the funds to construct a disinfecting chamber that could be used to sterilise the clothing and bedding of cholera cases.[59] The epidemic in Manchester reached its

---

55 Special Board, 24 May 1832.
56 H. Gaulter, *Origin and Progress*, p. 160.
57 B. Braidley, *Memoir of Benjamin Braidley, Esq.* (London, Longman, Brown, Green, 1845), p. 52.
58 Manchester Royal Infirmary Weekly Board Minutes, 20 August 1832, rescinded 10 December 1832.
59 William Henry was a member of the Special Board but unlike his son, William Charles Henry, he did not attend meetings. The same was true of the other eminent Manchester scientist of the day, John Dalton.

peak in mid-August with 278 reported cases and 132 deaths in one week. The instances of cholera declined after the first week of September, despite a serious outbreak in the New Bailey Prison, but revived once more at the end of the month. However, the worst was over and by mid-October the Board had decided to close the Commercial Street hospital. Isolated cases continued with the last reported one in January 1833.

The epidemic in Manchester did not reach the catastrophic levels that had been feared in 1831 and which might have been realised given the pace of industrialisation and urban growth. Why? Indeed the uneven pattern of cholera outbreaks across the country reveals to us the critical part played by water supplies in spreading the epidemic. The larger towns generally had a variety of sources of household water whereas villages and small towns often depended upon a single source. If this became contaminated the results could be devastating. Although the water supplies of large towns could become cross-contaminated, the variability of the epidemic's impact within these towns (the prevalence of cholera 'hotspots') is largely explicable by the variety of water supplies from river, canal, well and the roofs of houses. The chances of them all becoming infected was low. Although at the time the epidemic prompted the investigation of public health and private behaviour, its incidence tells us as much about the variability of the water supply in the first industrial city[60] as it does about differing perceptions of the moral and physical condition of the working class.

Officially the epidemic in Manchester comprised 1325 cases, of whom 706 died. But, as in other towns, the official statistics probably underestimated the extent of the epidemic. Some cases were misdiagnosed whilst others were concealed in order to avoid the terror of being removed to the cholera hospital and the ignominy of a cholera burial. As was evident in the summons against the radical clergyman Revd James Scholefield, who had allowed cholera victims to be buried in his churchyard in Every Street, Ancoats, families wanted loved ones to be buried in a churchyard of one's choice rather than hastily in a pit grave.[61] Scholefield admitted to four cholera burials whereas the authorities, aware of his reputation as an unlicensed doctor, his radical politics and influence among sections of the working class, suspected a considerably larger number.[62] Such behaviour helps to account for the discrepancy between the numbers of cholera deaths officially recorded and the cholera burials listed in the sombre pages of the sexton's register of the Collegiate

---

60   See J.A. Hassan, 'The Development and Impact of Water Supply in Manchester, 1568–1882', *Transactions of the Historic Society of Lancashire and Cheshire*, 133 (1984), pp. 25–45.

61   *Manchester Courier*, 1 September 1832.

62   Dispensation had been given to bury two cholera victims in the Every Street burial ground; see Special Board, 16 August 1832, 24 August 1832. See also the case of John Bradley of Little Pitt Street, who had attended his father's funeral in Scholefied's burial ground; Gaulter, *Origin and Progress*, p.172. On the radical 'Doctor Scholefield' see P. A. Pickering and A. Tyrrell, 'In the Thickest of the Fight: the Reverend James Scholefield (1790–1855) and the Bible Christians of Manchester and Salford', *Albion*, 26 (1994), pp. 461–82, and Owen R. Ashton and Paul A. Pickering, *Friends of the People: Uneasy Radicals in the Age of the Chartists* (London: Merlin Press, 2002).

Church for 1832.[63] Those entries also included cholera victims who died in neighbouring townships, some of whom had a legal right to be buried in Manchester.
What seems clear is that the demographic impact of the epidemic in Manchester
was moderate, especially given the public fears surrounding the disease in the
summer and autumn of 1831. The numbers lost in this local mortality crisis were
quickly replaced by the relentless flood of migrants into the town. What is also
clear is that in spite of the fears that the disease killed the rich and the poor, the
epidemiological data from Gaulter suggests a distinctive social and spatial distribution in which it was the poorer working classes living in slum areas who were
most at risk, more likely to catch the disease and much more likely to perish.
There were, as Morris argues, cholera cases among the middle classes,[64] but as
the epidemic took hold it became clear that it was the ill-housed and ill-fed poor
who were most vulnerable. When the sharp-eared Elizabeth Gaskell noted the use
of the phrase 'the curse of cholera', it was language that was far more likely to
be heard among the working classes living and working on the northern side of
the River Medlock than from her well-heeled neighbours in the residential suburb of Chorlton on Medlock where she was about to begin her married life.[65]

We cannot measure the impact of the epidemic on the economic life of the
town in any meaningful quantitative way, but it appears not to have been as great
as many had feared. The 'metropolis of manufactures' was not plunged into economic depression, especially once the spectre of quarantine had melted away. As
in other commercial communities, talk of quarantine measures was anathema,
whilst a weather eye was kept on how the epidemic was being reported. There
were obvious concerns that the reporting of the cholera riot in September 1832
by the metropolitan press might deter all-important London buyers from travel-
ling to the town.[66] But, as in other places, where shopkeepers and market stall-
holders must have experienced some falling off in trade, especially in the late
summer months, Manchester's markets remained open and the all-important business of the town continued. Compared to cholera, the protests that followed in
the wake of the rejection of the Reform Bill in May presented a more serious
threat to the town's trade.[67] The middle classes continued to travel into the town
centre, whether to patronise the shopkeepers or to listen to the playing of
Paganini.[68] Neither do the activities of the town's increasing numbers of societies

63   M. Powell and C. Hunwick, 'The Manchester Cathedral Sextons' Registers', *Local Historian*,
      39 no. 4 (2009), pp. 300–13.
64   Morris, *Cholera 1832*, pp. 91–3.
65   J. Chapple and A. Shelston, eds., *Further Letters of Elizabeth Gaskell* (Manchester, Manchester
      University Press, 2000), p. 20.
66   *Manchester Guardian*, 8 September 1832.
67   M. Goffin, ed., *The Diaries of Absalom Watkin. A Manchester Man 1787–1861* (Stroud, Alan
      Sutton, 1993), pp. 144–5.
68   Paganini performed an additional concert in Manchester due to public demand. Writing almost
      fifty years later, Josiah Slugg did not recall the cholera epidemic in 1832 but he did remember
      being in the crush of people attending one of Paganini's concerts at the Theatre Royal.
      J.T. Slugg, *Reminiscences of Manchester Fifty Years Ago* (Manchester, J.E. Cornish, 1881),
      pp. 298–9.

seem to have been seriously disturbed. Attendance at that most quintessential of all middle-class institutions, the Gentlemen's Concerts Society, now housed in its splendid new building on Peter Street, remained buoyant, takings recording only a modest fall even in the dire month of August.[69] Public events continued, whether it was the carnival pleasures of the Knott Mill Fair and the Manchester races, or more polite events which saw the Sunday School children processing through the streets.[70] Other communities were more cautious – Hyde and Glossop decided to cancel their annual wakes[71] – but in Manchester cholera does not appear to have seriously disrupted the recreational calendar. Moreover, throughout the epidemic the movement of people between towns continued almost unchecked. Outbreaks of cholera in Warrington, for example, were linked directly to cases in Manchester.[72]

1832 was also a year of political gatherings. The cholera had occurred at the same time as the struggle for parliamentary reform that culminated in the passage of the Great Reform Act in June 1832. Doctors such as Kay found themselves involved in both crises.[73] The reform crisis was the occasion of serious rioting in several towns, although not in Manchester. Nonetheless the town was the focus of popular support for reform in the shape of the Manchester Political Union founded in 1830 and the Political Union of the Working Classes and Others founded by followers of Henry Hunt in 1831. Reform meetings attracted considerable crowds. On one Monday afternoon in May 1832 an estimated 40,000 gathered on St Peter's Field to hear speakers and to sign a petition (25,000 signatures were obtained). *The Times*'s correspondent was of the opinion that 'the whole male population of the town' was there at some time during the event.[74] Thousands of people gathered to hear Hunt himself speak on the sacred site of Peterloo in July.[75] Although divided on class lines, there was broad support in Manchester for a reform that enfranchised the town for the first time, and despite the cholera, large crowds thronged the central streets in August 1832 at the height of the epidemic to enjoy an officially sanctioned Reform Celebration Holiday, an event planned by a committee chaired by Boroughreeve Benjamin Braidley. There was a procession of trades and societies with the police of the night watch resplendent in their new uniforms bringing up the rear. Aware that large crowds would gather, the Special Board of Health felt obliged to issue 500 copies of a placard

---

69   Manchester Gentlemen's Concert Society Accounts, 1831–1832 (Henry Watson Music Library, Manchester Central Library).
70   *Wheeler's Manchester Chronicle*, 16 June 1832.
71   Notices in *Stockport Advertiser*, 31 August 1832, 7 September 1832.
72   Two outbreaks of cholera in Warrington in June 1832 were linked to individuals from Manchester. These included Mary Miles and her infant son, James, who had fled to Warrington after her husband died of cholera in a lodging house in Blakely Street; see H. Gaulter, *Origin and Progress*, pp. 23–5, 42, and T.K. Glazebrook, *A Record of Events During the Presence of the Cholera at Warrington: in a Letter to Henry Gaulter* (London, Whittaker, 1833). Glazebrook was secretary of the Warrington Board of Health.
73   M. Goffin, ed., *The Diaries of Absalom Watkin*, p. 146.
74   *The Times*, 14 May 1832; *Manchester Times and Gazette*, 19 May 1832.
75   *Wheeler's Manchester Chronicle*, 21 July 1832; *Poor Man's Guardian*, 21 July 1832.

cautioning revellers to avoid intoxicating liquors since 'Drunkenness has often been followed by Cholera'.[76] However, the cholera was not enough to keep crowds out of the town centre. By the time Manchester's first parliamentary elections were held in December the epidemic was all but over.

However, the impression should not be given that the response to the cholera was uniformly sanguine. There is clear evidence of public anxiety and alarm during the epidemic, especially in the poorer quarters of the town, and also of the attempts by the Special Board to manage public opinion in the face of repeated disturbances bordering upon riot. The Special Board had the responsibility of communicating information and advice to a semi-literate populace about a disease with no known cause or cure that by its very nature had the potential to instil anxiety, suspicion and even panic. This involved them in attempts to manage news through such mechanisms as admitting reporters to a meeting of the Special Board in the wake of the Brogan case and by trying to secure that only official statistical information appeared in the newspapers.[77] The Board also tried more direct methods of communication by means of placards posted at prominent positions. Placards were prepared with information on a variety of matters, giving details of cholera hospitals and district committees, encouraging early applications for help in suspected cholera cases, warning against violent attacks on medical gentlemen, announcing the dispensing of free medicines, extolling the virtues of temperance and whitewashing as preventive measures and explaining arrangements for the burial of the dead.[78] The Board became aware of the potential for causing alarm and were cautious in the use of placards.[79] But on several occasions up to a thousand of these were plastered all over the town. Despite their informative content and the good intentions involved, for those who could not read well enough, and even for those who could, the proclamation in large and bold letters of the terrifying word 'CHOLERA' may have inadvertently contributed to a climate of fear. Gaulter certainly thought so:

> *The perpetual appearance of fresh placards headed by this frightful word – the daily parade of reports – the procession of the sling exciting and wounding the curiosity of the passengers – the rattling of the cholera van through the streets – the dead cart followed by a mourner or two at an awful distance, moving slowly towards a remote burying-ground branded with the double stigma of poverty and infection – all this ostentation of pestilence was most pernicious.*[80]

76   Special Board, 7 August 1832.
77   Special Board, 3 September 1832.
78   For examples see Special Board, 18 January 1832, Appendix 2; 18 June 1832; 20 August 1832; 8 September 1832, Appendix 1.
79   Special Board, 19 June 1832, 21 June 1832, 22 August 1832.
80   H. Gaulter, *Origin and Progress*, p. 137.

Popular Fears and Attitudes

The 1832 cholera epidemic sheds light on popular fears and attitudes. In particular, it reveals among some sections of the population suspicion of the medical profession bordering on outright hostility. Such hostility was a common feature of the popular response to the epidemic across Europe. In European cities it often centred upon conspiracy theories about the poisoning of the poor by doctors on behalf of the upper classes. In Britain it was rooted in fear of the 'resurrection men', a fear that had taken on an even more horrifying dimension as the details of the Burke and Hare case became public in 1828. Those horrors were stirred up again in 1831 in the trial and execution of the London burkers, Bishop and Williams.[81] Body snatching was largely a consequence of the demand for bodies for dissection by medical students. Manchester had two large medical schools which competed for cadavers as well as students.[82] The 1820s had seen frequent instances in the town of grave robbing,[83] incidents which help explain the installation of anti-bodysnatching measures in local burial grounds. 'As the season is fast approaching in which anatomical lectures are delivered' the Revd. James Scholefield reassured those considering using his churchyard in Ancoats that his new safety tomb (it included an alarm bell) guaranteed protection from local resurrectionists.[84] 'Burkomania' was evident when a house was stormed in Little Ireland on the suspicion that the occupant was dissecting the bodies of children, a rumour that quickly turned into one of a 'gang of monsters ... slicing flesh off corpses' and using it to make veal pies for sale in the local market. Henry Gillies' defence that the body parts found in his house arose from his occupation as an articulator of human and animal skeletons for the medical schools may have satisfied the authorities, but not the public, who recalled Gillies' involvement in an earlier case of bodysnatching.[85] The social rules governing the proper treatment of the body after death were what were being defended. Their importance was underlined in the decisions of the courts which could and did order the public dissection of executed criminals. As late as 1826 such acts of state power attracted considerable crowds to the Manchester Royal

---

81   The murder of Carlo Ferrari received extensive coverage in the provincial newspapers; see for instance *Manchester Times and Gazette*, 3 December 1831, 10 December 1831. Sarah Wise, *The Italian Boy. Murder and Grave-Robbery in 1830s London* (London, Jonathan Cape, 2004).

82   Manchester School of Medicine and Surgery, Pine Street; Manchester School of Anatomy, Bridge Street.

83   For example, the case of Edward Callaghan and John Stewart, 'two notorious resurrectionists' arrested for removing a body from Walker Croft burial ground; *Manchester Times*, 14 November 1828. Also, see J. Eaton, *Spoilation of the Grave. The Trial of J. Eaton, Sexton of 'St George's Chapel', Manchester, Convicted of Felony on May 11 1827 at the New Bailey Quarter Sessions* [Manchester, 1827].

84   Advert in *Manchester Times*, 29 August 1829; and similar adverts for safety tombs at the General Cemetery, Irwell Street, Salford; *Manchester Times*, 26 May 1832.

85   *Manchester Guardian*, 9 April 1831, 30 April 1831; *Preston Chronicle*, 16 April 1831.

Infirmary.[86] The government's intervention in the form of the Anatomy Act, which appointed inspectors – the first civil service inspectorate – to ensure that the cadavers dissected in medical schools were not obtained by criminal means, did little to change attitudes, especially as it identified the unclaimed bodies of paupers as a legitimate source of supply for the anatomists.[87]

Recommendations that cholera victims be buried within twenty-four hours flouted customary burial practices, helping to encourage both the concealment of cholera cases and clandestine burials. The haste in disposing of the corpse also stirred the deeply rooted fears surrounding premature burial.[88] A widespread disgust surrounding burial in the cholera pits also prompted appeals to the Special Board for burials to be allowed in family graves.[89] Cholera stiffened opposition to the authorities at the same time as confirming deep-seated suspicions surrounding surgeons and hospitals. There may not have been the same level of violence in Britain as there was in Paris or Moscow, but there were numerous minor attacks on property and persons throughout 1832. Of these, the most serious disturbances, involving troops as well as police to contain them, took place in Paisley in March and in Manchester in September. The riots were recourse to direct action by people who felt threatened as much by what they believed to be the hidden agenda of a medical profession bent on obtaining bodies for dissection as they were by fear of death from the cholera. Reports such as that in the *Manchester Guardian* in August 1832, which spoke of the first cohort of cholera dead in the town being subjected 'to a most rigorous post mortem examination', must have disturbed even the most intellectually advanced of its readers.[90] After all, attitudes towards the proper treatment of the body after death crossed social boundaries.

The Swan Street riot of 2 September has been outlined by a number of historians, though not subjected to detailed analysis.[91] The disturbance was occasioned by the opening by relatives and friends of the coffin of a cholera victim – a four-year-old Irish boy named John Brogan – which revealed that the head had been

86   The report in the *Manchester Guardian*, 26 August 1826 of the public dissection of Alexander Keand, who had been executed in Lancaster and his body brought to Manchester, records that the numbers attending the event were such that the surgeons stopped the dissection in order to show the body to the excited crowd.

87   R. Richardson, *Death, Dissection and the Destitute*, 2nd ed. (London, Phoenix, 2001); Julie-Marie Strange, *Death Grief and Poverty in Britain 1870–1914* (Cambridge, Cambridge University Press, 2005), pp. 7–8.

88   Joseph Taylor, *The Danger of Premature Interment, Proved from Many Remarkable Instances of People who have Recovered after being Laid out for Dead...* (London, Simpkin and Marshall, 1816). The local instance of Hannah Beswick, whose fears of premature burial resulted in her body being embalmed, was a stock episode in popular histories of Manchester. Beswick died in 1758 but was not buried until 1868, having been for a number of years an exhibit in the Natural History Museum. See also J. Bourke, *Fear. A Cultural History* (London, Virago, 2006), pp. 32–50.

89   Special Board, 11 August, 20 August, 29 August 1832.

90   *Manchester Guardian*, 4 August 1832.

91   The best short account is Morris, *Cholera 1832*, pp.110–12. Of the various nineteenth-century accounts see in particular Fred Leary, 'The Manchester Cholera Van', Notes and Queries, Query 513, *Manchester Weekly Times*, 26 September 1890.

replaced by a brick. This confirmed their worst fears that either the corpse had been violated by the carrying out of a post-mortem or the boy had been the victim not of cholera but of anatomists seeking bodies to dissect. A crowd of up to three thousand soon gathered and carried the coffin aloft as they marched on the Swan Street hospital. They demolished a wall in the hospital yard, broke the windows of the hospital itself, damaged beds and equipment inside, and released the patients. One of the hospital vans – the detested symbol of the epidemic amongst the poor – was destroyed. Police with cutlasses tried unsuccessfully to break up the crowd, which was calmed down only with the help of Daniel Hearne, the parish priest of St Patrick's Catholic Church, and finally dispersed by the presence of four troops of the Fifteenth Hussars called from Hulme barracks. There were thirteen arrests (predominantly of Irish men). It was later discovered that Robert Oldham, a medical student who had only recently started work at the hospital, and who successfully evaded justice despite a warrant for his arrest, had removed the boy's head.

The Swan Street riot so alarmed the Special Board of Health that it felt obliged to admit the press to the meeting when it was discussed.[92] The Board acted swiftly to allay public fears. But the fact is that the riot was not an isolated incident. It occurred at the height of the epidemic, but was the culmination of a sequence of hostile acts towards the hospital at Swan Street that dated back to the spring and had grown in intensity as the epidemic wore on. At the beginning of the year local residents had petitioned unsuccessfully for the removal of the hospital.[93] Once the hospital began to admit cholera cases crowds took to gathering outside the hospital gates and police officers were stationed to protect the medical men from attack. By the end of June one local paper reported the presence of a 'mob' of 'two to three thousand persons' besieging the hospital.[94] Police protection was necessary as the doctors left the premises. All this was taking place as reports circulated of attacks on cholera hospitals and personnel in other towns, including Liverpool.[95]

There were several cases in the press of men with Irish surnames charged with disorderly behaviour or causing a disturbance at the cholera hospital. The Brogan case which instigated the Swan Street riot was not even the first such incident of coffin opening in the town. In late June suspicions about the state of the body of a cholera victim at the funeral in the parish burial ground caused the mourners to forcibly open the coffin only to find the body was not covered in the customary shroud. Fear of poisoning was commonplace. After news spread of cases admitted in good health to Knott Mill cholera hospital and subsequently dying after being detained against their wishes, Gaulter reports that a 'mob which collected

---

92   Special Board, 3 September 1832.
93   Special Board, 11 February 1832.
94   *Wheeler's Manchester Chronicle*, 30 June 1832.
95   G. Gill, S. Burrell and J. Brown, 'Fear and Frustration – The Liverpool Cholera Riots of 1832', *Lancet*, 21 July 2001, pp. 233–7; S. Burrell and G. V. Gill, 'The Liverpool Cholera Epidemic of 1832 and Anatomical Dissection – Medical Mistrust and Civil Unrest', *Journal of History of Medicine and Allied Science*, 60 No. 4 (2005), pp. 478–98.

at the gates of the hospital loudly accused the doctors of poison, and even darker crimes.'[96] Such incidents so worried the Board that it made an appeal to the clergy and ministers of religion in the town to do all they could 'in their pulpits as in their Sunday Schools...to remove the present prejudices against the Cholera Hospitals from the minds of the poorer classes of the community.' Notwithstanding this plea the Board felt bound to protect the cholera van from interference by employing a man (in addition to the driver and bearers) 'to prevent bystanders approaching the patients'.[97] Such measures proved essential. For example, at the peak of the epidemic in mid-August as the cholera van fetched a patient from Little Ireland it was surrounded by a large crowd shouting and throwing stones; a window in the van was broken. The situation was so volatile in part due to the threat to traditional funeral rites, especially the wake common in Irish families, posed by the swift burial of cholera victims. In such circumstances the Board's decision to allow the remains of Brogan to be buried (in a lead coffin) at the recently opened St Patrick's, Livesey Street rather than in the common cholera graves was sensible.[98]

Lasting Impact of the Cholera

What of the lasting impact of the epidemic? It must have devastated the lives of the families of those who died and left an enduring legacy of personal and familial loss. In more general terms, however, the legacy is less sure. Cholera might have pricked the sanitary consciousness, but in Manchester as in the other major urban centres there was little permanent improvement in living conditions in working-class districts. Sewering and paving failed to keep pace with the increase in new streets and houses. Piped water trickled slowly into working-class districts. The Scavenging Committee had trialled birch besoms from Edinburgh, but the essential fact was that such a small group of workers, wherever their brooms came from, could do little more than sweep the main streets, weekly or fortnightly.[99] It comes as no surprise to read in 1835 of the Police Commissioners being pressed to take action over the 'accumulation of nightsoil and other filth in the streets on the southerly side of Oxford Street, generally called Little Ireland'.[100] Factors such as poor diet and overcrowding remained a fact of life for many of the working class in Manchester, even though doctors such as John Roberton had identified

96 Gaulter, *Origin and Progress*, p. 39.
97 Special Board, 19 July 1832.
98 A note accompanying the entry for John Brogan in St Patrick's burial register reads: 'The child whose corpse was mutilated in the cholera hospital by R. Oldham who was obliged to fly on this account. He appalled the population. The body after his head had been attached was reinterred in St Patricks burial ground in a lead coffin.' Hearne conducted the funeral and was reported as using the ceremony to deny reports that he had revived a person who had died of cholera. *Manchester Weekly Times*, 26 September 1890.
99 The permanent establishment of the scavenging department in 1830–31 comprised 38 men (of whom 24 were scavengers) and 19 horses. *Manchester Times,* 17 September 1831.
100 Proceedings of the Lamp, Scavenging, Fire Engine and Nuisance Committee, 28 October 1835. M9/30/4/3, p. 260.

them as predisposing causes for cholera.[101] Exhortations to personal cleanliness ran up against the apparently intractable problems of access to hot water and soap. Indeed, if the evidence collected in the early 1840s is representative, if anything living conditions in the already densely populated districts had probably deteriorated further. When the cholera returned in 1848–49 its killing path followed the grain of these deficiencies.[102]

An immediate aftermath of the epidemic was the founding in 1833 of the Manchester and Salford District Provident Society (DPS), though factors other than the cholera epidemic contributed to its establishment. Indeed, it is conceivable that the DPS would have been founded earlier had it not been for the cholera, since the model of the Liverpool society had been available as early as 1829 to replicate in Manchester.[103] Provident societies like that in Manchester and Salford attempted to regulate charitable giving to the poor, to ensure that only those perceived as 'deserving' were in receipt of the gift of charity. At the heart of this was a desire to reform working-class morals, to inculcate the virtues of thrift and self-reliance. Designed to complement the work of the DPS was the formation also in 1833 of the Manchester Statistical Society. The influence of Kay's *Moral and Physical Condition* was paramount in both the provident and the statistical societies. The latter was soon busy devising questionnaires and pursuing investigations into the living conditions and behaviour of the working classes, driven by a belief that public and voluntary interventions required hard empirical data. It adopted the questionnaire as a tool of social enquiry.[104] In addition the DPS devised plans for a network of district committees through which to organise the visits of middle-class volunteers to the working class in their own homes.[105] No doubt in order to assist in this process the DPS paid the surveyor Richard Thornton, who had produced the 1832 map for Bancks, nearly £70 for 'large district maps of the town'.[106] The DPS owed much to the Special Board of Health, not least the fact that it inherited the residue of the Cholera Subscription Fund and the Board of Health Clothing Fund. The link extended to the personnel of the DPS itself. Seventeen committee members had served on the Special Board as had most of

101 J. Roberton, *General Remarks on the Health of English Manufacturers, and the Need which Exists for the Establishment of Convalescents' Retreats* (London, J. Ridgway, 1831).

102 'Report on the Measures for the Relief of Cholera in Manchester' in *Report of the General Board of Health on the Epidemic Cholera of 1848 and 1849*, PP 1850 [1273], pp. 87–101; J. Leigh and N. Gardiner, *History of the Cholera in Manchester in 1849* (London, 1850).

103 *Liverpool Mercury*, 18 December 1829. Earlier provident societies were also founded in London and Brighton.

104 T.S. Ashton, *Economic and Social Investigations in Manchester 1833–1933. A Centenary History of the Manchester Statistical Society* (London, P.S. King, 1934); M.J. Cullen, *The Statistical Movement in Early Victorian Britain* (Hassocks, Harvester Press, 1975); D. Elesh, 'The Manchester Statistical Society; a Case Study of a Discontinuity in History of Empirical Research', *Journal of the History of the Behavioral Sciences*, 8 (1972), pp. 280–301, 407–17.

105 A.J. Kidd, 'Charity Organisation and the Unemployed in Manchester', *Social History*, 9 (1984), pp. 46–9.

106 The map was three times the scale of Bancks' 1832 plan. No copies have been located. *Manchester Times*, 6 July 1833.

the Society's officers. The by now ubiquitous Kay was one of the honorary secretaries.[107] The cholera epidemic had offered many insights into the lives of the town's working classes, not least the physical environment of the poorest quarters of the town, but it was the moral character of their existence that was of most concern in this institutional legacy of the work of the Special Board.

In November 1832, when Thomas Townend called for Manchester to hold a solemn day of thanksgiving, he recognised that the town had been fortunate in that it had 'been lightly afflicted' by cholera compared to places such as Liverpool and Glasgow.[108] To an extent this was due, as we have suggested, to the comparative variety of the public water supply. Manchester was also fortunate in being one of the last major urban areas to be infected. But some credit must also be given to the preparatory cleaning organised by the Special Board. Resources were limited and not all areas of the town were cleansed thoroughly. Most of the district committees acted reasonably promptly in the management of infected cases, and the policy of establishing hospitals and the swift removal of the infected and family members to those hospitals helped, though in the end only just over half (51.7 per cent) of all the cases were treated in the two hospitals.[109] Isolating and treating the infected in hospital in a large urban population was an expensive option and the somewhat tardy response to the cholera in towns such as Salford, Oldham and Stockport was in part due to questions of finance.[110]

Neither was the intervention of the Board necessarily easy. Clearing, let alone cleansing, the streets and courts of their human waste and other filth was an imperfect operation. As we have seen, the scavengers' cart did not reach some areas, whilst the pressure of numbers soon created fresh accumulations of filth in streets that had been cleared.[111] Lodging houses might be identified but not all could be spring cleaned with the whitewasher's brush. Reporting to the leypayers in August 1832, Kay spelt out some of the difficulties that tested the organisation and resources of the Special Board. Allen's Court was one slum in a district of slums located between the Irk and Long Millgate. Access to it was difficult, it required

> ... *the explorer to descend three flights of steps till he lands on the level of the river Irk; surrounded as it is by walls, with houses three or four stories high; the course of the river impeded by a weir; opposite a skin yard; in its immediate neighbourhood a tripe manufactory; opposite again a cat gut manufactory, and a manufactory where skins were prepared without the use of bark; within its own circuit some of the most loathsome nuisances; and inhabited by persons whose health was depressed by their occupations, their habits, and some by their extreme dissolute manners. In this court a*

107   *Manchester & Salford District Provident Society. First Annual Report* (Manchester, 1834).
108   *Manchester Guardian*, 17 November 1832.
109   H. Gaulter, *Origin and Progress*, p. 156.
110   *Manchester Courier*, 14 July 1832 on the reversal of the decision to establish a hospital in Oldham.
111   The Infirmary was drawing the attention of the Special Board to the need to do something about the filthy conditions and lack of ventilation in the Gibraltar district of the town in late April 1832; Manchester Royal Infirmary Weekly Board Minutes, 23 April 1832.

case was not reported owing to a misunderstanding, in which no blame was attributable to any medical gentleman. The case occurred on Sunday, the person died on the Wednesday, the body was kept in the court till Friday, and on Saturday thirteen cases occurred. They were not reported at an early period to the board, and he regretted to say that everyone of them had died. The operation of the board consequent upon the information of the state of the court, which only reached them on Saturday morning were prompt and decisive. Two officers of the reception house committee entered the court, separated the whole of the inhabitants, 30 in number, placed them in the reception house, and instituted measures by which the infection that existed might be subdued.'[112]

However, such sickening descriptions were to have more effect on later commentators than in advancing the emerging public health agenda. Cholera did not spark increased investment in the public health infrastructure, let alone increase the calls for reforming the key institutions of local government. The Police Act in 1828 appears to have had little noticeable impact on the effectiveness of the scavenging committee. Neither did the Police Acts of 1830 and 1832 suggest a new set of priorities. Despite the flurry of preventive measures during the epidemic, the cholera of 1832 did not prove to be a decisive moment in the public health of Manchester.

In terms of the wider middle class, the cholera was a crisis that saw them acknowledge common interests rather than the issues that divided them, though on occasions, as when the payments received for burying the cholera dead by the clergy at the Collegiate Church was sharply criticised, the fragility of these temporary alliances is evident.[113] Burial rights was one of the issues that defined the division between nonconformists and Anglicans. In Manchester it had resulted in the opening by dissenters in the fast growing suburban township of Chorlton on Medlock of one of the first nonconformist-controlled modern cemeteries.[114] The Rusholme Lane cemetery met a real need, and by 1830, less than ten years after its opening, it was the preferred location for over one-third of all burials in Manchester.[115]

Illuminating as cholera is for understanding the macropolitics of the middle classes, the disease also accelerated those processes that were creating the new social geography of the industrial city, causing the middle classes to regard the suburbs as their natural home. Doctors could argue over the exact epidemiological lessons of the epidemic, but to the middle classes it became evident that contrary to earlier views about the disease, it did not attack populations at random. Cholera hot spots were confined principally to the overcrowded and filthy inner-city districts of the city, not the new suburbs of Chorlton on Medlock, Ardwick, Rusholme and Broughton. As Henry Gaulter observed, 'the contrast between the localities which the rich and poor inhabit, exhibits perhaps the most striking example of the

---

112 *Manchester Guardian*, 4 August 1832.
113 *Manchester Times*, 20 October 1832.
114 J. Rugg, 'Ownership of the Place of Burial: a Study of Early Nineteenth-Century Urban Conflict in Britain', in R.J. Morris and R.H. Trainor, eds., *Urban Governance: Britain and Beyond Since 1750* (Aldershot, Ashgate, 2000), pp. 211–25.
115 35.7 per cent in 1830 according to the returns of burials presented to the Special Board, 5 May 1832.

substantial advantages, as far as health is concerned, which affluence can bestow, by enabling its possessor so to construct and to fix his residence as to place himself and his family beyond the reach of every ordinary source of malaria.'[116] It was a conclusion that other fever doctors had already reached, reinforcing the attitudes about the dirty and undeserving poor, in particular the low Irish.

Friedrich Engels overstated the anxieties associated with cholera when writing 13 years later that 'a universal terror seized the bourgeoisie of the city',[117] but for the middle classes the epidemic helped to change the still vague connection between the working classes, dirt and disease into an article of faith in the new system of class relations. Distinctions might be made within the working class, notably the DPS's hostility to what it saw as indiscriminate giving and the desire to restrict the gift of charity to the deserving poor, but the working class were now fixed in the imagination as those people who were ill-housed, ill-fed and who had unsatisfactory personal hygiene. The middle class were becoming much more sensitive to the stench of the poor. The cleaner, sweeter and healthier air of the suburbs was seen as offering protection against the sickening foul odours of city life. Theories of cholera transmission which stressed predisposing causes, especially the inappropriate (immoral) lifestyles of the poor, contributed to this change in attitudes. In a nutshell, cholera was contributing to the making of that distinctive social geography of the industrial city, a map of separations and disconnections that a later generation of concerned middle classes would decry and attempt to redraw.

Acknowledgment also needs to be given to the impact of the epidemic upon key individuals who were active in the Special Board. Whilst the public reputation of the town's medical profession was hardly enhanced, especially among the poorer classes, the lives of individual doctors were changed by the cholera. The careers of aspiring doctors like Kay and Gaulter were not to take off as they might have expected, though for different reasons. Kay took a key role in the epidemic. He was, as already noted, a conscientious member of the Special Board, active in the committee room, in the hospital, and in the field. He had experience of the Ancoats slums, and in this new crisis he was not beyond taking direct action. His account of visiting Bedford Court by the River Irk captures the man.

> '... one morning when he visited it [Bedford Court], he discovered heaps of putrid animal substances; the hoofs of cows and sheep emitting a most disgusting stench; there were also large tubs of size, some of which was in an absolute state of putrefaction. These disgusting nuisances he had dismissed in a summary way, by throwing them into the river, and he was happy to state that, all the houses in the court having been whitewashed, no other cases occurred there ...'[118]

Both editions of his pamphlet had received generous reviews and his name was now attached to liberal initiatives such as the DPS and Statistical Society. Such activity placed him in a strong position to advance professionally and personally.

---

116 H. Gaulter, *Origin and Progress*, pp. 118–19.
117 F. Engels, *The Condition of the Working-Class in England* (London, Panther, 1974), p. 76.
118 *Manchester Guardian*, 4 August 1832.

The trajectory of his career seemed clear but, as is well known, his plans for marriage collapsed, causing him to leave the crucible of Manchester for a civil service post in East Anglia and subsequent role as education reformer.[119] Gaulter's career was also on the up and in 1833 his closely researched anti-contagionist account of the epidemic, *The Origin and Progress of the Malignant Cholera in Manchester, Considered Chiefly in their Bearing on the Contagiousness and the Secondary Causes of the Disease*, was published. However, tragedy was soon to follow. In poor health, he decided to seek the restorative climate of Italy only to die in Naples in September 1833.[120]

This is not to suggest that the medical profession was full of self-sacrificing individuals, ready to respond to the crisis. The attitude of doctors such as Joseph Astbury Smith, who asked to withdraw from the Board because 'several of his patients had refused to employ him in consequence of knowing that his name is publicly posted on the walls as one of the surgeons to attend cholera patients',[121] needs to be placed alongside that of doctors such as Daniel Lynch, who filled the post of medical superintendent at the Swan Street hospital and who was to be exonerated after the Brogan incident, later receiving a public testimonial for his services during the epidemic. Lynch, whose father was visiting apothecary at the Infirmary, had himself qualified as an apothecary in 1828, becoming a MRCS in 1832. His assistants included the equally youthful and recently qualified surgeon, Samuel Gaskell (25), brother of Revd. William Gaskell, who arrived in Manchester having already treated cholera victims in Edinburgh.[122] Gaskell, like John Langford, no doubt hoped that through their work in the hospitals they would make a telling contribution to the understanding or treatment of the deadly disease.[123] Hindsight shows us that it was to be William Henry's experiments using heat to destroy disease that were to make the more lasting contribution to the public health, though the Special Board was hardly enthusiastic in acquiring his disinfecting apparatus.[124] But for every Lydgate willing to put his shoulder behind

119 R.J.W. Selleck, *James Kay-Shuttleworth. Journey of an Outsider* (Ilford, Woburn, 1994), pp. 88–103.
120 Gaulter was buried in the Protestant cemetery adjoining the church of Santa Maria della Fede, Naples. His death notice in the *Manchester Guardian*, 19 October 1833, referred to 'his high attainments as a professional man and a scholar, and for his familiar knowledge with general literature'. Notices of his book appeared in the medical press after his death, including a long review in the January number of the *Medical Quarterly Review*, 1 (1833–4), pp. 341–8.
121 Special Board, 9 July 1832.
122 John Chapple, *Elizabeth Gaskell. The Early Years* (Manchester, Manchester University Press, 1997), pp. 420–1, 426–8. Includes an informative account of 'the decapitation row' at the Swan Street hospital.
123 J. Langford, 'Treatment of Malignant Cholera with Tartar Emetic at Manchester', *The Lancet* (1832), ii. p. 781; S. Gaskell, 'Remarks on the Malignant Cholera as it Appeared in Manchester', *Edinburgh Medical and Surgical Journal*, 40 (1833), pp. 52–94.
124 Henry provided the majority of the funds to construct the disinfecting chamber. After the epidemic it went to the workhouse. See W.V. Farrar, K.R. Farrar and E.L. Scott, 'William Henry: Contagion and Cholera; the Textbook' in R.L. Hills and W.H. Brock, eds., *Chemistry and the Chemical Industry in the 19th Century: the Henrys of Manchester and Other Studies* (Aldershot: Variorum, 1997), pp. 27–52.

the wheels of the sanitary cart, the long list of surgeons and physicians in the commercial directories suggests there was a considerable number of Manchester doctors for whom working on a district committee, let alone serving in a cholera hospital, were not viewed as stepping stones to advancing their careers.

Similar patterns can be found in the legal profession. For the majority of young solicitors and attorneys, their profession offered them a royal road to a comfortable lifestyle. Only a minority took the fork that led them to grapple directly with the social problems of the age. In this respect special note should be made of Joseph Heron, whose duties as Honorary Secretary to the Special Board marked his entry into the public life of Manchester. Heron was 22 years old in 1831. Trained for the law, his agile mind and eloquence impressed even the more experienced members of the Board. He was also active outside the committee room, leading the discovery of the clandestine burials being conducted by Scholefield in Ancoats.[125] Heron was soon immersed in the liberal radical campaigns that yielded the municipal charter in 1838. 'His active usefulness as a volunteer in the public service' (the words are those of Richard Cobden) saw Heron appointed as the first town clerk of the new borough, a position he was to define, and in doing so he was to shape, probably more than any other individual, the public face of Victorian Manchester.[126]

Manchester had passed through its first major public health emergency of the nineteenth century. Some local doctors now had first-hand experience of this killer disease, but like cholera doctors in other parts of the country there was no agreement about how the disease was transmitted or what was the effective method of treatment. By the winter of 1832–33 the Special Board, like most of the 800 local boards of health, was being wound up. The correspondence between the Central Board and the Special Board reached a natural conclusion, leaving the job of making up the accounts as the final business to be overseen. The fears that surrounded cholera began to recede. By the time news arrived in Manchester in October 1833 that the town's most admired writer, Maria Jane Jewsbury, had died of the Asiatic Cholera, the anxieties surrounding the disease were fading fast. Mourned as she was, Jewsbury had died in Poonah.[127] The cholera morbus was back in its natural, its ancestral home in the subcontinent of India. It was to be another sixteen years before it returned to British shores.

---

125 *Manchester Courier*, 1 September 1832.
126 *Manchester Times and Gazette*, 2 December 1838; entry in *ODNB* by V.R. Parrott.
127 M.C. Fryckstedt, 'The Hidden Rill: the Life and Career of Maria Jane Jewsbury', *Bulletin of the John Rylands University Library of Manchester*, 66 (1983–84), 177–203; 67 (1984–85), 450–73.

EDITORIAL NOTE

In transcribing the minutes and correspondence we have made various alterations to the original text. These include correcting spellings, standardizing the use of capitals and expanding contractions. We have also, in the interests of space, not followed the original layout of the minutes. These changes are minor but their end result is a more fluent text.

THE PROCEEDINGS OF THE MANCHESTER
SPECIAL BOARD OF HEALTH 1831–33

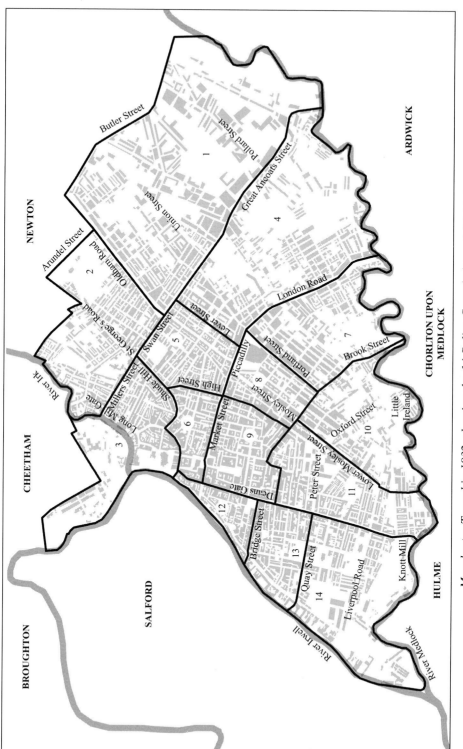

Manchester Township 1832 showing the 14 Police Commissioners' Districts.

At a meeting held at the Board Room of the House of Recovery
Aytoun Street
November 10, 1831

R.J.J. Norreys Esq., Chairman

Drs. Bardsley, Mitchell, Lyon, Carbutt, Davenport Hulme, William Charles Henry; Revd. James Crook; Messrs. John Bentley, J. Pryce, R. Buckley, John Holford, G. Wood, George Faulkner, J. Holt, Samuel Fletcher, Robert Ogden, J. S. Heron, J. Barker, Benjamin Braidley, S. Sheldon junr.

On the motion of the Boroughreeve of Manchester, seconded by Dr. Bardsley,

It was resolved, 1

> That a Special Board of Health be formed to prevent as far as possible the introduction and spread of <u>Cholera Morbus</u> into this Town and neighbourhood.

Moved by John Bentley Esq. Seconded by George Faulkner Esq.

Resolved 2

> That the members of the Board do consist of the Presidents, Vice-Presidents, Treasurers, Deputy Treasurers, House Stewards, and Auditors of the Manchester Royal Infirmary, and the House of Recovery, together with the Medical and Surgical Officers of those Institutions, and also Dr. Bardsley, Dr. Hulme, Lieutenant Colonel Shaw, the Revd. James Crook, George Faulkner Esq., the Magistrates of the Division, the Boroughreeve and Constables of Manchester and the Churchwardens and Sidesmen of Manchester with power to add to their number.

Moved by the Revd. James Crook. Seconded by Robert Ogden Esq.

Resolved 3

> That a committee be appointed consisting of

> The Boroughreeve and Constables

> The Churchwardens

> The Physicians of the Infirmary & House of Recovery

> The Revd. James Crook

> Dr. S.A. Bardsley

> George Faulkner Esq.

3

to fix upon a suitable building as a receptacle for patients who may be attacked with <u>Cholera Morbus</u> in this Town and neighbourhood and to provide such other accommodation and make such other arrangements for the management thereof as they may deem necessary.

Moved by Dr. Carbutt. Seconded by J.S. Heron Esq.

Resolved 4
> That the said committee do meet tomorrow at the Town Hall at 11 o'clock and that they do report their proceedings as soon as possible to the Special Board.

Committee Meeting, Town Hall
November 11, 1831

Benjamin Braidley Esq., Chairman
Drs. D. Hulme, Mitchell, Bardsley, Lyon, Carbutt; Revd. James Crook; Messrs. W. Haynes, G. Faulkner, George Wood

Memorandum
> Two letters were read from the Chairman of the Weekly Board of the Royal Infirmary requesting a report from time to time from the Special Board on the subject of Cholera Morbus.

Resolved 1
> That Mr. Thorpe do inform the Chairman of the Weekly Board that as the whole of the Officers of the Royal Infirmary are now members of the Special Board of Health the committee trust this arrangement will be sufficient without making such report to the Weekly Board.

Resolved 2
> That Mr. Thorpe do also send a copy of the resolutions passed yesterday to the Chairman of the Weekly Board.

Resolved 3
> That the Revd. James Crook, Dr. Bardsley, Mr. W. Haynes and Mr. George Faulkner be appointed a sub-committee to make enquiry as to the accommodations and general suitableness of the <u>Riding School</u>, or of any other building that they may be able to find, and that they be requested to report to this committee tomorrow.

Resolved 4
> That as no funds are yet provided for defraying any expences which may be incurred by the Special Board, Mr. Thorpe be instructed specially to request

the attendance of the Churchwardens at the committee tomorrow, and that a copy of this resolution be sent to them along with an earnest expression of the desire of the committee that they should attend.

Resolved 5

That Dr. Bardsley be requested to correspond on behalf of the Special Board with Dr. Clanny, the Chairman of the Board of Health in Sunderland, in reference to the reported appearance of the Indian Cholera in that neighbourhood, and to make such enquiries as may be necessary for the purpose of ascertaining whether that dreadful malady has really reached that place, and if so, how it appears to have been imported, together with such other information as he may think desirable.

Resolved 6

That the Treasurer of the House of Recovery be requested to allow for the use of the Special Board such of the early volumes of its proceedings as Dr. Carbutt may select.

Memorandum

Dr. Carbutt presented a list of streets which in his opinion were in such a filthy and impure state as probably to superinduce disease, viz:-

Watson St.	Hewitt St.	Cupid's Alley
Fleet St.	Little Peter St.	Cumberland St.
Lombard St.	Alport Town	Spinning Field
Wood St.	Queen St.	Tassle St.
Back Bridge St.	Bk Queen St.	Tassle Alley
Mulberry St.	Jackson's Row	Sounding Alley
	Bootle St.	

Resolved 7

That the above list of streets be transmitted to the Paving and Scavenging Committees, requesting their particular attention to them for the purpose of being cleansed as early as possible.

Resolved 8

That all the meetings of this committee be punctual at the hours named and that it do now adjourn until tomorrow at 11 o'clock.

Committee Meeting, Town Hall
November 12, 1831

Benjamin Braidley Esq., Chairman
Drs. Carbutt, Mitchell, Lyon, D. Hulme, Bardsley; Revd. James Crook; Messrs. R. Ogden, S. Fletcher, W. Haynes, G. Faulkner, W. Crossley

Resolved 1
    That the minutes of the last meeting be confirmed.

Memorandum 1
    Dr. Bardsley reported, that Mr. Brooks, the owner of the Riding School in
    Lower Mosley Street, had informed him that that building could not be let
    for the purposes of this committee, as he had agreed to keep it open as a
    gymnasium and riding school for the ensuing twelve months.

Memorandum 2
    The Revd. James Crook and Mr. Faulkner reported that they had not yet
    found any building suitable for the purposes of the Board but that they had
    requested Mr. Lings to prepare a list of empty houses, factories, &c. which
    should be sent to the Board when ready.

Memorandum 3
    Meeting of the Churchwardens reported that they had issued an advertise-
    ment convening general meeting of the inhabitants being Leypayers of the
    Township of Manchester for Thursday next for the purpose of adopting such
    precautionary measures as the meeting may deem expedient in order to pre-
    vent the introduction of cholera into the Town of Manchester and to sanc-
    tion the payment out of the poor's rates of whatever expences may be incurred
    in carrying these measures into effect.

Resolved 2
    That the Churchwardens, the Boroughreeve, Dr. Bardsley and Dr. Carbutt be
    appointed a sub-committee to prepare draft of resolutions to be submitted to
    the public meeting on Thursday next.

Resolved 3
    That the papers headed "The Epidemic Cholera" now presented by Dr. Lyon
    be inserted on the minutes. (See Appendix)

Resolved 4
    That this meeting be adjourned to Monday the 14th. Inst. at 11 o'clock.

Appendix

The Epidemic Cholera,

having made its appearance in this country it becomes necessary to take precautions against its arrival in this Town.
    The means by which it spreads from place to place are not satisfactorily ascer-
tained, but there is reason to think that personal communication with the sick
contributes largely to that end.

Whilst medical men differ on the above point they are universally agreed – that the persons most liable to an attack are,

Those who occupy crowded, dirty, and ill ventilated dwellings;

Those who are ill-clothed, and ill-fed;

Those who are weakened, or disordered by intoxication, or intemperance of any kind;

Those who after excessive fatigue are exposed to the night air.

The most efficient precautions, therefore that can be taken against an attack of cholera, or other dangerous disease, will consist in a strict observance of the following maxims.

Keep your habitation clean, dry, and well aired;

Clear away all filth and rubbish from the ground in front and rear of your house;

Avoid crowding a great number of persons into one room, especially during the night;

Procure the most comfortable clothing and the most substantial food in your power;

and, in order to do this,

Avoid spending your money in procuring the means of intoxication:

Abstain altogether from spirits and be temperate in the use of fermented liquors:

Be regular in your hours of labour and of rest:

Avoid unnecessary communication with the sick.

Committee Meeting, Town Hall
November 14, 1831

W. Haynes Esq., Chairman
Drs. Carbutt, D. Hulme, S.A. Bardsley, J.L. Bardsley, Lyon, W.C. Henry, Mitchell; Revd. James Crook; Messrs. S. Fletcher, G. Faulkner, R. Ogden, H. Forth

Resolved 1
    That the minutes of the last meeting be confirmed.

Resolved 2

That the state of

Major Street	Style Street	Scholes Street
Ashton Street	Nicholas Street	Ludgate Street
Dyke Street	Lower part of Blakeley Street	
Bayley Street	Boardman Street	Cable Street
New Mount Street	Thompson Street	Chaderton Street
Marsden Street	Worsley Street	Lamb Lane

and of a court behind No. 12 Queen Street be reported to the Scavenging Committee.

Memorandum

The Churchwardens reported a list of houses, factories, &c. in Manchester which are at present unoccupied.

Resolved 3

That the same be inserted on the minutes. (See Appendix)

Resolved 4

That the committee be adjourned to tomorrow Tuesday 11 o'clock.

William Haynes (signature)

Appendix

District	Assessment Number	No. of Door	Street, &c.	Name or Description of Building	Amount of Assessment
No. 1 Part 1st.	208	338	Oldham Road late Lancashire	House	£10
	317	516	Oldham Road late Lancashire	House	£10
	567		Murray Street	Late Public House	£30
	1784		George Leigh Street	Late Public House	£30
	1323		Bengal Street	Warehouse late Crighton	£28
Part 2nd.			Ancoats Grove	House	£20
		4	Holt Town	House	£23
			Bradford Road near the Colliery	House	£23

District No.1 Part 2nd.	Assessment Number	No. of Door	Street, &c.	Name or Description of Building	Amount of Assessment
		22/23	Canning Street		£10
		66	Mill Street		£7
		71	Mill Street		£7
		3	Beswick Street		£8
		7	Beswick Street		£6
		102	Mill Street		£25
			Pollard Street		£10
			Pollard Street	2 Houses	£10
			Polard Street		£6
			Salter Street	3 Houses	£12
			Mill Street	House, Yard & Stables	£51
			White Street	Yard, &c.	£40
			Canal Street		£6
			Canal Street	2 Houses	£14
			Whalley Street	2 Houses	£10
			Whalley Street	2 Houses	£6
			Kirkby Street	Empty Gas Works	
			Pot Street		£25
			Pot Street		£7
			Fawcett Street		£5
			Newton Street	Yard &c.	
			Henry Street		£6
			Henry Street		£6
			Back Cotton Street	2 Houses	£6
			Holt Town		£10
			Holt Town		£5
			Holt Town		£10
			Holt Town		£17
			Bradford Colliery	3 Houses	£9
			Pickford Street	Factory	£221
		9		Factory	£221
		15		Factory Johnson & Brooke	£42
		16		Factory	£108
		17		Factory	£114
		19		Factory	£126
		21		Factory	£221
District No.2	765	11	St. George's Road	House	£14
	834	81	St. George's Road	House	£10

District No.2	Assessment Number	No. of Door	Street, &c.	Name or Description of Building	Amount of Assessment
	901	91	St. George's Road	House	£10
	2235		Collyhurst	House	£10
	2264		Collyhurst	House	£18
	65		Collyhurst	House	£18
	2275		Collyhurst	House	£10
	2285		Collyhurst	House	£16
	4256		Swan Street	House	£35
			Swan Street	Peel & Co's Foundry	
	4278			Harpurhey Factory	£170
District No.3		37	Hanging Ditch	Late Smith	£20
			Apple Market	late Forster	£30
			Near the New Burial Ground. Walker's Croft	late Ridal Wood's Factory	£73
			Hodgson's Vaults Blackfriars		£25
District No.4			Crescent	House	£30
			Back Crescent	House	£10
	502	8	Ancoats Place	House	£14
	503	9	Ancoats Place	House	£14
	579		Mount Street	House	£30
	618	9	Cooper's Buildings	House	£6
	704		Ducie Street	Aldknow's Warehouse	£150
		21	Piccadilly	House and Shop	£55
			Lever Street	House	£10
			Friday Street	Warehouse	£12
			Friday Street	Office	£10
District No.5	56		Bridgewater Place	Warehouse	£50
	227		Swan Street	House and Shop	£20
	394		Shude Hill	House and Shop	£20
	574		Tib Street	House	£10
	5		Tib Street	House	£12
	6		Tib Street	House	£12
	902		Whittle Street	Warehouse	£12
	959		Church Street	Warehouse	£80
	962		Church Street	Warehouse	£80

District No.5	Assessment Number	No. of Door	Street, &c.	Name or Description of Building	Amount of Assessment
	7		Church Street	Warehouse	£80
	74		Church Street	Warehouse	£130
	1039		Garden Lane	Warehouse	£60
	1214		Back Turner Street	House	£30
	68		Thomas Street	House	£18
	9		Thomas Street	Warehouse	£20
	1270		Thomas Street	House	£16
	1392		James Street	House and Shop	£20
	3		James Street		£8
	1456		Edge Street	Shops	£80
	1525		Oak Street	House and Shop	£18
District No.7	762	68	Bloom Street	House	£16
District No.8		32	Falkner Street		£18
		15	Back George Street	Warehouse	£45
		28	Back George Street	Warehouse	£50
		40	Back George Street	Warehouse	£35
		47	Back George Street	Warehouse	£40
			Back Mosley Street	Warehouse	£25
		3	Bond Street	House	£10
District No.10		22	George Street		£50
		24	George Street		£50
		18	Lower Mosley Street		£10
			Oxford Road		£18
		48	Wakefield Street		£60
District No. 11	33	15	Cooper Street		£40
	34	16	Cooper Street		£40
	91	1	Chapel Street	late Goddard	£10
	106	32	Loyd Street	late Hughes	£10
	112	24	Loyd Street		£16
	315	15	Queen Street	Warehouse	£26
	350	24	Queen Street	Works	£20
	501	2	Mount	House	£10
	539		South Street	House	£25
	692	3	Jerusalem Place	House	£10
	1211	3	Back Alport	Works	£30
	1635	2	Lower Mosley Street	House	£50

District No.11	Assessment Number	No. of Door	Street, &c.	Name or Description of Building	Amount of Assessment
	1662	15	Great Bridge Street	House	£10
	1695	32	Great Bridge Street	House	£20
	1699	26	Great Bridge Street	House	£12
	1716	4	Great Bridge Street	House	£25
	2302	315	Deansgate	Works	£25
	2311	295	Deansgate	House	£14
	2321	283	Deansgate	Warehouse	£140
	2373	205	Deansgate	House	£10
District No.12			South Gate	Benjamin Williams Warehouse	£15
			St. Mary's	Mary Lynal, House	£25
			St. Mary's	– Roxby, House	£22
			North Parade	– Cardwell, House	£20
			Water Street	Flemming, Warehouse	£36
District No.13		21	Bridge Street		£35
		15	Water Street		£16
		30	Water Street		£20
		31	Water Street		£16
		46	Quay Street		£14
		52	Parliament Street		£14
		53	Parliament Street		£14
		54	Parliament Street		£14
			Dolefield	An old house	£15
		37	Gartside		£24
		7	Irwell Street		£15
		20	Irwell Street		£16
		27	Young Street		£12
		29	Young Street		£12
		23	Hardman Street		£15
District No.14		4	Great John Street	House	£30
		6	Great John Street	House	£30
		8	Great John Street	House	£30
		7	Quay Street	House	£26
		5	Quay Street	House	£55
			Water Street	House, late Mather	£25

Board of Health Committee, Town Hall
November 15, 1831

Benjamin Braidley Esq., Chairman
Drs. Mitchell, S.A. Bardsley, D. Hulme, Carbutt, Lyon; Revd. James Crook;
Messrs. G. Faulkner, W. Haynes

Resolved 1
 That the following buildings being thought suitable in point of <u>situation</u>,
Mr. Faulkner be requested to examine them, and to take such <u>two</u> of them
(say if possible one near George Leigh Street, and one near Wakefield Street)
as he may think proper, and for as short a period as he can, subject to the
option of taking them for such <u>further</u> period as may be wanted; viz:–

Murray Street	Millers Lane
George Leigh Street	Edge Street
Ducie Street	Wakefield Street
James Street	Quay Street

or, any other <u>two</u> houses, say one on the northern and the other on the southern side of Manchester.

Memorandum
 Read a communication from the Scavenging Sub-Committee on the subject
of cleansing the paved and unpaved streets.

Resolved 2
 That the same be entered on the minutes. (See Appendix)

Resolved 3
 That the following streets be reported to the Scavenging Committee as in a
very dirty state, viz: –

Lad Lane	Dyers Court
Back Lad Lane	Crown Street
Dyers Lane	Trumpet Street
Dole Street	

Sub-Committee of the Board of Health, Town Hall
November 15, 1831

Benjamin Braidley Esq., Chairman
Drs. Carbutt, S.A. Bardsley; Mr. Samuel Fletcher

 It was agreed that the following resolutions be submitted for the approval of
the meeting of Ley-payers to be held on Thursday next.

Resolved 1
    That it is expedient to adopt such immediate precautionary measures as may tend to check the spread of Cholera Morbus and abate its virulence in case that disorder should unfortunately be introduced into this Town.

    To be moved by Dr. Bardsley.

Resolved 2
    That for this purpose, a Special Board of Health be established, consisting of the Presidents, Vice Presidents, Treasurers, Deputy-Treasurers, House Stewards, Auditors, and Committees of the Manchester Royal Infirmary, the House of Recovery and the Ancoats Dispensary, together with the Medical and Surgical Officers of those institutions, Dr. Bardsley, Dr. Holme, Lieutenant Colonel Shaw, Revd. James Crook, Mr. George Faulkner, the Magistrates of the Division, the Boroughreeve and Constables of Manchester, the Churchwardens and Sidesmen, the Surveyors of the Highways, and the members of the Paving and Scavenging Committees under the Police Act, with power to add to their number.

    To be moved by Benjamin Braidley Esq. Boroughreeve.

Resolved 3
    That the expences which may be incurred in carrying the above resolutions into effect, be paid out of the poor's rate, and the Churchwardens of Manchester are hereby authorized to discharge the same.

    To be moved by Mr. Bradshaw.

Appendix

Scavenging Sub-Committee, Town Hall
November 14, 1831

Resolved
    "That in considering the communication from the Committee of the Board of Health it appears very desirable that every effort should be made to cleanse the streets of the Town whether they are paved or unpaved but that as this committee have already engaged the whole of the Scavengers which they have been authorized to do by the Commissioners and even gone about £10 per week beyond the means granted them they regret they cannot comply with their request as speedily as they could wish for want of funds, and as regards the list of streets presented by the Board of Health most of them are in an unpaved state and it is suggested that the owners of them should be compelled by indictment to cleanse them, and perhaps at the public meeting to be held

on Thursday next it may be properly recommended, in the mean time, to authorize the Churchwardens to assist in cleansing the unpaved streets."

(A true copy)
(Signed) John Thorpe junr.

Board of Health Committee, Town Hall
November 16, 1831

Benjamin Braidley Esq., Chairman
Drs. Mitchell, Bardsley, D. Hulme, Carbutt; Messrs. W. Haynes, G. Faulkner

Resolved
That the minutes of the last meeting be confirmed.

Memorandum
Dr. Bardsley read a letter which he had received from a medical friend at Sunderland (Dr. Winterbottom) which, with his permission, was directed to be inserted on the minutes, as also the letter sent by Dr. Bardsley to Dr. Winterbottom.

Copy of Dr. Bardsley's letter to Dr. Winterbottom.

Sir,
In conformity with the above resolution, I have the honour to address you on the subject of the cholera, which has appeared in your Town.

The alarm in this very populous and extensively commercial place, renders it imperative on the Board of Health to endeavour to obtain the best information in their power on a subject hitherto involved in doubt and obscurity. I shall therefore take the liberty for the sake of brevity and dispatch, to state my enquiry in the form of queries and respectfully solicit your attention to the same.

1st. Had any of the persons supposed to fall victims to the cholera been on board suspected vessels or come into contact with any of their crews?

2nd. Are the symptoms of the disease such as manifestly characterize Indian Cholera? or do they only differ in degree with those usually occurring in the autumnal cholera of Sunderland?

3rd. Is the disease confined to one quarter of your Town, or rather to contiguous dwellings? and does it affect persons in higher as well as lower stations of life, and who live in airy as well as crowded parts of the Town?

4th. What is the actual number of patients attacked by the malady up to the latest period? and what is the proportion between deaths and recoveries?

Your reply as early as convenient will be esteemed a favour by, Sir

> your very obedient servant,
> (Signed) S.A. Bardsley.

Ardwick
November 10, 1831

Copy of Dr. Winterbottom's Letter to Dr. Bardsley

> Sunderland
> November 14, 1831

My dear Doctor,

I sent you a hasty letter yesterday accompanied with a Sunderland newspaper which I hope would prove somewhat satisfactory – today I forward you a second edition of the same paper which contains some very important and satisfactory documents. I write to you now in Sunderland, having just returned from a meeting of the Board of Health; as a number of Medical Gentlemen were present I took the opportunity when the meeting had broken up, to read to them your queries: They told me they thought you would find them nearly all answered in the second edition of the paper now sent: however, I shall briefly notice them as well as I could collect from a private conversation with those who were present.

1st. How was the disease communicated? – Not known, certainly not brought by any vessel, i.e. as far as human foresight can decide.

2nd. Could communication with the crews of vessels be traced? Certainly not and it is a very curious fact that not an instance of any seaman being infected, has occurred; that is, of men now in the habit of going to sea.

3rd. "Number of patients"? About 30 and one half or perhaps a little more have died. The medical gentlemen think the symptoms resemble continental cholera.

4th. Respecting contiguity of houses, it does not seem to attach itself to particular quarters of the Town further than affecting the low, dirty and filthy parts; of which I am sorry to say there is no lack.

I am now the less anxious to extend my letter because you will receive much information from the paper sent, and also from Dr. Gaulter, a townsman of yours, now in Sunderland and who promised me after the meeting, to write his opinions to the Board of Health. Now, my dear Sir, allow me to say if I can give you any further information on this subject or any other, freely command me. I... *[Letter ends here but full version printed in press continues: I shall only observe that one of the modes pursued on such occasions as epidemics &c is to whitewash the houses of the poor, whilst they occupy the apartments – that is, they deluge them with water, not considering that* <u>*dry dirt*</u> *can do no harm; but when* <u>*wet*</u>*, it is brought into life. Another inconsistency – we allow the poor to live in cellars never visited by the cheerful light of the sun. Can we suppose the glorious luminary created for no other purpose than to light us through the streets or ripen cucumbers? Is it not a powerful agent – perhaps the* <u>*most powerful one*</u> *– of disinfecting the air, and of preserving the wonderful uniformity in the atmospheric mixture! Would it not be better, with regard to the poor, first to enlighten their houses, and* <u>*then*</u> *to enlighten their minds! I hope the cholera may have a better effect than many charity sermons, by proving to the rich that it is not a matter of indifference, – whether the poor do possess, or do not possess, the necessaries and comforts of life.*

Yours truly
Thos. M. Winterbottom

P.S. I was told, to day, what you probably know, but to me it was new – that the Epsom salt has a very prejudicial effect in this cholera; and that in India, when cholera prevails, it is forbid to be used by the soldiers or for them. (Manchester Times and Gazette, 19 November 1831)]

Board of Health, Town Hall
November 17, 1831

Benjamin Braidley Esq., Chairman
Drs. S.A. Bardsley, J.P. Kay; Revd. T. Tate, G. Dugard; Messrs. G.R. Chappell, G. Peel, G. Murray, J. Kennedy, P. Ewart junr., R. Ogden, E. Satterthwaite, S. Fletcher, J. Woollam, J. Hampson, Murray junr.

Resolved 1
That the resolution passed at the public meeting of Leypayers held this day be published in all the papers of Saturday next.

Resolved 2
That the first General Board be convened for Monday morning next at 11 o'clock.

Resolved 3
That in the meanwhile the Committee of the Special Board of Health which has been sitting every day for the last week be requested to continue their meetings daily.

Resolved 4

> That the Medical Gentlemen on the Board of Health be requested to meet here tomorrow at half past 12 o'clock to prepare the draft of a code of instructions and queries and to report the same to the Board on Monday next.

Resolved 5

> That the letter from the Infirmary Board now read be inserted on the minutes. (See Appendix)

Appendix

Manchester Royal Infirmary
November 15, 1831

Sir,

> I am directed gratefully to acknowledge the receipt of a copy of the proceedings of the Cholera Committee in compliance with the request of the Weekly Board, and to inform you that as the officers of this charity are now members of the Special Board of Health it will be unnecessary for your committee to communicate its further proceedings.
>
> I have the honour to be, Sir,
> Your most respectful and obedient servant
> (Signed) H.T. Neild
> Secretary

To the Chairman of the Cholera Committee
Town Hall

Board of Health, Town Hall
November 18, 1831

Drs. S.A. Bardsley, Mitchell, Lyon, Carbutt, D. Hulme; Revd. James Crook

Adjourned for want of attendance.

Board of Health, Town Hall
November 21, 1831

W. Haynes Esq., Chairman
Drs. Mitchell, Hulme, J.P. Kay, Lyon; Revd. J. Crook; Messrs. Addison, F. Fincham, J. Mountain, H. Beaver, J.S. Heron, G. Peel, H. Forth, J. Rooke, G. Faulkner, J.Walker, J. Butterworth, J. Potter, T. Kerr, R. Ogden, S. Fletcher, J. Woollam, J. Barker, T. Townend, J. B. Clarke; Lieutenant Colonel Shaw

Resolved 1

> That the proceedings of the public meeting of Leypayers, held on the 17[th.] Inst. now read, be inserted on the minutes.

Copy

Town Hall, Manchester
November 17, 1831

At a public meeting of the inhabitants of Manchester, being Leypayers, held here this day "for the purpose of adopting such precautionary measures as the meeting may deem expedient, in order to prevent the introduction of cholera into the Town of Manchester, and to sanction the payment out of the poor's rate of whatever expences may be incurred in carrying this measure into effect",

Robert Ogden Esq., Senior Churchwarden,
in the Chair.

Messrs.	Benjamin Braidley, Boroughreeve	
	S. Fletcher	
	W. Crossley	Churchwardens
Drs.	S.A. Bardsley	Drs. Mitchell
	W.C. Henry	D. Hulme
		Dr. Carbutt
Messrs.	W. Haynes	
	H. Forth	Constables
Messrs.	J. Bradshaw	Thomas Darwell
	Richard Potter	John Kennedy
	T. Flintoff	George Faulkner
	Thomas Birtles	Thomas Harbottle
	F.R. Hodgson	James Hampson
	George Murray	Archibald Prentice
	James Wroe	E. Evans
	Joseph Peel	Thomas Townend
	Frederick Fincham	J. Barker
	J. Woollam	James Holt
	George R. Chappell	and others.

1st. It was moved by Dr. Bardsley, seconded by Mr. Richard Potter, Cannon-Street, and resolved unanimously,

That it is expedient to adopt such immediate precautionary measures as may tend to check the spread of Cholera Morbus, and abate its virulence, in case that disorder should unfortunately be introduced into this Town.

2nd. Moved by Benjamin Braidley, Esq. Boroughreeve, seconded by Mr. Birtles, and resolved unanimously,

That for this purpose a Special Board of Health be established, consisting of the Presidents, Vice Presidents, Treasurers, Deputy-Treasurers, House Stewards, Auditors and Committees of the Manchester Royal Infirmary, the House of Recovery, and the Ancoats Dispensary, together with the Medical and Surgical Officers of those institutions; also Dr. S.A. Bardsley, Dr. E. Holme, Lieutenant Colonel Shaw, the Revd. James Crook, Mr. George Faulkner, the Magistrates of the Division, the Boroughreeve and Constables of Manchester, the Churchwardens and Sidesmen, the Surveyors of the Highways and the Members of the Paving and Scavenging Committees under the Police Act, with power to add to their number.

3rd. Moved by Mr. Bradshaw, seconded by Mr. Darwell, and resolved unanimously,

That the expences which may be incurred in carrying the above resolutions into effect, be paid out of the poor's rate, and the Churchwardens of Manchester are hereby authorized to discharge the same.

4th. Moved by Mr. Harbottle, seconded by Mr. S. Fletcher, and resolved unanimously,

That the foregoing resolutions be advertised in all the Saturday's papers, under the directions of the Board of Health now appointed.

(Signed) Robert Ogden, Chairman

5th. Moved by Mr. Thomas Townend, seconded by Mr. Darwell, and resolved unanimously,

That the thanks of the Leypayers be given to the Churchwardens for calling this meeting, and to Robert Ogden, Esq. for his conduct in the chair.

(Signed) Benjamin Braidley.

Resolved 2
That the proceedings of the provisional Board of Health be approved and adopted as the proceedings of this Board.

Resolved 3
That the sub-committee be requested to continue their enquiries as to suitable buildings both in regard to accommodation and situation for receiving patients and report the same.

Resolved 4
That the communication from the Central Board of Health now read be entered on the minutes. (See Appendix No.1)

Resolved 5

> That the report of the medical members of the Special Board now read be received and entered on the minutes. (See Appendix No.2)

Resolved 6

> That the code of instructions alluded to in the last mentioned report be forth-with printed for distribution. (See Appendix)

Resolved 7

> That the tables of queries for the use of Inspectors noticed in the same report be forthwith printed. (See Appendix No.3)

Resolved 8

> That a sub-committee be appointed for the division of the Town into districts with a view to form separate Boards of Health for the same, each board to consist, if possible, of a resident clergyman and a number of substantial house-holders and of one medical man at least.

Resolved 9

> That the said sub-committee be composed of the following persons viz:

> The Boroughreeve and Constables
> The Churchwardens and Sidesmen
> Colonel Shaw   Dr. J.P. Kay
> Dr. S.A. Bardsley   Mr. F. Fincham

> and that they be requested to report as early as possible the division and arrangements they may propose.

Resolved 10

> That each Board be instructed to correspond with the Special Board of Health in order that the plans adopted by it may be carried into execution by the District Boards.

Resolved 11

> That an Honorary Secretary and also a Stipendiary Secretary be appointed and that they be summoned to meet on Tuesday morning at nine.

Resolved 12

> That the medical members of the Special Board be appointed a committee to confer with that Board on such points as more immediately refer to medical subjects.

Resolved 13

> That the Special Board of Health meet daily at 11 a.m. and that a circular be

this day issued to call the meeting of to-morrow which shall contain this notification.

Resolved 14
> That Benjamin Braidley Esq. Boroughreeve be Chairman of the Special Board of Health.

William Haynes (signature)

Appendix No.1

Council Office Whitehall
November 14, 1831

Sir,

The Central Board of Health having maturely weighed all the information which has been transmitted to them relative to the progress of the Asiatic Spasmodic Cholera in various parts of Europe, but more particularly guided by the conclusions on this head to which Drs. Russell and Barry have arrived after a five months careful and laborious observation of the character of that disease in those parts of Russia which they have visited, beg leave to suggest for your consideration the following sanitary hints:

1. As to Precautionary Measures.

In order to ensure the adoption and realize the benefit of any system of sanitary arrangements in a large community, the first essential point is to divide that community into subordinate sections, and to form District Boards of Health, each to consist, if possible, of a resident clergyman and a number of substantial householders, and of one medical man at least.

These Boards should be charged with the following duties in their respective Districts, viz:

1st. To appoint Inspectors. Each Inspector to visit daily, and to enquire carefully after the health, means of subsistence, cleanliness, and comforts of the inmates of, say, (100 houses more or less) according to local circumstances.

2ndly. To receive and examine the reports of these Inspectors, which should be made up to a given hour on each day.

3rdly. To endeavour to remedy, by every means which individual and public charitable exertion can supply, such deficiency as may be found to exist in their respective districts in the following primary elements of public health, viz. the food of the poor, clothing, bedding, ventilation, space, cleanliness, outlets for domestic filth, habits of temperance, prevention of panic.

4$^{thly.}$ To report to their principal Boards respectively on the above heads, as well as on the actual state of health of their districts. The subordinate divisions of each district ought to be numbered or lettered, and each district named; the names of the members of each Board, of the Medical Men attached to each, and of the visiting Inspectors employed, should be placarded in conspicuous places.

Principal Boards of Cities, Towns, or Parishes to report directly to the Central Board in London: –

1$^{st.}$ On the actual state of health of their whole population.

2$^{ndly.}$ On the precautionary measures already carried into effect.

3$^{rdly.}$ On the measures contemplated.

4$^{thly.}$ On suspected sources, if any there be, from whence this particular disease might possibly spring.

With regard to precautions as to intercourse with suspected or really infected persons or places, the Board are confident that good sense and good feeling will not only point out, but morally establish, as far as may be practicable, the necessity of avoiding such communication as may endanger the lives of thousands.

But they strongly deprecate all measures of coercion for this purpose which, when tried upon the Continent, invariably have been productive of evil. The best inducement to a prompt acknowledgement of the disease having entered a family, as well as to an early and voluntary separation of the sick from the healthy, will always be found in the readiness and efficiency with which public charitable institutions attend to the objects noticed in s. 3.

It is with much satisfaction that the Board feel themselves authorized to declare and it will be no doubt highly consolatory to the public to learn, that under proper observances of cleanliness and ventilation, this disease seldom spreads in families, and rarely passes to those about the sick, under such favourable circumstances, unless they happen to be particularly predisposed.

It will not therefore be necessary, where there is space, and where due attention is paid to cleanliness and purity of air, to separate members of families actually affected by the disease, nor to insulate individual houses, unless in cases of crowded, filthy, badly ventilated habitations, and other contingencies, which involve the health and safety of all.

It having been proved by ample experience, in more than one city in Europe, that the fitting up and furnishing of hospitals for the reception of the poorer classes supposed likely to be attacked by the disease, at a period too long before its actual breaking out, has been productive of great waste of means, by the spoiling of various articles, and the consequent want of wholesome accommodation when most required, the Central Board would recommend that proper and sufficient house-room only be secured and prepared in the first instance, and that the charitable be called upon only to pledge themselves to furnish at a given notice such articles of bedding, furniture, &c. or the value of them, as they would have at once contributed.

By this means the deterioration of perishable articles will be avoided, and should the District entirely escape, the contribution will be saved.

The situation which the Board would recommend for temporary cholera hospitals would be, those most detached, insulated, and thoroughly exposed to free and open air; the description of house, such as would admit of the most perfect ventilation and cleanliness and the largest space around the sick.

The Board would recommend, when a family is reported to be in an unhealthy state by the Sub-Inspector, and the disease confirmed to be cholera by a medical member of the District Board, that the head of such family, if unable to afford proper accommodation at home, be advised to send the sick person forthwith to the temporary hospital, and that the other members of the family be supplied with such additional means and comforts as their state may require to enable them to resist the influence of the infected atmosphere in which they live.

2.   Medical and Dietetic Precautions

These will be found of considerable importance, from their contributing to prevent or diminish the susceptibility to infection which individuals may possess at the moment the disease breaks out.

No sudden nor extensive alterations should be made in the usual modes of living. All changes of food, to be useful, indeed, not to be absolutely prejudicial, should tend to render it drier, more nutritive and concentrated; moderately costive bowels, the almost invariable consequence of a dry invigorating Diet, will be found more conducive to exemption from cholera than an opposite habit.

Whenever aperients may become indispensable, those of a warm aromatic kind in moderate doses, or domestic means should alone be resorted to.

What is generally understood by salts, viz. Glauber's Salts and Epsom Salts, as well as other cold purgatives, should not be taken <u>in any quantities</u>, nor on any account without the express prescription of a medical man.

The Medical Members of the Board beg to state, in the most decided manner, that no specific preventative against cholera is known to exist, and that the drugs hitherto offered with this pretension, in countries where the greatest ravages have been caused by this disease, not only did not possess the negative virtue of doing no harm, but were found to be absolutely injurious.

The true preventatives are a healthy body, and a cheerful, unruffled mind. Looseness of bowels should be immediately checked, and any thing like periodical chills or cold perspirations should be met by quinine in suitable doses; but habitual drugging at all times <u>improper</u>, is to be deprecated in the strongest terms when epidemic disease is apprehended.

The Board have been anxious to lay before the public, as early as possible the above precautionary outlines, which they trust will tend, together with the suggestions emanating from the wisdom and observation of your and other local boards, if not to exempt the whole population of these realms from the scourge of Spasmodic Cholera, at least to enable them to meet it, in the event of its appearing amongst them, with physical and moral constitutions the least likely to suffer from its virulence.

The Central Board will avail themselves of the earliest opportunity to transmit to you any further sanitary suggestions which may occur to them on the subject of precautionary measures, as well as an outline of instructions now in preparation for communities supposed to be actually attacked.

> I have the honor to be, Sir,
> Your most obedient servant
> (Signed) E. Stewart. Chairman

To the Chairman of the Board of Health at Manchester
(Franked) C.C. Greville.

Appendix No.2

At a meeting of the medical members of the Board of Health

Dr. Bardsley, Chairman
Drs. Mitchell, Lyon, Pendlebury, J.P. Kay, Hulme, Carbutt, Mr. Addison

Resolved 1
   That the code of instructions for preserving the health of the public and guarding against the introduction and spread of cholera be submitted to the Board. (See Appendix).

Resolved 2

That in case the Special Board of Health should think proper to adopt a system similar to that recommended by the Special Board of Health of London for the purpose of a minute inspection of the streets and houses of the Town the Medical Committee beg leave to submit to them the accompanying forms of inquiry – one concerning the state of the houses requiring the attention of the Churchwardens and Overseers – another for the purpose of obtaining a report of the state of streets, courts, &c. to be forwarded to the Scavenging Committee. (See following Appendix).

Appendix No.3

Table No.1.
Inquiries concerning the State of Houses

District No. ——   Inspectors, —— —— ——
Inspector's Tables

Name of Street, Court, &c.	No.	No.	No.	No.	No.	No.
1. Is the House in good repair?						
2. Is it clean?						
3. Does it require Whitewashing?						
4. Are the Rooms well ventilated or can they be without change in Windows, &c?						
5. Is the House damp or dry?						
6. Are the Cellars inhabited?						
7. Are these inhabited Cellars Damp or ever flooded?						
8. Are the soughs in a bad state?						
9. Who is the Proprietor?						
10. What number of Families or Lodgers does the House contain?						
11. What is the state of the Beds, Closets, and Furniture?						
12. Is a private Privy attached to the House?						
13. Will the tenants assist in Cleansing the Streets & Houses?						
14. Will they allow the Town's authorities to whitewash them, if they cannot conveniently do it themselves?						
15. Are the tenants generally healthy?						
16. What is their occupation?						
17. Remarks concerning Food, &c.						
18. Habits of Life						
19. General observations						

Inquiries concerning the state of Streets, Courts, Alleys, &c.

District No. ——   Inspectors, —— —— ——

Names of Streets, Courts, Alleys, &c. &c.	Name	Name	Name
Is the street, court or alley narrow, and is it ill ventilated?			
Is it paved or not?			
If not, is it under the Police Act?			
Does it contain heaps of Refuse, Pools of Stagnant Fluid, or deep Ruts?			
Are the public and private Privies well situated, and properly attended to?			
Is the Street, Court, or Alley, near a Canal, River, Brook, or Marshy land?			
General observations			

Board of Health, Town Hall
November 22, 1831

Dr. S.A. Bardsley, Chairman
Drs. J.P. Kay, Lyon; Revd. James Crook; Messrs. T. Entwistle, F. Fincham, G.R. Chappell, John Barker, Thomas Weatherby

Resolved 1
　　That the Boroughreeve and Mr. Barker be requested to engage an assistant secretary.

Resolved 2
　　That Mr. Newberry be added to the Special Board.

Resolved 3
　　That Dr. Gaulter be added to the Special Board.

Resolved 4
　　That the Very Revd. the Warden and the Clergy of the Collegiate Church be added to the Special Board – that they and also Mr. Newberry and Dr. Gaulter be informed of their appointment.

Resolved 5
　　That the Secretary be instructed to get the circular prepared by the sub-committee for the formation of the District Boards immediately printed and circulated.

Resolved 6

> That that part of the clause in the Manchester Police Act relating to the throwing of any kind of rubbish in the streets be added to the code of instructions to the poor and that Mr. Fincham be requested to superintend the printing.

S.A. Bardsley (signature)

Board of Health, Town Hall
November 23, 1831

Mr. George Faulkner, Chairman
Drs. Mitchell, D. Hulme; Messrs. T. Townend, Woollam, Weatherby, F. Fincham, Jo. Holford

Resolved 1st.

> That the proceedings of the meeting of the Board yesterday be confirmed.

Resolved 2nd.

> That Dr. D. Hulme be added to the committee appointed for the purpose of looking out in the Town for suitable buildings to be used as hospitals.

Board of Health, Town Hall
November 24, 1831

Dr. S.A. Bardsley, Chairman
Drs. H. Gaulter, Lyon, J.P. Kay, D. Hulme; Revd. Mr Wray; Messrs Woollam, Joseph Rooke, Frederick Fincham, G. Faulkner, J. Sandiford, T. Weatherby

Resolved 1

> That the committee appointed for the formation of the District Boards still sit to complete those arrangements.

Resolved 2

> That it be submitted to the Medical Committee whether it would not be desirable, under the contingency of the cholera unhappily breaking out in this Town, to be provided with a number of warm air spirit baths.

Resolved 3

> That 2000 copies of Table No.1 and 300 of Table No.2 with 100 backs be immediately ordered from the printer.

Resolved 4

> That a special meeting of the Medical Committee be called for to-morrow morning at 12 o'clock to take into consideration important subjects in connection with their appointment.

S.A. Bardsley (signature)

Board of Health, Town Hall
November 25, 1831

John Kennedy, Esq., Chairman
Dr. J.P. Kay, Revd. Mr. Crook, Mr. Dugard; Messrs. J.S. Heron, Hall, T. Townend,
J. Rooke, J.R. Taylor, J. Sandiford

Resolved 1
   That the proceedings of the Board yesterday be confirmed.

Resolved 2
   That the committee for the formation of the District Boards be summoned
   for tomorrow morning at 10 o'clock.

Resolved 3
   That suitable circulars for calling the meetings of the various committees be
   ordered to be printed.

Resolved 4
   That Mr. Joseph Grave junr. be appointed a member of the Special Board
   and that he be duly informed of that appointment.

Resolved 5
   That a committee be appointed to analyze the reports of the District Inspectors
   in order to classify the information obtained for the direction of the execu-
   tive operations of the Special Board of Health.

Resolved 6
   That the committee do consist of the following gentlemen with power to add
   to their number – a quorum to consist of three – and that they be requested
   to meet on Monday evening at 6 o'clock.

The Boroughreeve & Constables	The Churchwardens	
Revd. James Crook	Messrs. J.S. Heron	Messrs. J. Kennedy
Revd. G. Dugard	H. Beaver	J. Woollam
Dr. J.P. Kay	J. Barker	F. Fincham
Mr. Joseph Grave junr.	J. Murray	T. Townend

Board of Health, Town Hall
November 26, 1831

Dr. S.A. Bardsley, E. Lyon

Memorandum

Received – orders of the Privy Council relative to the removal of nuisances and medical reports – transmitted to the Boroughreeve to be immediately placarded.

Adjourned – the attendance insufficient to form a Board.

S.A. Bardsley (signature)

Board of Health, Town Hall
November 28, 1831

Benjamin Braidley Esq., Chairman
Drs S.A. Bardsley, E. Lyon, D. Hulme; Revd. James Crook; Colonel Shaw; Messrs. G. Faulkner, Joseph Grave, T. Weatherby, F. Fincham, Addison, Mr. Danson

Resolved 1

That circular letters be addressed to the clergymen and ministers of the several places of worship in Manchester and its vicinity to which burial grounds are attached requesting them to make a weekly return of the number of burials in their respective churchyards during the last five months of the year 1830 and also since the commencement of the month of July last up to the present time.

Resolved 2

That the code of instructions for the prevention and early treatment of cholera presented by the Medical Committee be immediately advertised in all the Manchester papers. (See Minute Book of the Proceedings of the Medical Committee – Appendix. Page 2)

Board of Health, Town Hall
November 29, 1831

Adjourned – the attendance insufficient to form a meeting.

Board of Health, Town Hall
November 30, 1831

Dr. S.A. Bardsley, Chairman
Drs. E. Lyon, J.P. Kay, J.D. Hulme; Colonel Shaw; Mr. H. Beaver

Resolved 1

That a notice be issued particularly requesting the attendance of the Boroughreeve, Constables & Churchwardens on Thursday morning at 11 o'clock to meet the committee appointed for the selection of suitable buildings as temporary hospitals.

Resolved 2
> That 150 backs and also 3000 copies of the precautionary address be ordered
> from the printers.

S.A. Bardsley (signature)

Board of Health, Town Hall
December 1, 1831

At 12 o'clock there being an insufficient number of persons present to form a meeting the parties desired that the Churchwardens or one of them be requested to attend at the adjourned meeting of tomorrow at the same hour.

Board of Health, Town Hall
December 2, 1831

George Faulkner Esq. Chairman
Drs. Lyon, S.A. Bardsley, J.D. Hulme; Revd. James Crook; Colonel Shaw, Messrs. T. Townend, F. Fincham, Weatherby, J. Woollam, Haynes, J.S. Heron, Bradshaw

Resolved 1
> That the Revd. James Crook, Mr. G. Faulkner, Dr. Lyon & Dr. Kay be
> requested to inspect the buildings now proposed as temporary hospitals or
> any other that may appear eligible and to report to the General Board at the
> meeting on Monday.

Resolved 2
> That Mr. Winstanley be added to the committee appointed for the classifica-
> tion of the district reports [and] to be informed of that appointment.

Resolved 3
> That Dr. Johns be added to the General Board and be duly informed of that
> appointment.

Board of Health, Town Hall
December 3, 1831

There not being a sufficient number of persons present to constitute a meeting it was adjourned to Monday at 11 o'clock.

Board of Health, Town Hall
December 5, 1831

Dr. S.A. Bardsley, Chairman
Drs. D. Hulme, E. Lyon, Johns; Revd. James Crook; Colonel Shaw; Messrs. F. Fincham, G. Faulkner, J. Woollam, T. Weatherby, E. Connell

Resolved 1

>That the sub-committee for the inspection of the buildings proposed as hospitals be requested to prosecute and complete their enquiries and to report to the Board as early as possible.

Resolved 2

>That the several District Boards in connection with this Board be requested to make enquiries whether in case of the cholera appearing in this Town, the Sunday schools in their respective districts may be obtained and used and at what expense.

Adjourned to Monday 11 o'clock.

S.A. Bardsley (signature)

**Board of Health
December 7, 1831**

Dr. S.A. Bardsley, Chairman
Drs. J.P. Kay, Lyon, Johns, Messrs. F. Fincham, J. Woollam, T. Townend, Mr. T. Weatherby

Resolved 1

>That the Committee of Classification be summoned to meet at 4 o'clock tomorrow (Thursday) to arrange the reports of Inspectors which have been received from the various districts.

Resolved 2

>That the sub-committee be requested to intimate to Mr. Guest that the Board will accept of his offer of the factory in Union Street at the rent of £2 per week after suitable repairs have been made and that the Committee be directed to make arrangements for putting it in a proper state for the reception of patients.

Memorandum

>Received a communication from the Scavenging Committee.

Resolved 3

>That the same be entered on the minutes of this Board. (See Appendix)

Resolved 4

>That Mr. P. Ewart junr. & Mr. F. Fincham be requested to wait on the landlords of the houses in Little Ireland to represent to them the uncleanly state of that part of the Town.

Resolved 5

That for the purpose of securing a full attendance at this Board the members be requested to attend for the future on Monday, Wednesday and Saturday in each week at 1/2 past 2 o'clock p.m. for the transaction of business and that notice be given to each member not present by circular.

Adjourned till Saturday 11 o'clock.

S.A. Bardsley

Appendix

Gentlemen

The Scavenging Committee beg to inform the Board of Health that they have in conjunction with the Churchwardens of Manchester placed twenty men to clean the unpaved streets, courts and alleys in various parts of the Town and they expect to have an increased number of men in a few days.

Town Hall,
December 5, 1831

To the Board of Health.

Board of Health, Town Hall
December 10, 1831

George Faulkner Esq., Chairman
Drs. E. Lyon, H. Gaulter, Johns; Messrs. S. Fletcher, L. Buchan, J. Potter, Mr. Winstanley, J.S. Heron

Resolved

That the proceedings of the last meeting of this Board be confirmed and also the proceedings of the Committee of Classification of the 8[th.] Instant.

Adjourned till Monday 1/2 past 2 o'clock.

Board of Health, Town Hall
December 12, 1831

Dr. J.P. Kay; Messrs. F. Fincham, T. Townend, T. Weatherby

The attendance being insufficient to constitute a meeting, it was adjourned till Wednesday at 1/2 past 2.

Board of Health, Town Hall
December 14, 1831

George Faulkner Esq., Chairman
Drs. J.P. Kay, Lyon, Johns; Revd. Mr Hollist; Messrs. J. Barker, T. Townend,
J. Grave junr., James Hampson, J. Woollam, Mr. Howarth

Resolved 1

> That Mr. Thorpe be requested to engage a clerk to assist the Stipendiary
> Secretary in preparing the classified reports of the state of the houses in this
> Town.

Resolved 2

> That Dr. J.P. Kay and Mr. T. Townend be requested to present the classified
> reports respecting the uncleanly state of the houses to the Churchwardens and
> Overseers.

Resolved 3

> That 100 copies of the Inspector's Table No.2 be immediately ordered from
> the printer.

Resolved 4

> That a sub-committee be formed to draw up a report of the state of Little
> Ireland and to communicate personally with the Magistrates that the
> committee do consist of the Revd. H. Fielding, Mr. Peter Ewart junr.,
> Mr. Frederick Fincham, Dr. Ferneley, Dr. Johns and Dr. Lyon and that they
> be forthwith informed of that appointment with a request to meet tomorrow
> at 1/2 past 2 precisely.

Resolved 5

> That Drs. Kay and Pendlebury with Messrs. Ransome and James Hampson
> be requested to form a sub committee and adopt the same course with regard
> to Clay Street.

Resolved 6

> That the following resolution be submitted for consideration at the meeting
> of the Board on Saturday: – "That 1/2 past 2 the hour at present appointed
> for the meetings of this Board having been generally complained of as incon-
> venient the future attendance of the Members be fixed for 11 o'clock and that
> they have due notice of this change."

Adjourned till Saturday. 1/2 past 2.

Board of Health, Town Hall
December 17, 1831

George Faulkner Esq. Chairman
Drs. S.A. Bardsley, D Hulme, E. Lyon, Johns; Revd. H. Fielding; Messrs. J. Thorpe, F. Fincham, T. Townend, T. Weatherby, J. Woollam, J. Potter, P. Ewart junr.

Resolved 1
> That 1/2 past 2 the hour at present appointed for the meetings of this Board having been generally complained of as inconvenient the future attendance of the Members be fixed for 11 o'clock <u>precisely</u> and that due notice be given to the members of this change.

Resolved 2
> That in future no resolution passed at any meeting of this Board shall be rescinded without 4 days previous notice being given by posting the same up in the Board Room.

Resolved 3
> That Dr. Bardsley be requested to draw up a communication to be forwarded to the Central Board in London appointed by order of the Privy Council and to have the same ready to be submitted for the adoption of this Board at their next meeting on Monday.

Adjourned till Monday 11 o'clock.

Board of Health, Town Hall
December 19, 1831

R. Ogden Esq., Chairman
Drs. S.A. Bardsley, Johns, J.P. Kay, Lyon, J.D. Hulme; Revd. H. Fielding; Lieutenant Colonel Shaw; Messrs. F. Fincham, T. Townend, J. Barker, S. Fletcher, J. Woollam, J. Bentley, P. Ewart junr.

Resolved 1
> That the proceedings of the Board on Saturday be confirmed.

Resolved 2
> That the agreement with Mr. Guest for engaging his factory in Union Street be concluded and that the sub-committee be requested to see that it is properly cleansed and fitted up with the requisite apparatus for warming the rooms and that no other steps be taken until the actual necessity occurs it being ascertained that beds and other furniture can be provided in 24 hours.

Resolved 3
> That a Deputy Chairman be appointed to this Board.

Resolved 4

That the address now read by Dr. Bardsley be adopted by this Board and forthwith transmitted to the Chairman of the Central Board in London. (See Appendix No.1)

Resolved 5

That the several District Boards of Health be empowered to add to their number.

Resolved 6

That the letter now read by Dr. Bardsley be adopted by this Board and that a copy be addressed and transmitted to the Chairman of each District Board. (See Appendix No.2)

Resolved 6 *[sic]*

That a letter be addressed to those parties who have not yet made a return of the number of interments in the cemeteries with which they are connected requesting them to send in their report as soon as possible.

Appendix No.1

Town Hall, Manchester
December 19, 1831

Sir,

The Special Board of Health established at a meeting of the ley-payers – November 17[th.] 1831 for the purpose of adopting such precautionary measures as may be deemed expedient to check the spread and abate the virulence of the Asiatic Spasmodic Cholera in case of its appearance in this Town, having completed their system of sanitary arrangements, are desirous to communicate to the central Board of Health in the metropolis an outline of their proceedings up to the present period and classed under the following heads.

1[st.] "On the actual state of health of their whole population."

From the reports of the medical members of the Board it appears, that continued fever (many cases of which assume the typhoid character) is much more prevalent at this season than has occurred for several years past. The house of recovery for fever patients is not capable of containing the number of applicants for admission, (a circumstance very rarely occurring since its establishment in 1809) and the fever is rather upon the increase in the neighbouring Townships. There have likewise occurred a few cases of the common, but <u>none of the spasmodic Asiatic Cholera</u>. The measles and scarlatina, both of the mild sort, have appeared in different parts of the Town and its vicinity. Upon the whole, the Town has been more unhealthy than usual during the autumnal months; But it is necessary to remark, that the fever is chiefly confined to the <u>indigent</u> classes, and especially those who reside in dirty, ill-ventilated dwellings and are irregular in their mode of living.

2nd. "On the precautionary methods already carried into effect."
The Town of Manchester has been divided into 14 Districts, and each district placed under a district Board of Health at the head of which a clergyman has been appointed, assisted by a medical gentleman, and respectable householders, Visitors, or Inspectors have been chosen, and furnished with books containing queries of most importance in regard to cleanliness – space – outlets for domestic filth – deficiency in bedding and other matters relating to the primary elements of public health. The answers to these queries have been transmitted to the Special Board and when properly classed and arranged will be promptly attended to. Already the streets have been generally cleansed and great pains are taken to remove all offensive accumulations of filth near the habitations of the poor, as well as to purify their houses internally by whitewashing &c.

A commodious factory favourably situated for ventilation, and nigh to the quarter of the Town most densely inhabited by the working classes has been rented; and will be kept in readiness to be converted into a hospital, for the reception of cholera patients, should unhappily this malady extend its ravages amongst us it will not be very difficult to provide other similar accommodations according to the urgency of circumstances. The Churchwardens are authorised to pay out of the Poor rates all expences incurred in carrying these measures into effect, and the greatest readiness in co-operating with the Board of Health is received by the different Committees of the Town Police for Scavenging, paving, &c. Precautionary measures similar to the above have been also adopted by the Townships joining to, and nearly connected with Manchester. The Boards of Health of these district Townships will communicate with the Special Board of Manchester. This Board trust under Divine Providence, that the plans of precaution already adopted and to be followed up as circumstances may require will answer the purpose for which they were designed, viz: to mitigate the severity and check the spread of Spasmodic Cholera.

I am, Sir &c. &c.

To the Chairman of the Central Board of Health
Council Office
Whitehall
London

Appendix No.2

Special Board of Health
Town Hall, Manchester
December 19, 1831

Reverend Sir,

In order to ensure the adoption and realize the benefit of any system of sanitary arrangement in this large and populous Town, the Special Board beg to direct your attention to the following statement of the duties with which the District Boards are charged, in the instructions communicated to this Board, by the central one established in the metropolis, by the order of government.

1st. "Each Inspector to visit daily, and to enquire carefully after the health, means of subsistence, cleanliness and comforts of a certain number of poor families according to local circumstances."

2nd. "To receive and examine these reports which should be made up to a given hour on each day."

3rd. To report to the principal Board on the above heads, as well as on the actual state of Health of the District and that the Chairman of the District Board be requested to attend the meetings of this Board as often as convenient. The Special Board hold their sittings thrice a week viz: on Monday, Wednesday and Saturday precisely at 11 o'clock and they beg to suggest whether it might not be advisable for the District Board to adopt the same plan.

I am, Sir, &c. &c. &c.

To the Chairman of the Board of Health for District No. —

Received from the Central Board a number of copies of the following address.

19/12/31

Central Board of Health,
Council Office, Whitehall, 13th. Dec. 1831.

Sir,

Agreeably to the Intimation given by this Board in the concluding Paragraph of their Circular, dated 14th. Ult, I have the Honor to transmit the subjoined "Sanitary Instructions for Communities supposed to be actually attacked by Spasmodic Cholera," with some Observations on the Nature and Treatment of the Disease, drawn up by Drs. Russell and Barry.

Every Individual being deeply interested in the Preservation of the Public Health, it is the bounden Duty of all to endeavour to arrest the Spread of Disease at its very Commencement. In order to attain this important Object

1st. The most efficient Arrangements should be made by the Local Boards of Health, and other Authorities, to obtain the earliest, and most correct Intelligence of every suspicious Case which may occur within their Jurisdiction.

2nd. All unnecessary Communication should be prevented, as far as possible, between the infected and the healthy.

3rd As Space, Cleanliness, and pure Air are of the most vital Consequence, both to the Recovery of the sick Person and to the Safety of those about him, the Patient labouring under Spasmodic Cholera should either be placed in a separate, well-ventilated Apartment of his own House, if it afford such Accommodation, and be attended by as few Persons as the Circumstances of his Case will admit, or be induced to submit to an immediate Removal to such Building as may have been provided for the Reception of Persons whose Circumstances will not afford the Advantages at Home, of Space, Air, and Separation from the healthy.

4th When an Individual shall have been attacked with this Disease, and placed under the most favorable conditions, as already pointed out, both for the Recovery of his own, and the Safety of the Public Health; – the Room or Apartment where he may have been attacked, and from which he may have been removed, should be purified by scrubbing, lime-washing, free Ventilation and Fumigation by heated Sulphuric Acid and Common Salt, with Black Oxyde of Manganese, or the same Acid with Nitre; or, when these Materials cannot be obtained, by strong Vinegar thrown upon heated Bricks. The Bed, Bedding, and Clothes should be immersed in Water, washed with Soap, and afterwards fumigated as above.

5th To correct all offensive Smells, Chloride of Lime may be applied; but great Caution is recommended in the Use of this Material, its Fumes continued for any Length of Time, having been found highly prejudicial to Health, more particularly in delicate Persons.

6th A Number of steady Men, proportionate to the District in which they are to act, should be appointed to limewash and purify, as ordered above, under the Direction of Medical Authority, such Apartments as may be pointed out by the Inspectors of the Local Board.

7th Those who die of this Disease should be buried as soon as possible, wrapped in Cotton or Linen Cloth saturated with Pitch, or Coal Tar, and be carried to the Grave by the fewest possible Number of Persons. The Funeral Service to be performed in the open Air.

8th It is of the utmost Importance to the Public Health that an improved Diet, and Flannel Clothing, at least Flannel Belts and Woollen Stockings, should be given to the Poor. No Person should ever allow himself to sit down and get cool, with wet Feet: Indeed the most particular Attention should be paid to keeping the Feet dry and warm. Repletion and Indigestion should be guarded against; all raw Vegetables, acescent, unwholesome Food and Drink avoided. Temperance should be most rigidly observed in every thing. In short, no Means should be neglected which may tend to preserve individual Health. The Neglect of any or all of these Cautions would not of themselves produce the specific Disease called Spasmodic Cholera; but such Neglect would most assuredly dispose the Individual living in an infected Atmosphere to be attacked by this Disease, when most probably he might otherwise have escaped.

The most effectual Means by which this Disease may be prevented from extending, is to enable the Poor, who are generally the first attacked, to oppose to its Influence, as far as practicable, those Ameliorations in Diet, Clothing, and Lodging which public, and private Charity will, it is hoped, not fail to produce.

Observations on the Nature and Treatment of the Disease, drawn up by Drs. Russell and Barry.

"Of the Two great Classes of Functions performed by the Organs of which Man is composed, One only is attacked in this Disease. The Operations of the Senses and of the Intelligence are either left untouched, or are affected but in a secondary Manner.

Those Functions, on the contrary, by which Existence as a living Being is preserved; those complicated Powers, by Means of which we are for ever appropriating and converting into a Part of ourselves Portions of the Matter around us; are all and at once deranged by the Attack of this terrible Malady. Nutrition is annihilated; Respiration becomes difficult, irregular, and inefficient; the involuntary Muscles no longer perform their Task; the voluntary are drawn into Contractions by other Powers than the Will; the Blood ceases to circulate; its Physical Properties are altered; its serous Portion is suddenly thrown out upon the intestinal mucous Surface of the Body; the Secretions are all arrested; and animal Heat is no longer produced.

Under such rapidly destructive, and almost universal Derangement of Function, the most energetic Efforts should be directed to reproduce what the Disease has rendered Nature unable to keep up; viz,

1st. Fluidity, Heat, and Motion in the Blood.

2nd. Regulated Action in the voluntary, and involuntary Muscles.

Lastly, but above every other Consideration, renewed Energy in the Nervous Centre, the Source of all Vitality and Function.

No Remedy at all approaching to the Nature of a Specific has been as yet discovered for this Disease. In fact, no One Mode of Cure can be usefully employed under all the Circumstances of any Disease. The Grades of Intensity, and the grouping of the Symptoms with which Spasmodic Cholera makes its Attacks, vary with the Conditions of the Subject; its Treatment, therefore, must vary with these Grades and Conditions.

The leading preliminary Symptoms generally are, either Diarrhoea, Spasms, Apoplectic Vertigo with Nausea, imperfect vomiting, or various Combinations of these Symptoms.

When the Diarrhoea affords Time for distinct Treatment, it ought to be arrested at once by the most prompt and efficient Measures; – by Opium in moderate Doses; Astringents; local Bleeding by Leeches, if the Subject be plethoric; by Cordials and Sulphate of Quinine, if there be cold Sweats; by confining the Patient strictly to Bed, and keeping up Heat; by Diet; by Emetics.

Should Spasms be the first and leading Symptom, Subnitrate of Bismuth, Cupping along the Course of the Spine, Cordial, and Antispasmodic Medicines, Opium, Frictions, and dry Warmth are indicated.

But when the Patient is suddenly seized with Vertigo, Nausea, Coldness, Loss of Pulse, Blueness of the Skin, shrinking of the Features and Extremities, with more or less watery Discharges and Cramps; constituting an aggravated Case of the worst Type; whether this State shall have come on without Warning, or shall have supervened upon either, or both of the preliminary Sets of Symptoms already mentioned, Time must not be wasted upon inert Measures. Such a Patient will inevitably perish, and within a very few Hours, if the paralysed vital Functions be not quickly restored.

Let him then be immediately placed between warm Blankets; and should no Medical Person be at hand, let Two Table-spoons full of common Kitchen Salt, dissolved in 6 oz. of warm Water, be given immediately, and at once, if he be an Adult Let dry and steady Heat be applied along the Course of the Spine, and to the Pit of the Stomach, (if no other Means be at hand,) by a Succession of heated Plates or Platters. Let the upper and lower Extremities be surrounded with Bags of heated Bran, Corn, Ashes or Sand, and assiduously rubbed with a warm Hand, and a little Oil or Grease to protect the Skin. Energetic, complete vomiting will probably be produced by the Salt; and perhaps bilious purging, with Tenesmus.

Should a Medical Man be on the Spot, a moderate Bleeding, if it can be obtained, would be desirable, previously to, or immediately after the Administration of the Salt, or of any other Emetic which may be preferred.

The extensively deranged Action of those Organs, whose Nerves are chiefly derived from, or connected with, the Spinal Marrow; the anatomical Characters found about that great Source of Vitality, after Death, in many

Cases of this Disease; together with the Success stated by Dr. Lange, Chief Physician at Cronstadt, to have attended the Practice mentioned below, founded upon these Views, in Twelve out of Fourteen aggravated Cases, fully justify the following Recommendation.

In Cases such as those just described, let the actual Cautery be freely applied to One or Two, or more Places on either Side of the Spine, as if for the Purpose of forming good-sized Issues. Should the heated Iron have produced any Excitement of the nervous Power, and the Salt-emetic have caused any Portion of the Bile to flow through its proper Duct, a great Step will have been accomplished towards Recovery from the Stage of Collapse. Cordials and Opiates judiciously administered; Sinapisms and other external Stimulants; Mercurials, with mild Aromatic Aperients, which the Intelligence and Activity of British Medical Practitioners will not fail to adapt to the actual Circumstances of each Case, will conduct the Patient safely to the Stage of Re-action.

The Organs, during the Collapse of this Disease, probably owing to deficient Vitality, often give no Indication of having been acted upon by repeated Doses of certain powerful Medicines, which under other Circumstances would have produced the most pronounced Effects. It is therefore suggested, that this temporary Insensibility of the System should not inculcate the Administration of such repeated Quantities as could, by Accumulation, when the Organs begin to recover their Vitality, give rise to unfavourable Results.

Thirst being a most distressing Symptom of this Disease, the Quality and the Temperature of the Drink should perhaps be left to the Choice of the Patient; but the Quantity taken at a Time should not exceed Four Ounces, and should be acidulated with Nitrous Acid, if the Patient will bear it.

Should the Disease prove extensively, and rapidly epidemic in a large Community, it would be prudent to establish Stations at convenient Distances from each other, where Medical Assistance and Medicines might be procured without the Risk of Disappointment or Delay. The Details of these Arrangements are left to the Wisdom of Local Boards of Health.

As the Symptoms of the consecutive Stage of feverish Re-action in Cholera differ but little, if at all, from those of ordinary Typhus, except perhaps in the greater Rapidity with which they but too often run to a fatal Termination; and as this Kind of Fever is treated in no Part of the World with more Success than in England, the entire Management of this Stage of the Disease is left to the Zeal and Science of the Profession at large.

Attentive Nursing, and assiduous, well-directed Rubbing, are of the utmost Importance; a strictly horizontal Position, however, must be maintained until the Heart shall have, partly at least, recovered its Action. An erect or even semi-erect position, during the Collapse, has been often observed to produce instant Death. Warm Baths, therefore, for this and other Reasons, are worse than useless; evaporating Fluids, and indeed all Moisture applied to the Skin, seem to be contra-indicated for obvious Reasons. Hot Air Baths, so contrived as to be applicable in a recumbent Posture, and admitting Access to the Patient for the Purpose of Friction, may be of use."

> I have the Honor to be,
> Sir
> Your most obedient servant,
> E. STEWART, Chairman.

Board of Health, Town Hall
December 21, 1831

Benjamin Braidley, Chairman
Drs. E. Lyon, J.P. Kay, W. Johns; Revd. James Crook; Colonel Shaw; Messrs. J. Bentley, J. Barker, J. Woollam, F. Fincham, J.S. Heron, T. Townend, G. Faulkner,

Resolved 1
> That the proceedings of the Board on Monday the 19th Instant be confirmed.

Resolved 2
> That the Constables of Manchester be appointed Deputy Chairmen of this Board.

Resolved 3
> That the letter now read from Mr. Matthews, surgeon be forthwith referred to the Nuisance Committee of the Police.

Resolved 4
> That Mr. W.R. Whatton, Surgeon, be added to the Special Board and that he be duly informed of that appointment.

Resolved 5
> That a copy of the communication of Mr. Woollam be submitted to the Nuisance Committee. (See Appendix No.1)

Resolved 6
> That the District Boards be requested severally to furnish the Special Board with an account of the number of sections into which the District is sub-divided and the names of the Inspectors with their respective places of

residence and that this request be transmitted with the circular prepared by Dr. S.A. Bardsley.

Resolved 7

That a committee be formed to correspond with the landlords of houses requiring repairs, soughing, ventilation and where the erection of additional privies would be desirable and that the committee do consist of Dr. J.P. Kay, Dr. E. Lyon, Revd. James Crook, Mr. J.S. Heron and Mr. P. Ewart junr.

Resolved 8

That it be recommended to the medical gentlemen of Manchester and the neighbouring districts in all cases of cholera or suspected cholera coming under their observation that no report to that effect be made public, until it has been reported to the Medical Committee of this Board and ascertained clearly whether it be cholera or not and that a circular be sent privately to each medical and surgical practitioner in Manchester and the vicinity to this effect.

Resolved 9

That the report of the sub-committee appointed to examine the state of Little Ireland now presented by Mr. Fincham and which has been submitted to the consideration of the Magistrates be inserted on the minutes. (See Appendix No.2)

Resolved 10

That the Classification Committee be requested to meet at 4 o'clock on Friday afternoon.

Adjourned till Saturday 11 o'clock.

Appendix

No.1

I beg to notice that the nuisance so often complained of in Queen Street, Deansgate in the yard of Maguiness and others has not yet been attended to, and to request that this notice may be handed to the Nuisance Sub-Committee, and desire their immediate attention to the same – 21st· December 1831.

(Signed) John Woollam

No.2

Gentlemen,

the undersigned having been deputed by the Special Board of Health to inquire into the state of Little Ireland beg to report that in the main street & courts abutting, the sewers are all in a most wretched state and quite inadequate to carry off the surface water, not to mention the slops thrown down by the inhabitants in about 200 houses.

The privies are in a most disgraceful state, inaccessible from filth, and too few for the accommodation of the number of people – the average number being <u>two</u> to 250 people. The upper rooms are with few exceptions very dirty and the cellars much worse, all damp, and some occasionally overflowed. The cellars consist of two rooms on a floor each 9 to 10ft square some inhabited by 10 persons, others by more: in many the people have no beds and keep each other warm by close stowage on shavings, straw &c.; a change of linen or clothes is an exception to the common practice. Many of the back rooms where they sleep, have no other means of ventilation than from the front rooms.

Some of the cellars on the lower ground were once filled up as uninhabitable but one is now occupied by a weaver and he has stopped up the drain with clay to prevent the water flowing from it into his cellar and mops up the water every morning.

We conceive it will be impossible effectually to remove the evils enumerated and offer the following suggestions with a view to their partial amelioration.

First, to open up the main sewer from the bottom and to relay it.

Secondly, to open and unchoke all the lateral drains and secure a regular discharge of the water &c. into the main sewer.

Thirdly, to enforce the weekly cleansing and purification of the privies.

Fourthly, if practicable to fill up the cellars.

Fifthly, to provide the inhabitants with quick lime and induce them to white-wash their rooms where it can be done with safety.

Sixthly, if possible to induce the inhabitants to observe greater cleanliness in their houses and persons.

In conclusion we are decidedly of opinion that should cholera visit this neighbourhood a more suitable soil and situation for its malignant development cannot be found than that described and commonly known by the name of Little Ireland.

Henry Fielding, Clerk
Edmund Lyon M.D.
Frederick Fincham
William Johns M.D.
Peter Ewart junr.

Members of the Board of Health in Manchester
Town Hall, 19 December 1831

To
The Magistrates of the District &c. &c.

Board of Health, Town Hall
December 24, 1831

The Very Revd. Dr. Calvert, Chairman
Drs J.D. Hulme, J.P. Kay, S.A. Bardsley, W. Johns, E. Lyon, H. Gaulter; R. W. Whatton; Rev. James Crook; Colonel Shaw; Messrs. Benjamin Braidley, T. Townend, F. Fincham, S. Fletcher, T. Weatherby, Mr Milne

Resolved 1
   That the proceedings of the Board on the 21st Inst. be confirmed.

Resolved 2
   That the certificates of the general state of health of this Town now presented from Messrs. Bruce & Ritchie, Leeds to facilitate the entry of vessels laden
   with goods shipped at Liverpool into the Spanish ports – be signed by the
   Chairman of the Board.

Resolved 3
   That the Classification Committee be requested to meet after the adjournment
   of the Board on Monday.

Resolved 4
   That in consequence of a report made to the Magistrates respecting a nuisance to be removed by their orders – the Magistrates having expressed
   doubts, whether this Board be constituted in pursuance of a special order of
   the Privy Council – the President of this Board be requested to address the
   Clerk of the Privy Council requesting an official order to constitute this an
   efficient Board of Health – provided that in the opinion of the Clerk of the
   Council, it be not already deemed a legal board.

Resolved 5
   That Dr. S.A. Bardsley be requested to undertake the office of Medical
   Correspondent to this Board.

Adjourned to Monday 11 o'clock.

Board of Health, Town Hall
December 26, 1831

Benjamin Braidley Esq., Chairman
Drs. S.A. Bardsley, J.P. Kay, H. Gaulter; Revd. James Crook; Colonel Shaw; J. Bentley, H. Forth, S. Fletcher, T. Townend, E. Connell

Resolved 1
> That the minutes of the last meeting of this Board be now confirmed.

Memorandum
> Received a note from Mr. Guest enclosing a letter from Mr. George Murray declining to let the factory in Union Street to this Board for the purposes of a temporary cholera hospital.

Resolved 2
> That the sub-committee appointed to fix upon a building as a temporary hospital be requested to examine the factory in Pollard Street, pointed out by Dr. J.P. Kay or any other building that may appear desirable and ascertain whether it may be hired and rendered suitable for the purposes of this Board and that they report as early as possible the result of their enquiries.

Resolved 3
> That the Special Board recommend to the Medical Committee to take into consideration the propriety of making further medical arrangements to check the spread of Asiatic Cholera in case of its appearance in this Town and that they report to the Special Board.

Adjourned to Wednesday 11 o'clock.

Board of Health, Town Hall
December 28, 1831

Henry Forth Esq., Chairman
Drs. S.A. Bardsley, Mr. Johns, Pendlebury, J.P. Kay, E. Lyon, J.D. Hulme, H. Gaulter; Revd. G. Dugard, James Crook, James White; Messrs. T. Townend, F. Fincham, J. Kennedy, Howarth

Resolved 1
> That the proceedings of the Board on Monday be confirmed.

Resolved 2
> That the sub-committee appointed to examine the factory in Pollard Street reported to this Board that that building though not so convenient as might be desirable could be made available as a temporary hospital in case a more suitable building could not be procured and that Mr. Swindells the proprietor expressed himself perfectly willing to let it for that purpose.

Resolved 2 *[sic]*
> That the thanks of this Board be presented to Mr. Swindells for the obliging manner in which he has offered his factory for the purpose of a temporary Hospital, and should a building be required in that neighbourhood the Board

will gladly avail themselves of the offer of which due notice will be given to Mr. Swindells.

Resolved 3

That the Nuisance Committee be earnestly requested to cause the receptacle for offal &c. in Back John Street to be inspected and proper measures to be carried into force for removing the bad effects resulting from it to the health of the neighbourhood.

Resolved 4

That Mr. Henry Houldsworth be requested to give in writing to the Board his plan for heating bran on the steam boilers in factories and for providing a convenient portable sling, or machine in every such large establishment, with a view to the speedy and safe conveyance of patients, who may be suddenly seized in the mills with cholera, in case that disease should unfortunately appear in this Town – and that the Board beg to express their thanks to Mr. Houldsworth for his communication.

Adjourned till Saturday 11 o'clock.

Henry Forth (signature)

Board of Health, Town Hall
December 31, 1831

Benjamin Braidley Esq., Chairman
Drs. S.A. Bardsley, J.D. Hulme, W. Johns, E. Lyon, J.P. Kay; Revd. The Very Revd. Dr. Calvert, George Dugard; Colonel Shaw; Messrs. Whatton, J.S. Heron, T. Townend, T. Weatherby, J. Rooke, P. Ewart junr.

Resolved 1

That the proceedings of the Board of the 28th Instant be confirmed.

Resolved 2

That the communication from the Central Board in reply to the letter addressed by Mr. Braidley (in accordance with the resolution of the 24th. Inst.) to the Clerk of the Privy Council be entered on the minutes. (See Appendix No.1)

Resolved 3

That all communications to this Board proposing remedial means for cholera be referred to the Medical Committee to be by them reported to the Special Board if deemed necessary.

Memorandum

The required communication from Mr. Henry Houldsworth regarding the supply of heated materials to cholera patients was received and referred to the Medical Committee.

Resolved 4

That the proceedings of the Medical Committee of the 30th Instant be received, entered and adopted as the proceedings of this Board. (See Appendix No.2)

Resolved 5

That 250 copies of the first and second resolutions contained in those proceedings be immediately printed and transmitted to the different medical practitioners of Manchester.

Resolved 6

That Mr. Braidley, Mr. J.S. Heron and Mr. J. Fletcher be constituted a committee to examine the accounts, fix the salaries &c. belonging to this Board.

Resolved 7

That a meeting of the Medical Committee be requested for Monday next immediately after the meeting of the Special Board to take into consideration the communication of Mr. Houldsworth and to fix on a suitable plan for the slings or other means to be adopted for the conveyance of patients and that they be authorized to order without delay a sufficient number for immediate use.

Resolved 8

That the factory in Pollard Street offered by Mr. Swindells for a temporary hospital be immediately taken and that the following gentlemen be appointed a committee to fix the terms of occupancy and to superintend its fitting up &c. viz: Dr. J.D. Hulme, Messrs. F. Fincham, G. Faulkner & P. Ewart junr.

Resolved 9

That a committee be appointed to select a suitable site or sites of ground on which to erect one or more temporary hospitals and that they be desired to obtain estimates for the erection of such buildings.

Resolved 10

That the committee do consist of Dr. J.P. Kay, Messrs. W.R. Whatton, J.S. Heron and P. Ewart junr., and that they be requested to report to the Board as early as possible.

Adjourned till Monday 11 o'clock.

Appendix

Central Board of Health
Council Office, Whitehall
27[th.] December 1831

No.1

Sir,

In reply to your letter to Mr. Bathurst of the 24[th.] Instant which has been laid before this Board, I am directed to transmit to you the enclosed Circular of the 29[th.] ulto.

I have the honour to be, Sir
your obedient humble Servant,
(Signed) H. Maclean Secretary

Benjamin Braidley Esq.
Board of Health
Manchester

Enclosure

Extract of a letter from the Clerk of the Council in reply to communications from Boards of Health requesting information as to their re-appointment under the Orders in Council of the 21[st.] November 1831, for the purpose of obtaining accurate returns of disease, and for the removal of nuisances: –

"I am directed to acquaint you that the Lords of His Majesty's Most Honorable Privy Council do not think it necessary that a new Board of Health should be appointed with the powers mentioned in the orders of the 21st November 1831, except in the event of the cholera breaking out in your Town or in the immediate neighbourhood; or in the event of some other case of great urgency occurring, the circumstances of which will be taken into consideration upon the same being specially represented to their Lordships."

The Order of the 21[st.] of November was not intended to cancel the Boards of Health then in existence nor to prevent the formation of any others that might have been contemplated in consequence of the Order of the 20th October; and their Lordships are of opinion that such Boards of Health may be very beneficially employed in discharging the duties marked out in the circular of the Central Board of Health of the 14th November 1831."

29 November 1831

No.2

Medical Committee
December 3, 1831

Dr. S.A. Bardsley, in the Chair

Resolved unanimously 1[st.]

That it be recommended to the Special Board that a circular be addressed to the medical practitioners of Manchester & the neighbourhood, viz:

physicians, members of the College of Surgeons, and Licentiates of Apothecaries Hall desiring them to forward their names and address to the Special Board if willing to become members of the Boards of Health formed in their respective districts, in the event of the appearance of cholera in this Town or neighbourhood.

Resolved unanimously 2nd.
That the following form of circular be also submitted to the Special Board – viz:

Sir,
I am directed by the Special Board of Health to enquire whether you will permit your name to be added to the Board of Health for District No. —

The Board also request that you will inform them whether you are willing to give your medical services to the district in which you reside if the cholera appear in Manchester.
The Board desire that if you express your willingness to afford your assistance in this emergency you will insert your name and address in the note containing the answer which you may return to the Secretary of the Board.

Resolved unanimously 3rd.
That it is the opinion of this committee that in the event of the cholera appearing in this Town the establishment of temporary hospitals in various populous districts, in addition to the one already resolved upon, will be an indispensable measure, and that it will be expedient to make arrangements for the medical attendance and superintendence of such hospitals.

Board of Health, Town Hall
January 2, 1832

Benjamin Braidley Esq., Chairman
Drs. S. A. Bardsley, William Johns, J.D. Hulme, J.P. Kay; Rev. James Crook; Mr. T. Townend

Resolved 1
That the proceedings of the Board on the 31st. of December be now confirmed.

Memorandum
Dr J.P. Kay reported that the committee had engaged Mr. Swindells premises in Pollard Street at the rent of 10 shillings per week – the rent to commence when occupied. Dr. Kay also reported that enquiries were in progress relative to a fit site or sites of ground on which to erect cholera hospitals and also for the estimates of the expence of such erections.

Resolved 2

That Dr. James David Hulme be added to the Building Committee.

Resolved 3

That the contemplated erection of temporary hospitals being for the benefit of the public, the Finance Committee be respectfully requested to allow the Board to make use of the services of Mr. Shoreland for that purpose when required.

Adjourned till Wednesday 11 o'clock.

Board of Health, Town Hall
January 4, 1832

H.J. Forth Esq., Chairman
Drs J.P. Kay, S.A. Bardsley, J.D. Hulme, Edm. Lyon, William Johns; Revd. George Dugard, James Crook, James White; Colonel Shaw; Messrs. J.S. Heron, W.R. Whatton, T. Townend, R. Addison, P. Ewart junr.

Resolved 1

That the proceedings of the Board on the 2nd. Inst. be confirmed.

Memorandum 1

The Classification Committee presented Mr. Gardiner's weekly report of the number of houses whitewashed – ordered to be entered on the minutes. (See Appendix)

Memorandum 2

Dr. Kay and Mr. Heron reported that they had made enquiries respecting several plots of land on which to erect temporary hospitals but that no definitive arrangements had yet been made.

Memorandum 3

The committee appointed to superintend the fitting up of Mr. Swindells mill reported that Mr. Gardiner had been written to requesting him to have the top room of that building immediately whitewashed and the windows cleaned – also that it will be in a fit state for the reception of patients if necessary by the end of the week.

Resolved 2

That this Board having adopted Mr. Swindells mill in Harrison Street as a temporary hospital, the Scavenging Committee be requested to have the approaches to the said building (viz: from Pollard Street through North Street and part of Harrison Street) immediately scavenged and cleansed.

Resolved 3
> That Mr. Townend and the Rev. James White be deputed to wait upon the Churchwardens to request them to point out a suitable spot of ground belonging to the Town for the burial of persons dying by cholera, if it should be required.

Resolved 4
> That Mr. Thorpe be requested to engage two additional clerks to assist in preparing the abstracts from the reports of the District Inspectors and any other business that may be required.

Resolved 5
> That the circular ordered by a resolution passed December 1st. to be addressed to the Medical Gentlemen of Manchester and the neighbourhood be sent only to those resident in the Township.

Adjourned to Saturday 11 o'clock.

Henry Forth.

Appendix

Churchwardens' Office
January 3, 1832

Gentlemen,
> I beg to report that during the past week from 24th December to 31st: 100 houses were whitewashed.

I am Gentlemen
Your obedient servant
(signed) N. Gardiner

Board of Health, Town Hall
January 7, 1832

Colonel Shaw, Chairman
Drs. S.A. Bardsley, E. Lyon, J.D. Hulme, William Johns; Revd. James White, James Crook, George Dugard; Messrs. W.R. Whatton, T. Weatherby, J.S. Heron, S. Fletcher, T. Townend

Resolved 1
> That the proceedings of the Board on Wednesday be confirmed.

Memorandum 1

Mr. Townend and the Revd. James White reported that they had made the necessary enquiries of the Churchwardens respecting a plot of ground for the burial place of persons dying by cholera, – that the Churchwardens stated that the Parish Ground would be insufficient to receive the bodies of such victims of that malady, being both too small and already nearly filled. The deputation also stated that from the examination of some of the deeds preserved in the Town's Office (of which extracts are subjoined, See Appendix) they were impressed with an idea of the liability of the Lord of the Manor to find a burial place for persons dying by this disorder.

Resolved 2

That the Rev. James White, Mr. T. Townend and Mr. S. Fletcher be appointed a deputation to wait on the Law-Agents of the Lord of the Manor to consult with them on the subject.

Resolved 3

That a committee be appointed to consider the best means of conveying the bodies of persons dying by cholera to the Burial Ground and that the committee do consist of Mr. Whatton, Mr. Weatherby and Mr. Townend: – that they be also requested to wait on the Churchwardens to ascertain whether a sufficient number of coffins are prepared in case a great mortality by cholera should prevail and if such will be issued when required.

Resolved 4

That it be recommended to the Chairman of the different District Boards to appoint a druggist in their respective district to make up the prescriptions for pauper patients attacked by Spasmodic Cholera given by the Medical Gentlemen whose offers of gratuitous services have been accepted by the General Board – that the druggist appointed in each district be desired to furnish drugs to all orders signed by such Medical Gentlemen – (a list of whom shall be supplied to them and also to the several District Boards) and that all debts thus contracted be liquidated on those signed orders being presented to the Accounts Committee of the Board.

Resolved 5

That the necessity of envelopping the bodies of persons dying by cholera in pitched cloth be submitted to the consideration of the Medical Committee.

Resolved 6

That the discussion on the propriety of immediately erecting temporary hospitals being fixed for Monday next when estimates will be presented and it appearing that such a measure would be attended with considerable expense it is particularly desirable that the Churchwardens and Sidesmen should be present on the occasion, and that they be specially requested to attend.

Resolved 7

That the agreement with Mr. Swindells for the hire of his factory in Harrison Street now read be confirmed.

J. Shaw (signature)

Appendix

Extracts for
The Burgesses of Collihurst Land

Name of the Person who gave the Charity	When given	Whether by Deed or Will	For what purpose given	Whether in land or money	Annual produce
Rowland Mosley E^{sqr.} Lord of the Manor of Manchester	21st. November 15th. James 1st	An Amicable Decree in the Dutchy Court of Lancastcr for a conveyance by Deed	That the Inhabitants of Manchester at all times when any Infection of the plague shall happen in Manchester shall have Right and Liberty to erect and build Cabins for the Relief and harbouring of Infected Persons upon six acres of Collyhurst next to Manchester & to Bury the Dead there.	Yearly Rent for ever to be issuing out of all the Collyhurst Lands	£ – s – d 10. 0. 0

Collyhurst Rent of Ten Pounds per annum: –

21st. November 15th. King James the First An Amicable Decree made in the Dutchy *[sic]* Court in a cause there depending between William Radcliffe and others Inhabitants of Manchester plaintiffs and Rowland Mosley Esq. Lord of the Manor of Manchester Defs.: about the Waste Land at Collyhurst Whereby it is ordered that the said Rowland Mosley his heirs and assigns should Inclose and Improve the Waste Ground called Collyhurst and have and enjoy the same free from Common of pasture: – yet that the Inhabitants of Manchester at all times when any Infection of the plague should happen in Manchester should have Right and Liberty to erect and build Cabbins for the reliefe and harbouring of Infected persons upon six acres of Collyhurst aforesaid next to Manchester and to bury the Dead there And that the said Rowland Mosley should convey and assure unto the said William Radcliffe &c and their Heirs a Yearly rent of Ten pounds for the use of the poor of Manchester for ever to be issuing out of all the said Collyhurst Land and to be payable at the Feast days of the Annunciation of the Blessed Virgin Mary and St. Michael the Archangel by equal portions with Clause of Distress to be contained therein &c

**Board of Health
January 9, 1832**

Henry Forth Esq. Chairman
Drs. Bardsley, E. Lyon, J.D. Hulme, W. Johns, J.P. Kay; Revd. James White, James Crook, George Dugard; Colonel Shaw; Messrs. J.S. Heron, S. Fletcher, T. Townend, J. Barker, W.R. Whatton, E. Connell, Joseph Rooke, R. Ogden

Resolved 1
> That the proceedings of the Special Board of the 7th Instant be confirmed.

Memorandum 1
> Mr. Townend reported that the Churchwardens having consulted their Law Clerk respecting the liability of Sir Oswald Mosley to provide a plot of land as a burial ground, have undertaken to address a note on the subject to Sir Oswald's Agent.

Memorandum 2
> The Classification Committee presented the report from Mr. Gardiner of the number of houses whitewashed during the foregoing week – ordered to be entered on the minutes. (See Appendix)

Resolved 2
> That the Building Committee be empowered to engage the building offered by Messrs. Peel and Williams and have it prepared for the immediate reception of patients and that they be requested to advertise for similar buildings in other districts for the same purpose.

Adjourned till Wednesday 11 o'clock.

Henry Forth

Appendix

Churchwardens Office
January 9, 1832

Gentlemen

> I beg to report that from the 31st of December 1831 to the 7th of January 1832, 70 Houses and the room in Mr. Swindell's Factory were whitewashed and cleansed.

I am
Gentlemen
your Obedient Servant
Signed N. Gardiner

**Board of Health, Town Hall
January 11, 1832**

Colonel Shaw, Chairman
Drs. W. Johns, J.P. Kay, J.D. Hulme, S.A. Bardsley; Revd. George Dugard;
Messrs. J.S. Heron, T. Weatherby, T. Townend, E. Connell, W.R. Whatton

Resolved 1
　　That the proceedings of the Board on the 9th Instant be confirmed.

Memorandum
　　The Building Committee presented a communication from Messrs. Peel,
　　Williams and Peel offering the required portion of their building in Swan
　　Street for the purposes of the Board at the rent of £1. 5s. 0d. per week.

Resolved 2
　　That the thanks of this Board be transmitted to Messrs. Peel, Williams and
　　Peel for the liberal and obliging manner in which they have acceded to the
　　application of the Board.

Resolved 3
　　That the communication from the Scavenging Committee now read be entered
　　on the minutes. (See Appendix)

J. Shaw

Appendix

Extract from the minutes of the Lamp, Scavenging and Fire Engine Committee of
January 9th 1832.

Resolved
　　That the Board of Health be respectfully informed that when this committee
　　has a horse in the stable at liberty it is at all times at their service.

(a true Copy)

Signed J. Thorpe junr.

Town Hall
January 10, 1832

**Board of Health, Town Hall
January 14, 1832**

W. Crossley, Esq., Chairman
Drs. J.P. Kay, S.A. Bardsley, J.D. Hulme; Revd. James Crook; Colonel Shaw;
Messrs. W.R. Whatton, T. Townend, J.S. Heron, P. Ewart junr.

Resolved 1
    That the proceedings of the Board on the 11th Inst. be confirmed.

Memorandum
    Received a letter from Mr. H.C. Morris, Norwich Union Office, Market Street
    complaining of the unhealthy stench arising from a privy or sewer in the
    adjoining house. Also from Mr. W.R. Whatton complaining of the filthy state
    of the square opposite Bloom Street.

Resolved 2
    That the letters of Messrs. Morris and Whatton be referred to the Nuisance
    Committee with a request that they will take immediate steps for the removal
    of the nuisances complained of.

Resolved 3
    That the Medical Committee be requested to take into consideration the expe-
    diency of appointing one or more Inspectors who shall daily visit the lodg-
    ing houses frequented by vagrant paupers and report any cases of sickness
    of a doubtful character occurring there.

Adjourned till Monday 11 o'clock.

**Board of Health, Town Hall
January 16, 1832**

Benjamin Braidley Esq. Chairman
Drs. H. Gaulter, W. Johns, S.A. Bardsley; Revd. James Crook, Revd. George
Dugard, Colonel Shaw; Messrs J.S. Heron, H. Forth, W. Crossley, T. Townend,
T. Weatherby, J. Rooke, Mr. R. Addison

Resolved 1
    That the proceedings of the Board on Saturday be confirmed.

Resolved 2
    That the weekly report received from Mr. Gardiner be entered on the min-
    utes (See Appendix) and that in future Mr. Gardiner be requested to direct
    the reports to the Classification Committee.

Resolved 3
    That Mr. J.S. Heron having read an extract of a letter from a friend of his as
    to a new mode of communicating heat to cholera patients, he be requested
    to furnish a copy of the same to the Medical Committee.

Resolved 4

That Mr. Joshua McWilliams of No.2 Angel Street, St. George's Road be appointed druggist for District No.2 and Mr. Smith of London Road, druggist for District No.4.

Resolved 5

That the Building Committee be requested to provide all the common utensils necessary for the furnishing one hospital for the use of the patients and attendants.

Resolved 6

That a committee be appointed consisting of Dr. Kay, Colonel Shaw, Dr. Bardsley and the Honorary Secretary to draw up a report of the measures already agreed upon as proper to be adopted in case of the appearance of the cholera in this Town and that they be requested if possible to present such report to this Board at their meeting on Wednesday.

Appendix

Churchwardens' Offices
January 16, 1832

Gentlemen

I beg to report that from the 7th to the 14th of January 69 Houses were whitewashed.

I am
Gentlemen
your Obedient Servant
(Signed) N. Gardiner

**Board of Health
January 18, 1832**

Benjamin Braidley Esq., Chairman
Drs. Bardsley, Kay, Lyon, Gaulter, D. Hulme, Johns; Revd. James White, H. Fielding, T. Tate; Colonel Shaw; Messrs. F. Fincham, J. Woollam, J.S. Heron, T. Townend

Resolved 1

That the proceedings of the last meeting of this Board be confirmed.

Resolved 2

That Mr. Gaulter of Piccadilly be appointed druggist for District No.6 and Mr. Robert Barker of the Market Place druggist for District No.12.

Resolved 3

> That the communication from the Finance Committee now read be entered on the minutes. (See Appendix No.1)

Resolved 4

> That a committee be appointed consisting of Dr. S.A. Bardsley, Dr. Kay, Mr. Henry Houldsworth and Mr. Woollam to make enquiries of the different occupiers of factories whether they would allow the factories in their respective occupations to be made the depôts of bran and also to allow the same to be heated on their respective boilers.

Resolved 5

> That Colonel Shaw be added to the Building Committee.

Resolved 6

> That the report of the sub-committee (appointed at the last meeting to prepare a draft of the measures already resolved on by this Board for the mitigation of cholera – to be published in case of its appearance in this Town) be received and entered on the minutes (See Appendix No.2) and that its various suggestions be approved and adopted as part of the proceedings of this Board and that the organization arising out of such resolution be completed as quickly as possible.

Resolved 7

> That in future this board shall meet only twice a week viz: on Wednesday and Saturday at 11 o'clock and that the members of the Board be informed by the Secretary of the change.

Resolved 8

> That the minutes of the Medical Committee of the 16th. Inst. now read; (recommending the appointment of all legally qualified gentlemen to the Medical Committee of the Board and also suggesting that the stipendiary overseers should visit the pauper lodging houses daily) be received and approved of and that the Medical Committee be desired to take the necessary measures for carrying the same into effect.

Resolved 9

> That Dr. Hull be added to this Board and that the Secretary be requested to inform him of such nomination.

Resolved 10

> That Mr. James Brereton, Great Ancoats Street opposite Brownsfield be appointed druggist for District No.1.

Resolved 11

> That the report of the Classification Committee now presented by Dr. Kay be received and entered on the minutes.

Copy of the
Report of the Proceedings of the
Classification Committee

January 17, 1832

List of District Boards

District	Name	Address
No.1	George Murray Esq., Chairman	
	Revd. Thomas Tate, Honorary Secretary	Oldham Road
No.2	Revd. James White, Chairman.	St. George's
	Robert Guest, Surgeon, Honorary Sec.	19 Oldham Street
	Thomas Weatherby	Marshall Street
	John Gerrard	Great Ancoats Street
	John Barker	Cannon Street
	Hugh Beaver	Jersey Street
	– Jackson	Swan Street
No.3	Revd. Mr. Wray, Chairman	Strangeways
	J. Roberton, Surgeon	King Street
	John Wallis	Mayes Street
	J.S. Heron	Bank Street
	Joseph Rooke	Horrock's Lane, Red Bank
No.4	Revd. George Dugard, Chairman	Grosvenor Street, Oxford Road.
	S.A. Bardsley	Ardwick
	A.M. Heath, Surgeon	Piccadilly
	Fawdington, Surgeon	Lever Street
	Henry Houldsworth	Newton Street
	Edmd. Buckley	Mather Street
	Alfred Binyon	Mayfield
	Joseph Compton	Mayfield
No.5	Rev. W. Piccope, Chairman	Charlotte Street
	R.P. Bamber, Surgeon	Oldham Street
	B. Roberts, Surgeon.	Lever Street
	Sam. Horne	Church Street
	George Faulkner	New High Street
	Thomas Crewdson	Cannon Street
No.6	Revd. R. Remington, Chairman	Mosley Street
	Thomas Ashton, Surgeon	Mosley Street
	George Wood	New High Street
	William Crossley (Resigned)	York Street
	– Prince	Market Street
	Samuel Smith	Old Millgate
	William Clarke	Market Place

District	Name	Address
No.7	Revd. N. Germon, Chairman (Resigned)	Greengate
	W.R. Whatton, Surgeon, Chairman	5 Portland Place
	Lewis Williams	Piccadilly Mills
	S. Sheldon junr.	Shude Hill
	Joseph Turner	Piccadilly
	Joseph Peel	Pollard Street
	Thomas Ogden	Shepley Street
No.8	Revd. J. Hollist, Chairman	Grosvenor St. C.R.
	– Clough, Surgeon	York Street
	H. Dadley, Surgeon	Falkner Street
	H. Forth	St. Peter's Square
	Thomas Birtles	Bolton Court, Half Moon Street
	Hugh Hornby Birley	York Street
	James Burt	Bond Street
No.9	Revd. D. Smith, Chairman (Resigned)	
	Revd. Mr. Jackson, Chairman	
	Dr. J.P. Kay	Mosley Street
	H. Newberry (Resigned)	Brown Street
	J.E. Taylor (Resigned)	Market Street
	– Wilson	King Street
	– Satterfield	St. Ann's Square
	Thomas Ollivant	Exchange Street
	– Leeke	St. Ann's Square
No.10	Rev. Henry Fielding, Chairman	George Street
	– Ferneley, Surgeon	Oxford Road
	– Ferneley junr. M.D.	Oxford Road
	John Holt (Resigned)	Bond Street
	Peter Ewart junr.	East Street
	Thomas Sharp	Falkner Street
	D. Bellhouse (Resigned)	Nicholas Street
No.11	Rev. W. Marsden, Chairman	Quay Street
	J.A. Ransome junr., Surgeon	St. Peter's Square
	Jonathan Bannerman	Mosley Street
	William Haynes	Cannon Street
	Frederick Maude	at Mrs Marshall's, Cooper Street
	R.C. Sharp	Mosley Street
	Bulkely Price	Brown Street
No.12	Revd. W. Hutchinson, Chairman	13 Charlotte Street
	Ed. Stephens, Surgeon	Bridge Street
	John Kenworthy	Star Yard
	Samuel Berry	St. Mary's Gate

District	Name	Address
No.12	John Briddon	Blackfriars
	Richard Cope	Exchange Street
No.13	Revd. Mr. Huntington, Chairman	Great John Street
	R. Hurst, Surgeon	50 Garside Street
	Mark Phillips	Somerset Street
	John Woollam	Quay Street
	Thomas Golland	Deansgate
	Thomas Lingard	Old Quay
No.14	Revd. Mr. Shaw, Chairman	Byrom Street
	– Miller, Surgeon	Brazennose Street
	Thomas Bazeley	St. John Street
	George Kenworthy	St. John Street
	William Anthony	St. John Street
	James Holt	St. John Street
	J.R. Taylor	St. John Street

Table of Inquiries
concerning the state of Streets Courts &c.
See Table. No.2. Appendix No.3.

Report of the
Operations of the Scavenging Committee
(dated December 5)
See Appendix

Table of Inquiries
concerning the State of Houses.
See Table No.1. Appendix No.3.

Churchwardens & Overseers
Uncleanly state of the Houses

District	Street &c	No.	Cellar or not	Does it require white-washing	Number of families or lodgers	Will the tenant assist in cleaning	Proprietor

Churchwardens' Reports
of Houses cleansed

See	Appendix	Dated	January 3
See	Do.	Do.	January 9
See	Do.	Do.	January 16

Houses not in Repair

District	Street, Court, &c.	No. of House	Proprietor	Not in Repair	Damp	Ill ventilated	Wanting a Privy

Board of Health,
Town Hall, Manchester
1832

Sir,

I am directed to inform you, that the Inspectors of District No. _ have reported that No. _ in _____ Street, of which you are the proprietor, in an imperfect state of repair, damp, require ventilating and soughing, and the erection of a privy.

The Committee appointed by the Special Board of Health for the purpose of corresponding with landlords, request your immediate attention to the state of the above mentioned house and feel assured that you will at the earliest period remove the evils reported, especially when you consider the circumstances which at present threaten the community.

I am, Sir,
Your obedient Servant
(Signed) Joseph Heron
Hon. Secretary

Number of Sections into which the
several Districts are subdivided

District		
	No. 1	
	No. 2	Thirty six Sections
	No. 3	Six Sections
	No. 4	Nine Sections (Verbal Answer)
	No. 5	Six Sections

No. 6   Three Sections (Verbal Answer)
No. 7
No. 8   Seven Sections
No. 9   Seven Sections
No. 10   Four Sections
No. 11
No. 12   Four Sections
No. 13   Eighteen Sections
No. 14

List of Districts from
which the Reports of the Inspectors are evidently
not all returned

District No.1
Several reports wanting – cannot say for which section they are required, very
few of the reports from this district having the number marked. One report has
been sent in without either name of the Inspectors or the number of the section
marked.

District No.2
The reports from Sections 14, 15, 22, 24 and 36 are not yet returned
by the Inspectors.

District No.3
Number complete

District No.4
Number complete

District No.5
Number complete

District No.6
Number complete

District No.7
The reports from Section 6 & 10 are not yet received.

District No.8
Number complete

District No.9
Number complete

District No.10
Number complete

District No.11
No reports have yet been returned from this District.

District No.12
Number complete

District No.13
Number complete

District No.14
No reports have yet been obtained from this district

List of Inspector's Reports remarkably imperfect and the Districts to which they relate

	District
Report of Messrs Butterworth & Hurst	No.1
Report of Messrs O. Newton & E. Tootal	No.2
Report of Messrs Patchett & Timperley	No.2
Report of Messrs Wetherald & Cooper, Knowles &c.	No.4
Report of Messrs Wood & Smith	No.7
Report of Messrs Plant & Major	No.7
Report of Messrs Marsden & Carver, Scott & Co.	No.7
Report of Messrs George Faulkner	No.7
Report of Messsrs Wainwright, T. Smith & Co.	No.13.

End of the Report of the Classification Committee
January 17th

Resolved 12
That circulars be addressed to the Chairmen of the District Boards informing them of the number of the reports of inspectors which are either imperfect or deficient and requesting that these reports may be immediately corrected or supplied.

Resolved 13

That the Scavenging Committee be requested to furnish the Board as early as possible with a report of the nature and extent of their operations founded on the information furnished by the Classification Committee.

Resolved 14

That the Classification Committee be requested to report to the Churchwardens those particular habitations which appear to be most destitute of food, fuel, clothing and bedding.

Resolved 15

That as the greater part of the reports of houses requiring cleansing have been transmitted to the Churchwardens they be requested to urge the cleansing of those habitations at the earliest possible period.

Resolved 16

That those District Boards which have not yet furnished the Special Board with a list of their Inspectors and the sub-divisions to which they are respectively appointed be requested by circular to do so at the earliest period.

Resolved 17

That the recommendation of the Classification Committee concerning the purchase of fuel be entered on the minutes (See Appendix No.3) and transmitted to the Churchwardens.

Adjourned till Saturday 11 o'clock.

Appendix No.1

Extract from the Minutes of the Finance Committee of January 12th 1832.

Resolved,

"That the Board of Health be informed that Mr. Shoreland's services may be had by the Board as requested by them."

(a true Copy)
(Signed) Jonathan Thorpe junr.

Town Hall
Manchester, 17 January 1832

Appendix No.2

Placard &c

Special Board of Health
Town Hall, Manchester

By the reports now before this Board ＿＿cases of cholera have appeared in ＿＿＿

The following is a detail of the preparations which have been made in anticipation of the arrival of the disease in Manchester and of the instructions by which the public may know how the measures for meeting it are now to be carried into effect.

1. The Special Board of Health constituted of the principal fiscal authorities of the Town, of the Medical Gentlemen officially connected with the public charities and others, of which the Boroughreeve is chairman, will during the prevalence of cholera in Manchester, assemble daily in the Boroughreeve's room at the Town Hall, at eleven in the morning, to which place all communications intended for the Board may be addressed. The Secretary will also attend at the Town Hall during the whole day, to open and transmit all communications addressed to the Board or to its Medical Committee.

2. The Town has been divided into districts according to the fourteen Police Sections, in each of which a district Board of Health has been established. Gentlemen have been appointed by the respective District Boards to inspect the streets and houses and to ascertain the state of health and the general condition

District	Chairman's Name	Residence	Place where District Boards assemble daily
No.1			
No.2	Revd. James White	St. George's	Police Lockups, Swan Street
No.3	Revd. Mr. Wray	Strangeways	Chapter House, Collegiate Church
No.4	Revd. G. Dugard	Grosvenor Street, Oxford Road	Vestry Room St. Andrew's Church
No.5	Revd. J. Piccope	Charlotte Street	Vestry Room St. Paul's Church
No.6	Revd. R. Remington	15 Mosley Street	
No.7			
No.8	Revd. John Hollist	Grosvenor Street, Chorlton Row	St. James's Sunday School Room, Pine Street
No.9	Revd. E.D. Jackson	Long Millgate	Town Hall, King Street
No.10	Revd. H. Fielding	37 George Street	
No.11	Revd. W. Marsden	Quay Street	
No.12	Revd. Mr. Hutchinson	Cooper Street	Vestry Room of St. Mary's Church
No.13	Revd. Mr. Huntington	St. John Street	St. John's Sunday School
No.14			

of the inhabitants in the several divisions. Reports will be continually made by these Inspectors to the District Boards and by them to the Special Board. The following list of the chairmen of the District Boards, and of the places where these boards assemble (at eleven o'clock every morning) is subjoined for the information of all persons desirous of making any applications to them.

3. For the reception of persons affected with cholera ___ hospitals have been prepared whose situation is minutely described below viz:

No.1. Mr. Swindell's Factory, Harrison Street, North Street, Pollard Street, Ancoats.

No.2. The Phoenix or old Soho Foundry, formerly occupied by Messrs. Peel and Williams, Swan Street, Shude Hill.

No.3. The factory formerly occupied by John Worthington, Commercial Street, Knott Mill.

These hospitals have been furnished with commodious beds, and with all the apparatus and every other accommodation desirable for the comfort or the treatment of those affected with cholera. Respectable nurses have been selected. A resident Medical Officer has been appointed to each hospital, and all cases of this disease will here receive the constant gratuitous attention of the medical practitioners.

4. The names and the places of residence of Medical Gentlemen who have offered their services to attend cholera patients, requiring gratuitous assistance, in their respective Districts, are subjoined, as also, the names and addresses of Druggists appointed in each District, to furnish medicines for pauper cholera patients, to the orders of Medical Gentlemen whose services have been accepted by the Board of Health.

District	Name of Medical Attendants	Residence of Medical Attendants	Druggist's Name	Druggist's Residence
No.1			Mr. James Brereton	Gt. Ancoats Street, opposite Brownsfield
No.2			Mr.Joseph McWilliams	2 Angel Street, St. George's Road
No.3	George Haigh	7 Hunts Bank		
	E. Holroyde	20 Long Millgate		
			Thomas Pritchard	Old Millgate

District	Name of Medical Attendants	Residence of Medical Attendants	Druggist's Name	Druggist's Residence
No.4	James Braid	10 Piccadilly		
	T. Fawdington	6 Lever Street		
			W. Smith	London Road
No.5	Robert Thorpe	21 Oldham Street		
	Alex Murray MD	94 Oldham Street		
	C. Phillips MD	37 Piccadilly	Gaulter	Piccadilly
	R.P. Bamber	95 Oldham St.		
No.6			Gaulter	Piccadilly
No.7	W.R. Whatton	5 Portland Place		
No.8	George Greaves	18 Charlotte Street		
	Lewis Henry Nathan	56 George Street		
	W.J. Wilson	Mosley Street	R. Woodall	Piccadilly
	C. Clough	22 York Street		
No.9	J. Ainsworth	King Street		
	H.T. Worthington	47 Princess Street		
	John Thorpe	76 King Street	Bullock	King Street
	John Walker	29 Princess Street		
	John Alexander	4 Princess Street		
No.10	W.C. Henry MD	29 Mosley Street		
	J.P. Kay MD	35 Mosley St.		
			L. Simpson	32 Princess Street
No.11	B. W. Booth	1 Clarence Street		
	Henry Ollier	44 Brazennose Street		
			Howard	208 Deansgate
No.12	W. Owen	58 Bridge Street		
			Robert Barker	Market Place
No.13	W.B. Stott	12 Quay Street		
	R.J. Hunt	50 Gartside Street		
			S. Thompstone Junr.	194 Deansgate
No.14	W. White	12 St. John Street		

5. Slings have been prepared, for the conveyance of persons affected with cholera from their respective dwellings to the hospitals, some of which will be deposited in the house of each of the druggists appointed in the several districts.
A carriage will also be stationed for the same purpose at the hospital situated in Swan Street, Shude Hill.

6. On the removal of persons affected with cholera, the Special Board of Health conceive that the immediate cleansing, whitewashing and fumigating of the house in which they lived are measures essential to the safety of the remaining inhabitants, and persons are appointed by the Board who will perform this duty.

7. The Workhouse Burial Ground has been selected by the Churchwardens for the interment of persons dying of cholera, as also the following if necessary.

8. Means of conveying the bodies of the dead to the places thus selected for the interment of those dying of cholera, will be stationed at the hospitals in Swan Street, Shude Hill and at ＿＿＿＿

The Board feel confident that the arrangements which have been made are sufficient to meet the occasion which has called them forth; and that the inhabitants of this great Town will, by the calmness and firmness with which they will meet the emergency, and by the energy and liberality with which they will assist the operations of the Board, retard as much as possible the progress as well as mitigate the evils of the disorder.

Appendix No.3

Classification Committee
January 17, 1832

Resolved

> That this committee feeling that an abundant supply of fuel to the poor of Manchester during the severity of the winter season would be most conducive to the maintenance of the health of the inhabitants, suggest to the Board the propriety of recommending the Churchwardens to make a large purchase of coals at the lowest wholesale prices in order to dispose of them to the poor at the same rate, inasmuch as they are at present subjected to the payment of a very great percentage which forms the profits of the inferior dealers.

Board of Health, Town Hall
January 21, 1832

Benjamin Braidley Esq., Chairman
Drs. S.A. Bardsley, J.P. Kay, E. Lyon; Rev. James Crook; Colonel Shaw; Messrs. J. Townend, J.S. Heron

Resolved 1
> That the proceedings of the last meeting of this Board be confirmed.

Resolved 2
> That Mr. Gaulter of Piccadilly be appointed druggist for No.5 District.

Resolved 3
> That a certain number of recommendations for Home Patients signed by Trustees of the Infirmary be committed to such Medical Gentlemen as are appointed by the District Boards to visit cases of suspicious disease.

Resolved 4
> That a certain number of these recommendations be signed by such trustees as are members of the Special Board and that their distribution be entrusted to the Medical Committee.

Resolved 5
> That the subject of providing proper conveyances for the dead from the hospitals to the places of internment be referred to the Building Committee and that they be requested to act upon it immediately.

Board of Health, Town Hall
January 25, 1832

Colonel Shaw, Chairman
Drs. J.D. Hulme, J.P. Kay, E. Lyon, W. Johns, J. Hull; Rev. James Crook; Messrs. T. Townend, J.S. Heron, W. Crossley, F. Fincham, J. Rooke, P. Ewart junr.

Resolved 1
> That the proceedings of this Board on the 21st. Instant be confirmed.

Resolved 2
> That Mr. L. Simpson of 32 Princess Street be appointed druggist for No.10 District.

Resolved 3
> That the communications from the Churchwardens and Mr. Gardiner dated January 21st. be entered on the minutes of the Board. (See Appendix Nos. 1 and 2)

Resolved 4
> That a deputation consisting of Dr. J.D. Hulme, Dr. E. Lyon and Mr. T. Townend be appointed to wait on the Churchwardens and obtain their concurrence in the propositions of the Medical Committee of the 24th Inst. relative to the appointment of, and advertisement for, resident apothecaries and

having agreed with them on the terms of the advertisement that the deputation be authorised to insert the same in three of the Manchester papers.

Resolved 5
>That the minutes of the Accounts Committee of January 23rd. be now confirmed.

Resolved 6
>That Mr. T. Townend be requested to undertake the duties of Treasurer to this Board.

Resolved 7
>That Mr. Townend having stated his inability to attend to the duties proposed, in consequence of expected absence from Town, Mr. J.S. Heron be requested to undertake the office of Treasurer.

Adjourned till Saturday 11 o'clock.

J. Shaw (signature)

Appendix No. 1

Churchwardens' Offices
21st January, 1832

Gentlemen,
>We have considered the recommendation contained in the copy of the resolution of the Board of Health of the 17th Inst. in reference to a supply of fuel for the poor, And we beg respectfully to inform you, that we do not consider the adoption of the plan proposed, to fall within the range of our duty as Churchwardens.

We are,
Gentlemen
Respectfully
Your most Obedient servants
Signed R. Ogden
Samuel Fletcher
W. Crossley

To
The Board of Health

Appendix No.2

Churchwardens' Offices
21st January, 1832

Gentlemen,

In reply to yours of the 19th Inst., wherein you hand a copy of a resolution, urging the necessity of cleansing as early as possible those habitations that have been reported upon as requiring it, I am directed by the Churchwardens to state to you, that steps had been taken for that purpose before receiving your communication on the subject.

I am, Gentleman,
Your most Obedient Servant
(Signed) N. Gardiner

Board of Health, Town Hall.
January 28, 1832

Benjamin Braidley Esq., Chairman.
Drs. J. D. Hulme, S.A. Bardsley, J. P. Kay, E. Lyon; Rev. W. Marsden, George Dugard; Colonel Shaw; Messrs. William Haynes, T. Townend, Clarke, J.S. Heron

Resolved 1

That the Churchwardens having expressed their intention of keeping a separate account of the expenses incurred by this Board the appointment of a Treasurer will be unnecessary and that accordingly the resolution of the last meeting of this Board appointing Mr. J.S. Heron to that office be rescinded.

Resolved 2

That the other minutes of the preceding meeting of this Board be now confirmed.

Resolved 3

That Mr. Howard of No. 208 Deansgate be appointed druggist for District No. 11.

Resolved 4

That Mr. S. Thompstone junr. No. 194 Deansgate be appointed druggist for District No. 13.

Resolved 5

That a letter be addressed to the Churchwardens requesting them to direct all the stipendiary overseers to visit the common lodging houses and in the event of any suspicious case of disease occurring to report the same to the Secretary of this Board until further arrangements can be made on the subject.

Resolved 6

That Mr. Peter Ewart junr. be a member of this Board and that the Secretary be requested to inform him of that appointment.

Resolved 7

That the thanks of this meeting be given to Messrs. Clarke for their kindness in offering the use of their boiler house as a depôt for the boxes of slings and blankets.

Resolved 8

That the Revd. G. Dugard be appointed Chairman of the Board of Health for District No.1 and that Mr. James Kennedy be requested to act as Honorary Secretary to that Board.

Resolved 9

That the Building Committee be empowered to engage the factory near Knott Mill for the purposes of a temporary hospital.

Adjourned till Wednesday 11 o'clock.

Resolution omitted in entering the proceedings of this day's meeting.

That the minutes of the General Medical Committee of the 17th Inst. be adopted and confirmed by this Board.

Board of Health, Town Hall
February 1, 1832

Henry Forth Esq., Chairman
Drs. J.P. Kay, W. Johns, E. Lyon; Revd. Mr Huntington, W. Marsden;
Colonel Shaw; Messrs. J.S. Heron, R. Addison, T. Weatherby, F. Fincham

Resolved 1

That the proceedings of the last meeting of the Board be confirmed.

Resolved 2

That this Board having heard the report of Mr. J.S. Heron on behalf of the Building Committee of the state of the negotiations for taking the factory near Knott Mill, do authorize and request the Building Committee to conclude the agreement for taking the same upon the terms now mentioned viz: for 6 months certain and 2 Months notice after that time from the party wishing to determine the tenancy or upon such other terms as may appear most desirable and that the Building Committee be requested to prepare one room in such factory for the reception of patients.

Resolved 3

That Mr. F. Fincham and Mr. P. Ewart junr. be requested to make enquiries as to the best form of box and the best materials for constructing such boxes to be placed on the boilers of the various factories and to contain blankets, slings, &c, and to report to the Board at the next meeting the result of such enquiry.

Resolved 4

That the communication from Mr. Clarke be acknowledged by the secretary with an intimation that an answer will be returned to him in the course of a few days.

Resolved 5

That the report of Mr. Harrison be acknowledged and referred to the Medical Committee and that the thanks of this Board be transmitted to the Churchwardens for its communication.

Resolved 6

That the report of Scavenging Committee (dated January 30th) now read be entered on the minutes. (See Appendix)

Resolved 7

That a further communication be made to the Scavenging Committee stating the opinion of this Board that their reply to the request of this Board dated January 18th. does not give the information desired, requesting further information on those points and also a list of those streets cleansed by the Scavenging Committee which are not on the Town's Books.

Resolved 8

That the publication entitled "The Cholera Gazette" be supplied to this Board as published for the use of its members.

Henry Forth (signature)

Appendix

Extract from the minutes of the Lamp, Scavenging and Fire Engine Committee of January 30th 1832.

Resolved

That the following report be transmitted to the Board of Health in reply to their letter of the 18th. Instant.

(Copy)

The Scavenging Committee begs to inform the Special Board of Health that prior to the receipt of Inspectors' reports, two additional gangs of scavengers had been engaged in cleansing the Streets generally and more particularly some that are not on the Town's Books, where it was practicable. The committee has also to report that 40 to 50 hands receiving parish relief, have been placed by the Churchwardens at the disposal of the committee, and are now employed under its direction in the general cleansing of the Town. The committee begs to assure the Special Board that every effort shall be made to carry the recommendation of the Inspectors into effect but so many streets are inaccessible for carts in consequence of their unpaved state and the funds at the disposal of the committee being no more than sufficient for the ordinary business of the Town that a considerable time must elapse before all can be accomplished.

(a true copy)
(Signed J. Thorpe junr.)

Town Hall
January 31, 1832
To the Board of Health

Board of Health, Town Hall
February 4, 1832

Henry Forth Esq., Chairman
Drs. J.D. Hulme, S.A. Bardsley, J.P. Kay, W. Johns; Revd. George Dugard; Colonel Shaw; Messrs. S. Fletcher, J.S. Heron, F. Fincham, T. Weatherby, P. Ewart junr.

Resolved 1
That the proceedings of the Board on Wednesday be confirmed.

Resolved 2
That the report of the Building Committee of the 2nd. Instant relating to the agreement with the executors of the late Thomas Waddington for the use of their factory in Commercial Street, Knott Mill be now confirmed and entered on the minutes of this Board. (See Appendix No.1)

Resolved 3
That Mr. Thomas Prichard, Old Millgate be appointed druggist for District No.3.

Resolved 4
That the letter from Mr. Henry Houldsworth now presented as the report of Messrs. Fincham and Ewart junr. be entered on the minutes of this Board and referred to the Medical Committee. (See Appendix No.2)

Resolved 5
That the Medical Committee be recommended to issue a circular to the owners of factories requesting them as far as possible to enforce cleanliness of person among the workpeople in their employ.

Resolved 6
That the Medical Committee be requested to take into consideration the expediency of warning the public not to give credence to any reports of the cholera having made its appearance in Manchester as the earliest intimation will be given by the Board of Health to the public should any case occur.

Resolved 7

That Dr. J.D. Hulme and Mr. F. Fincham be appointed a deputation to wait on Mr. Wood, the agent of Mr. Fitzgerald, to ascertain whether or not the report is correct that it is his intention to employ colliers from Newcastle upon Tyne or its vicinity in his coal-pits in this neighbourhood.

Adjourned till Wednesday 11 o'clock.

Henry Forth (signature)

Appendix No.1

Building Committee
February 2, 1832

Memorandum

The Trustees of the late Thomas Waddington agree to let to the Board of Health and the latter to rent from them the factory house and outbuildings in Commercial Street, Knott Mill as follows for six months from the present date certain at the weekly rent of two guineas at the expiration of that term either party to be at liberty on giving one month's notice from its close unless the Board of Health then give the Trustees notice that they will continue to occupy it at the same rent to the close of the present year.

Appendix No.2

To Peter Ewart junr., Esq.

Dear Sir

I regret that I was not at the factory when you called this morning: having been on the sick list this last week, I have been later than usual in getting to work.

The only point our clerk has mentioned, to which you adverted when inspecting the situation of our boilers, was whether or not a bag would not be better than boxes to keep the slings and blankets in for the use of cholera patients. I was led to recommend a box in consequence of having found that the heat in the interior of a box placed upon the top of a boiler will be 130° to 140° whereas in a bag there will be a difficulty in getting a heat of 115°. And also from the comparative ease with which the slings and blankets may be tossed into a box and the lid shut down and locked as compared with putting them into a bag, and further the advantage which a box offered of connecting a pipe with it to one of the flues by which to carry off any effluvia which may arise from the blankets &c. The shape of the box which I thought might be convenient and the position on the boiler, are shown by the annexed sketch.

If you think bags would be better there is probably some objection to the boxes which I have overlooked, which is very likely as I have not had time to give the thing more than a casual thought.

> I am, Dear Sir,
> Yours most truly
> (Signed) H. Houldsworth

P.S. The box would require to be as long as the slings and about 2ft 6ins wide. The convex surface of the boiler would form a large heating surface as compared with the area of the box.

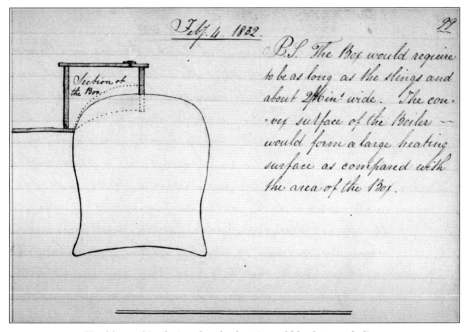

Houldsworth's design for the heating of blankets and slings

Board of Health, Town Hall
February 8, 1832

Colonel Shaw, Chairman
Dr. J.P Kay, W. Johns, J. Hull; Revd. Thomas Tate, James Crook; Messrs. J.S. Heron, P. Ewart junr., T. Weatherby, Ralph Shaw, James Sandiford

Resolved 1
   That the minutes of the preceding meeting of this Board be now confirmed.

Resolved 2
   That the proceedings of the Medical Sub-Committee of the 7th Instant be adopted by the Board and that the address to the Public be advertised in the Courier, Chronicle, Times and Guardian journals of Saturday next in the following terms:

Special Board of Health
Town Hall, Manchester
February 8, 1832

The Medical Committee of the Special Board of Health having been informed from various quarters that reports are in circulation of the occurrence of Asiatic Cholera in Manchester, deem it their duty to assure the public, from careful investigation into the supposed cases of cholera, that there is not the least foundation for such reports, as none of the characteristic symptoms of that formidable malady have in any one instance been detected. The public are requested not to place confidence in any other than the authenticated statements of this committee relative to the appearance of cholera in Manchester; the Special Board of Health having made arrangements by which the occurrence of any case of this disease may be immediately communicated to it and then announced to the public. The Board have also great satisfaction in assuring the public that the measures which they have concerted for preventing the introduction and spread of cholera are so far completed, by the appointment of district inspectors, the provision of suitable hospitals, the aid of medical practitioners, and various other regulations, as will most probably effect the object for which the Board was established.

Resolved 3
   That the communication from the Scavenging Committee of the 7[th.] Instant be entered on the minutes. (See Appendix No.1)

Memorandum
   A petition was presented from parties resident in the neighbourhood of the Phoenix Foundry (189 Signatures attached) remonstrating against the use of that building for the purpose contemplated by the Board.

Resolved 4
   That the said petition be referred to the Special Board on Saturday next and that the Medical Committee be specially requested to meet on Friday at 12 o'clock to consider the best means of allaying the anxiety expressed by certain inhabitants of Swan Street and neighbourhood with regard to the proximity of their dwellings to the hospital provided by the Board for the reception of cholera patients.

J. Shaw (signature)

Appendix

Extract from the minutes of the Lamp, Scavenging and Fire Engine Committee of yesterday.

Memorandum

Read application from Mr. J.S. Heron on behalf of the Board of Health for the old timber now taking away from the Military Guard House.

Resolved

That the Board of Health be respectfully informed that they may have the timber now taking out of the Military Guard House at a valuation.

(a true copy)
(Signed) J. Thorpe junr.

Town Hall,
February 7, 1832

Board of Health, Town Hall
February 11, 1832

Benjamin Braidley Esq., Chairman
Drs. E. Lyon, J.P. Kay, W. Johns, S.A. Bardsley; Revd. Huntington; Colonel Shaw; Messrs. T. Weatherby, T. Townend, J. Sandiford, J.S. Heron, F. Fincham

Resolved 1

That the minutes of the preceding meeting of this Board be now confirmed.

Resolved 2

That the document prepared by Dr. J.P. Kay, Dr. E. Lyon and Dr. S.A. Bardsley, at the desire of the General Medical Committee in reply to the petition from the owners and occupiers of property in the vicinity of the Phoenix Foundry now read be adopted and entered on the minutes of the proceedings of this Board. (See Appendix)

Memorandum

A deputation from the above mentioned petitioners attended and heard the reply to their petition read. Ordered, that a copy be furnished for their perusal to Mr. Hesketh, Cornhill.

Resolved 3

That Dr. Kay and Dr. Lyon be requested to take measures for the publication of the said reply in the Manchester papers and also by the distribution of 5000 circulars and that they be authorized to make such additions to the same as may tend to allay the alarm of the petitioners.

Resolved 4

That the proceedings of the General Medical Committee of the 10th. Instant be confirmed and adopted as the proceedings of this Board.

Resolved 5

That Mr. Braidley, Dr. Lyon and Dr. Bardsley be requested to prepare a form of enquiry to be transmitted to the authorities of Preston, Huddersfield and Rochdale in accordance with the 3rd. resolution of the General Medical Committee.

Resolved 6

That the minutes of the Medical Sub-Committee of this day be adopted as the proceedings of this Board.

Resolved 7

That the reports of streets cleansed now presented from the Scavenging Committee be referred to the Classification Committee.

Appendix

Copy of the Reply to the Petition
of the Inhabitants, &c.
of Shude Hill and the Vicinity.

This petition having been referred to a numerous meeting of the General Medical Committee (which consists of all the legally qualified Medical Gentlemen of Manchester), they conceived that the groundless alarm expressed by the inhabitants, concerning the proximity of the Swan Street Hospital, might be allayed by a statement of the reasons which induced the Board to select that building for the reception of cholera patients.

1. Persons affected with cholera cannot, from the nature of the disease, be removed to a great distance from their habitations without such fatigue, and also from exposure to the atmosphere, such physical depression, as are likely to prove fatal. The spread of spasmodic cholera may however be most effectually checked and the disease most easily treated, by removing the poor from their close and ill ventilated habitations to commodious hospitals where all the apparatus necessary to the treatment of the malady may be conveniently applied, and the exertions of the medical faculty may be efficiently concentrated. The situation of the hospital must be determined by a consideration of these circumstances, and the Special Board has therefore chosen buildings in the immediate vicinity of districts densely populated by those most liable to

the disease, viz: the poor, the ill-clothed, the badly fed, and those destitute of the comforts and conveniences of life.

The Board after prolonged and diligent inquiries, has been unable to procure any site, suitable for the purpose, on which to erect a temporary hospital for the reception of cholera patients, and particularly the hopes of effecting this object were baffled in the neighbourhood of Shude Hill. Independently of this practical impossibility, and also <u>of the great expense of erecting a building, and of the want of adequate powers [at the time], to employ the funds</u> of the Town for this purpose, the Special Board with the advice of its Medical Committee, considered the premises situate in Swan Street as in every respect most eligible, both as concerned the safety of the patients, and the health of the surrounding inhabitants.

2. The hospitals, chosen in the various sections into which the Town has been divided, are intended for the reception of those cases of cholera only, which occur in the districts respectively surrounding them and the inhabitants of the immediate vicinity of the Phoenix Foundry would be exposed <u>to extreme danger</u> were the disease suffered to propagate itself without impediment amongst the surrounding habitations of the poor. <u>The safety of the petitioners will be most effectually promoted by the removal of all persons affected with cholera in their district to the Swan Street Hospital</u>, which has been especially provided by the Board for that purpose. *[Alterations in pencil made to the original in this part of the appendix].*

3. The advantages which a district visited by any contagious epidemic thus derives from the removal of all persons affected with the malady to a Hospital is not attended with any countervailing evil, for experience proves that from the attention paid in such establishments to cleanliness and ventilation contagions equally malignant with that of cholera are <u>not propagated from them to the houses situated in their vicinity.</u>

4. The Swan Street Hospital, from its elevated position and its comparative insulation from the neighbourhood by its court and the wall with which it is surrounded, is <u>particularly well adapted</u> to prevent the propagation of cholera from the patients which it may contain.

5. The vicinity of the Shudehill market is not objectionable. The Medical Committee assure the petitioners *[inhabitants]* that all known facts are opposed to the opinion, that contagion may be communicated from a well ventilated hospital, by a current of air, which must, in this case, traverse a wide street before its contact with those who may be predisposed to its reception.

The Medical Committee feel the greater confidence in conveying these assurances to the petitioners**[inhabitants]*, as it is on record, and is also well known to many of the inhabitants of this Town, that in the year 1796, when a malignant epidemic of typhus fever prevailed in Manchester, objections, similar to those now raised *['stated in the petition to the Special Board' crossed out and replaced by 'now raised']* were urged against the erection of Fever Wards in Portland Street; in the densely populated vicinity of which street upwards of four hundred pauper patients were affected with the disease. The epidemic was controlled by the erection of the House of Recovery, and that the petitioners *['inhabitants' replaced by 'petitioners']* need not be informed that this establishment is now considered one of the most salutary institutions of the Town, and is regarded with no apprehension by persons residing in its immediate vicinity and no instance of the propagation of Typhus Fever to any dwelling in the vicinity has occurred. Consequently, the surrounding property, so far from being depreciated, has rather increased in value.

6. Experience, as communicated from the highest authorities, proves that the contagion of cholera exerts its influence only in a very limited sphere. The disease is chiefly communicated by injudicious personal intercourse, by exposure to the atmosphere of an ill-ventilated apartment inhabited by those suffering from the disease, or to infection from clothes and bed linen which have been long in contact with the patient, and, even then, has the power of affecting only a limited number of persons predisposed to its reception "who are rendered eminently susceptible by cold, intemperance, fatigue, fear, anxiety, diarrhoea and other previous diseases". These and other considerations render it evident that the spasmodic cholera is not, as popular anxiety appears to apprehend; more contagious than many epidemics, and is even less so than some well-known infectious diseases. Drs. Barry and Russell, who formed the Medical Commission at St. Petersburgh, state, "that, in a generally infected atmosphere, the additional danger of infection incurred by approaching one or more individuals labouring under this disease was not greater than would occur from approaching one or more typhus patients under similar circumstances."

Benjamin Braidley (signature)
Boroughreeve, Chairman

**Board of Health
February 15, 1832**

W. Haynes Esq., Chairman
Drs. S.A. Bardsley, J.P. Kay, E. Lyon, J.D. Hulme; Revd James Crook; Colonel Shaw; Messrs. J.S. Heron, J. Woollam, T. Weatherby, Brunditt, J. Sandiford, T. Townend, P. Ewart junr.

Resolved 1
    That the minutes of the proceedings of this Board on the 11th. Instant be now confirmed.

Resolved 2

That the letter transmitted to the authorities of Preston, Huddersfield and Rochdale dated 13th. Inst. be entered on the minutes. (See Appendix)

Resolved 3

That the committee appointed January 16th. to draw up a plan of the arrangements adopted by this Board, for the information of the public, consisting of Dr. Bardsley, Dr. Kay, Colonel Shaw, and Mr. Joseph Heron be reappointed and that they be requested from time to time to revise their report and communicate their corrections and alterations to the Special Board. It being understood that the plan already agreed upon shall still be the groundwork of the one contemplated in this resolution.

That the corrected report last presented by the committee previous to the appearance of cholera shall in the event of that disorder appearing be forthwith printed and placarded for the direction of the public generally and for the promulgation of the entire system of arrangements made by this Board.

Resolved 4

That Mr. John Spear Heron be added to the above committee.

Resolved 5

That the Board of Health conceives that the continued operations of the Scavenging Committee are essential to the health of the Town in the prospect of the introduction of cholera and therefore suggests to the Churchwardens the propriety of extending their grant of money to the Scavenging Committee.

Resolved 6

That the publication of the reply to the petition of the owners and occupiers of property in the neighbourhood of the Phoenix Foundry be suspended for the present.

Resolved 7

That Mr. J.S. Heron and Mr. P. Ewart junr. be requested to wait upon Messrs. Peel, Williams and Peel and furnish them with a copy of the answer of the Board to the petitioners against the establishment of the cholera hospital in Swan Street.

Signed W. Haynes (signature)

Appendix

Special Board of Health
Town Hall, Manchester
February 13, 1832

Sir

The Manchester Special Board of Health, having reason to believe that an unrestricted intercourse of pedlars, itinerant collectors of old clothes, and other vagrants will be one of the most likely means of transmitting the Pestilential Cholera from town to town; and being anxious to adopt any reasonable precautions which may tend to avert so great a calamity from this populous and important district; – considering also that the Town of (Preston) (Huddersfield) (Rochdale) is one of the principal avenues by which travellers from the North to the South must necessarily pass: they have thought it expedient to make enquiry, what measures (if any) for the supervision and restraint of vagrants have been taken by the authorities in (Preston) (&c.) (&c.).

On behalf of the Board, therefore, I have to request the favour of your communicating any information which you may be able to supply on this subject. And I would further beg leave to suggest that, if no steps of the nature alluded to have yet been taken, it may be worthy of consideration whether some regulations cannot be enforced, which might contribute in some degree to the security of your own Town; as well as that of the district to the southward.

I have the honour to be,
Sir
your Obedient Servant
(Signed) Benjamin Braidley
Chairman

To
The Chairman of the Board of Health
or Chief Magistrate at (Preston) (Rochdale) (Huddersfield)

Board of Health, Town Hall
February 18, 1832

Henry Forth Esq., Chairman
Drs. J.P. Kay, J.D. Hulme, W. Johns, E. Lyon; Revd. George Dugard, W. Marsden, James Crook; Colonel Shaw; Messrs. T. Townend, J. Sandiford, P. Ewart junr., George Peel, J. Woollam, T. Weatherby, J.S. Heron, F. Fincham

Resolved 1

That the proceedings of the last meeting of this Board be confirmed.

Resolved 2

That the communications from the Vicar of Huddersfield and the Mayor of Preston be acknowledged by the Secretary and that a copy of the resolution passed by the Medical Committee and confirmed by this Board as to the propriety of visiting and inspecting lodging houses for the accommodation of vagrants or paupers be transmitted at the same time.

Resolved 3

> That a copy of the medical arrangement by district be transmitted by this Board to the Churchwardens with a request that they will furnish to the stipendiary overseers appointed to inspect the lodging houses a list of the medical gentlemen appointed in their respective districts and that the Churchwardens be requested to transmit to this Board a list of such overseers in each district and that when such list be transmitted to this Board each medical gentleman be furnished with the names of the overseers in their respective districts and at the same time be informed of the nature of the duties they will be called upon to perform.

Resolved 4

> That this Board beg to recommend to the Churchwardens that they require that the overseers shall keep a list of the lodging houses in their respective districts and make returns to the Churchwardens of their daily visits stating the existence or non existence of suspicious disease and the number of applications which they may find it necessary to make to the Medical Inspectors of their districts.

Resolved 5

> That the Revd. Mr. Crook, Dr. Lyon and Dr. Johns be requested to wait upon the Churchwardens for the purpose of arranging with them best method of cleansing and purifying the houses from which cholera patients may have been conveyed; as also to ascertain from them whether any and what steps have been taken by them for providing a burial place for those dying of the cholera and to state to them that it is the opinion of this Board that some decisive steps should be immediately taken for the obtaining such burial place.

Resolved 6

> That Colonel Shaw, Dr. J.D. Hulme, Dr. J.P. Kay, and Mr. F. Fincham be appointed a sub-committee to confer with the Trustees of the Duke of Bridgewater and the Liverpool Board of Health on the best means of carrying into effect the inspection of boats on the various canals.

Resolved 7

> That the petition now presented to the Board not being accompanied by any signatures it be returned to Mr. Haigh.

Henry Forth (signature)

Board of Health
February 22, 1832

Colonel Shaw, Chairman
Drs J. P. Kay, S. A. Bardsley, E. Lyon, Dr W. Johns; Revd. James Crook, George Dugard; Mr T. Townend

Resolved 1
> That the proceedings of the Board on the 18th Instant be now confirmed.

Memorandum
> The Revd. James Crook, Dr Lyons and Dr Johns reported the result of their interview with the Churchwardens, viz; That in case of the cholera appearing in Manchester before any other plot of ground can be provided, the Churchwardens will appropriate a portion of the Parish Burial Ground for the interment of persons dying by that disease; – they were not prepared to give a definite answer relative to the appointment of persons to cleanse and fumigate the houses from which the patients had been taken.

Resolved 2
> That Mr Langford and Mr Lynch (having been recommended by the Medical Committee) be provisionally appointed resident Medical Officers to the cholera hospitals and that they be informed of that appointment.

Resolved 3
> That, the supervision of the boats arriving from London or other places where cholera exists being of the utmost importance that the subject be discussed at the meeting of this Board on Saturday the 25th Inst; and that the Churchwardens be required to attend.

J. Shaw (signature)

Board of Health, Town Hall
February 25, 1832

Dr. S.A. Bardsley, Chairman
Drs. J.P. Kay, W. Johns; Revd. James Crook; Messrs. T. Weatherby, S. Fletcher, J. Sandiford, John Woolman, J.S. Heron, T. Townend, George Peel

Resolved 1
> That the proceedings of the Board on the 22nd. Inst. be confirmed.

Resolved 2
> That the further consideration of the propriety of appointing a Medical Officer to inspect the boats on the canals be postponed until such time as the Churchwardens shall think themselves sufficiently prepared to discuss the subject.

S.A. Bardsley (signature)

Board of Health, Town Hall
February 29, 1832

Colonel Shaw, Chairman
Dr. J.P. Kay, S.A. Bardsley, E. Lyon; Revd. W. Marsden; Messrs. Robert Ogden, Samuel Fletcher, E. Connell, F. Fincham, T. Weatherby, J. Sandiford

Resolved 1
That the proceedings of the last meeting of this Board be now confirmed.

Resolved 2
That the Boroughreeve be requested to write to the County Members for a copy of "the Cholera Prevention Bill" begging the favour of an immediate reply and that a special meeting of this Board be called for Monday next at 11 o'clock a.m. to examine the said Bill and ascertain the powers granted therein.

Resolved 3
That the communication from the Scavenging Committee of the 27th. Inst. be entered on the Minutes. (See Appendix No.1)

Resolved 4
That the report of the number of boats &c. employed on the canal be entered on the minutes also the list of pauper lodging houses presented by Mr. Ogden. (See Appendix Nos. 2 & 3)

J. Shaw (signature)

Appendix No.1

Extract from the Minutes of the Lamp, Scavenging and Fire Engine Committee of February 27th, 1832.

Resolved
That the communication from the Board of Health now read be inserted on the minutes.

Resolved
That the Board of Health be respectfully informed that this committee has not funds to pay for cleansing unpaved streets and that any similar reports should in consequence be transmitted to the Churchwardens for their consideration.

(a true copy)
(Signed) Jonathan Thorpe junr.

To
The Board of Health
Manchester

Appendix No.2

	Thomas Bache	Kenworthy & Co.	Pickford & Co.	Robins, Mills & Co.
1. Number of boats employed?	26	16	90 to 100	20
2. Number of men, women and children in each boat?	4 Men	4 Men	4 Men	4 Men
3. How often the boats arrive from London and the ordinary hours of arrival?	Everyday hours very uncertain generally from 12 am to 12 am	Everyday say Morning	Everyday generally morning	Everyday morning
4. What number of passengers may be expected by the boats in the summer?	Not one a month upon the average	Very few. Three or four a month	Impossible to give an idea	Not more than one in ten boats
5. Does the same crew navigate the boat all the way from London?	Yes	Yes	Generally	Yes

F.A. Walsh (signed)

Numerical List of
Pauper Lodging Houses

		Number			Number
			Brought Up		168
District No.	1......	–	District No.	8......	–
	2......	108		9.......	–
	3......	51		10......	12
	4......	–		11......	26
	5......	6		12......	–
	6......	–		13......	60
	7......	3		14......	1
			Total Number		267

Board of Health, Town Hall
March 3, 1832

Drs. J.P. Kay, S.A. Bardsley; Colonel Shaw; Mr. Weatherby

Attendance insufficient to form a quorum.

Special Meeting
Board of Health, Town Hall
March 5, 1832

Benjamin Braidley Esq., Chairman
Drs J.P. Kay, W. Johns, S.A. Bardsley; Revd. C.D. Wray, James Crook, E.D. Jackson, Huntington, George Dugard; Colonel Shaw; Messrs. H. Forth, W. Crossley, S. Fletcher, T. Townend, John Potter, T. Harbottle, Norreys, Bradshaw, P. Ewart junr., Kerr, J. Sandiford, J. Walker, J. Woollam, Chappell

Resolved 1
That a Committee be appointed consisting of Dr. Bardsley, Colonel Shaw, Dr. Kay, Revd. C.D. Wray, and Revd. James Crook for the purposes of drawing up a memorial to the Lords of the Privy Council requesting them to legalize this Board under the act passed by the legislature for the prevention of cholera that it be presented to this Board at their next meeting and having met with their approval that it be signed by the Chairman and transmitted to the Clerk of the Council in waiting.

Memorandum
Dr. Kay reported that he had made enquiries of the Committee of the Ardwick and Ancoats Dispensary whether they would allow their apothecary to undertake the inspection of the boats on the canals arriving from London – that they expressed their willingness to give every assistance to the Board, but would wish that a form of queries should be furnished to be filled up by that gentleman and that a person should be provided to give him notice of the arrival of the boats.

Adjourned till Wednesday 11 o'clock.

Board of Health, Town Hall
March 7, 1832

Colonel Shaw, Chairman
Drs. J.P. Kay, S.A. Bardsley; Revd. W. Marsden; Messrs. Benjamin Braidley, P. Ewart junr., T. Kerr, F. Fincham, T. Townend

Resolved 1
That the proceedings of the last meeting of this Board be confirmed.

Resolved 2

That the memorial now read be received and entered on the minutes and that a copy thereof signed by the Boroughreeve be immediately transmitted to the Privy Council. (See Appendix)

Resolved 3

That the second resolution of the Medical Sub-Committee of the 2[nd.] Inst. be received and adopted as the proceedings of this Board.

J. Shaw (signature)

Appendix

To the Right Honorable
The Lords
of His Majesty's Privy Council &c. &c. &c.

Special Board of Health
Town Hall
Manchester

My Lords

This memorial humbly sheweth that the Special Board of Health established in Manchester in conformity with the recommendation of the Privy Council of the 20[th.] of October, and consisting of "the Presidents, Vice-Presidents, Treasurers, Deputy-Treasurers, House-Stewards, Auditors and Committees of the Manchester Royal Infirmary, the House of Recovery, and the Ancoats Dispensary, together with the Medical and Surgical officers of those Institutions; also Dr. S.A. Bardsley, Dr. E. Holme, Lieutenant Colonel Shaw, the Revd. James Crook, Mr. George Faulkner, the Magistrates of the Division, the Boroughreeve and Constables of Manchester, the Churchwardens and Sidesmen, the Surveyors of Highways, and the Members of the Paving and Scavenging Committees under the Police Act, with power to add to their Number," has been for some months past actively engaged in organizing measures to prevent the introduction and spread of cholera in the Town.

A general meeting of the Leypayers of the Township was called, and the Churchwardens and Overseers were empowered to employ the funds of the parish as the emergency should appear to require. District boards were established, and inspection of the streets and houses of the Town ensued, and measures were taken to cleanse the habitations of the poor, and to scavenge the streets. Subsequently, three hospitals have been provided, stipendiary medical residents have been elected. Nine physicians have offered their services gratuitously and surgeons have been on the same terms appointed as District Medical Officers, and also druggists to dispense medicines in the several police divisions of the Town. The Board has also been careful to provide means of conveying the sick in carriages, and by slings distributed in various depôts. A place of burial has also been selected in a situation remote from dwelling houses.

The fiscal authorities having already incurred a considerable expense in the execution of these arrangements, and doubting the legality of appropriating the poor's rates to these general purposes, are unwilling to become responsible for any further expenditure on the part of the Special Board of Manchester, until its operations are sanctioned by the Privy Council. Some desirable arrangements yet remain unaccomplished. The Special Board, knowing that cholera is most frequently propagated along lines of water conveyance, is anxious to establish in one of its hospitals, conveniently situated for the purpose, an inspection of the crews and passengers arriving by the canal boats from London, in order that any cases of suspicious disease may be forthwith removed to the hospital. The Board has already ascertained that this inspection can be performed without any interruption of commercial intercourse, and that it would be encouraged by the proprietors of boats navigated on these canals who would cheerfully aid its execution. With a similar design the Board is also desirous of having a daily inspection of all the pauper lodging houses of the Town. For the accomplishment of these objects it will be necessary to appoint competent officers with salaries. The Special Board regrets to add that its exertions in cleansing the streets and houses of the Town, and especially in removing many gross and disgusting nuisances have been paralyzed from the want of confidence which the authorities have felt concerning their power to expend the funds of the Town for these purposes.

Existing in the constant apprehension and actual danger of the ingression of the disease the Board is unable to apply those preventive measures which are absolutely required by the circumstances in which the Town is placed.

The adoption of many arrangements which might be desirable to prevent the spread of the disease when once introduced is also for the same reason delayed.

In consideration of the foregoing circumstances this memorial humbly represents that it is of great importance that the sanction of the Privy Council should be given,

1stly. To the present constitution of this Board.

2ndly. To the liquidation of all expences "reasonably or properly incurred" in the execution of arrangements necessary for preventing the introduction and spread of cholera upon receiving the order in writing of a Justice of the Peace dwelling in or near the parish, commanding the Churchwardens and overseers to pay a sufficient sum of money for such purposes, according to the provisions of the Act for preventing the spread of cholera.

3rdly.   To the monthly transmission of a statement of all expences so incurred by this Board to the Privy Council.

Signed on behalf of the Special Board of Health
Benjamin Braidley
Boroughreeve and President of the Board

Board of Health, Town Hall
March 10, 1832

Colonel Shaw, Chairman
Drs. S.A. Bardsley, J. P Kay; Revd. James White; Messrs. E. Connell, T. Townend, F. Fincham, Mr. P. Ewart

Resolved 1
    That the proceedings of the last meeting of this Board be now confirmed.

Resolved 2
    That notice be given to the Assistant Secretary that his services will not be required by this Board after the end of one month from this day.

Resolved 3
    That the communication from the Nuisance Sub-Committee (dated 8th inst.) be entered on the minutes of the Proceedings of this Board. (See Appendix)

J. Shaw (signature)

Appendix

Extract from the minutes of the Nuisance Sub-Committee of March 7th. 1832.

Memorandum
    Read the reports of the Inspectors respecting the complaints of the Board of Health.

Resolved
    That the same be entered on the minutes.

Resolved
    That this committee cannot inspect any more cases from the Board of Health until they have more inspectors.

(a true copy)
(Signed) Jonathan Thorpe junr.

Town Hall, Manchester
March 8, 1832.

Board of Health, Town Hall
March 14, 1832

Dr. J.P. Kay; Revd. J. Crook; Colonel Shaw

No communication having been received from the Privy Council in reply to the memorial transmitted by this Board, the meeting adjourned till Saturday.

Board of Health, Town Hall
March 17, 1832

H. Forth Esq., Chairman
Drs. J.P. Kay, S.A. Bardsley; Colonel Shaw; Messrs. T. Townend, P. Ewart junr.

Resolved 1
That the proceedings of the Board on the 10$^{th.}$ Instant be confirmed.

Resolved 2
That no reply having been received from the Privy Council the Boroughreeve and Constables be requested to transmit a copy of the Memorial to Mr. Heywood begging him to communicate upon the subject with the Clerk of the Council and that the Boroughreeve and Constables be requested to call a special meeting at their discretion on the receipt of a reply.

Henry Forth (signature)

Special Meeting
Board of Health, Town Hall
March 19, 1832.

Benjamin Braidley Esq., Chairman
Drs. S.A. Bardsley, J. Hull, W. Johns; Revd. George Dugard, James White, W. Marsden, James Crook, Huntington, Cecil D. Wray; Colonel Shaw; Messrs. P. Ewart junr., Bradshaw, Joseph Rooke, F. Fincham, T. Townend, J. Potter, E. Connell, J. Holford, W. Garnett, D. Dockray, J. Woollam

Resolved 1
That the proceedings of the last meeting of this Board be approved of.

Resolved 2
That a special meeting of the Board of Health be called for 11 o'clock tomorrow to make a selection of 50 or 60 names from the present members of the Board to be transmitted to the Privy Council for the purpose of being legally appointed a Board of Health and that the object of the meeting be stated in the circular.

Resolved 3

That the following list of names be submitted to the special meeting of the Board tomorrow.

The Boroughreeve and Constables for the time being.

The Churchwardens for the time being.

The Very	Revd. Dr. Calvert	Drs.	S.A. Bardsley
	Revd. C.D. Wray		J. Mitchell
	Revd. W. Marsden		E. Lyon
	Revd. George Dugard		E. Carbutt
	Revd. James Crook		J.L. Bardsley
	Revd. James White		J.D. Hulme
	Revd. H. Fielding		William Henry
	Revd. Huntington		W.C. Henry
			J.P. Kay
Messrs.	~~J. Bradshaw~~		H. Pendlebury
	J. Holford		H. Gaulter
	J^{o.} Kennedy		E. Holme
	George Hall		J. Hull
	R.J.J. Norreys		W. Johns
	J. Bentley		C. Phillips
	E. Connell		
	J. Barker	Messrs.	J. Thorpe
	H. Houldsworth		J.A. Ransome
	T. Townend		J. Ainsworth
	D. Dockray		R. Thorpe
	T. Weatherby		W.J. Wilson
	F. Fincham		T. Turner
	Jos^{h.} Rooke		R. Addison
	J. Woollam		W.R. Whatton
	P. Ewart junr.		
	George Faulkner	Colonel Shaw	
	J^{o.} Potter		
	T^{o.} Potter	Messrs.	H.H. Birley
	J^{o.} Dalton		Oswald Milne

Mr Joseph Heron
Honorary Secretary

Resolved 4

That the letter from Mr. Maclean in answer to the memorial presented by this Board to the Privy Council be entered on the minutes. (See Appendix)

Appendix

Central Board of Health
Council Office, Whitehall
March 14, 1832.

Sir

In reply to your letter of the 7th. Inst. to the Lords of the Council, which has been referred to this Board, stating the measures adopted by the Board of Health established at Manchester, & requesting the sanction of the Privy Council to the present constitution of the Board also to the liquidation of all expences properly incurred in making the necessary arrangements for preventing the introduction or spread of cholera, and to the monthly transmission of a statement of all expences so incurred to the Privy Council; I am directed to state to you with reference to the first point, that upon the list of names of the existing Board being transmitted to me, the same shall be submitted to the Lords of the Council for confirmation: at the same time it would be desirable that no more members should be placed upon the Board than may be considered absolutely necessary for the purposes required, and that the number should not exceed 50 or 60.

As to the second and third points of your letter, I am to refer you to the Order in Council of the 6 Inst. relative to the mode of raising funds, in consequence of the passing of the Cholera Prevention Act.

I am further directed by the Board to express to you their approbation at the judicious arrangements which have been already adopted by the existing Board at Manchester.

I am
Sir
your most Obedient Servant
(Signed) William Maclean
Secretary

Benjamin Braidley Esq.
President of the Board of Health
Manchester

Special Meeting
Board of Health, Town Hall
March 20, 1832

William Haynes Esq., Chairman
Drs. S.A. Bardsley, J.D. Hulme, J.P. Kay; Revd. Dr. Smith, James Crook, George Dugard, W. Marsden; Colonel Shaw; J. Thorpe, Joseph Rooke, P. Ewart junr., Jo Barker, Jo Bentley, L. Buchan, Butterworth

Resolved

> That the list of names now read over, being the proposed constitution of a Board of Health for the Town of Manchester be submitted to the Lords of the Council for confirmation.

Adjourned till Saturday 11 o'clock

William Haynes (signature)

**Board of Health, Town Hall
March 24, 1832**

Colonel Shaw, Chairman
Drs. S.A. Bardsley, J.P. Kay; Revd. George Dugard; Mr. P. Ewart junr.

Resolved 1

> That the proceedings of the last meeting of this Board be confirmed.

Resolved 2

> That the Revd. George Dugard having requested permission to make temporary use of the cholera hospital in Harrison Street as a Sunday school a deputation be appointed to wait on Mr. Swindells to obtain his consent to the appropriation of the rooms for such purpose – to report to the Board at their next meeting – and that the deputation consist of the Revd. G. Dugard and Dr. J.P. Kay.

Resolved 3

> That copies of the memorial presented by this Board to the Privy Council, of the Cholera Prevention Act and of the Order in Council of the 6th. Inst. be granted for the use of the Salford Board of Health as requested by Mr. Garnett and at the same time that a copy of the intended placard containing the arrangements adopted by this Board be furnished for their guidance.

J. Shaw (signature)

Sealed.   At the Council Chamber Whitehall
                           the 23rd. March 1832.
                           By the Lord of His Majesty's Most
                           Honorable Privy Council.

It is this day ordered by Their Lordships that a Board of Health be constituted in the Town of Manchester consisting of the following members – viz:

The Revd. Dr. Calvert   Drs. S.A. Bardsley
     Revd. C.D. Wray   J. Mitchell

Revd. W. Marsden
Revd. George Dugard
Revd. James Crook
Revd. James White
Revd. H. Fielding
Revd. Huntington

Messrs. J. Holford
J. Kennedy
George Hall
R.J.J. Norreys
J. Bentley
E. Connell
J. Barker
Henry Houldsworth
T. Townend
D. Dockray
T. Weatherby
Frederick Fincham
Joseph Rooke
J. Woollam
P. Ewart junr.
George Faulkner
J. Potter
T. Potter
J. Dalton

E. Lyon
E. Carbutt
James L. Bardsley
J.D. Hulme
William Henry
W.C. Henry
Physicians J.P. Kay
H. Pendlebury
H.J. Gaulter
E. Holme
Jo. Hull
William Johns
Charles Phillips

Messrs. J. Thorpe
J.A. Ransome
James Ainsworth
R. Thorpe
W.J. Wilson
Surgeons T. Turner
R. Addison
W.R. Whatton

Lieutenant Colonel Shaw
Messrs. H.H. Birley
O. Milne
Honorary Secretary Joseph Heron

And the said Board are to proceed in the execution of the duties required of them accordingly.

(Signed) C.C. Greville

Board of Health, Manchester
March 28, 1832

Lieutenant Colonel Shaw, Chairman
Drs. S.A. Bardsley, E. Lyon, J.P. Kay, J. Hull, J.D. Hulme, W. Johns, H. Gaulter, Jo Mitchell; The Very Revd. Dr. Calvert, Revd. James White, James Crook, George Dugard, W. Marsden, H. Fielding; Messrs. R.J.J. Norreys, J. Holford, J. Woollam, J. Kenworthy, J. Rooke, P. Ewart junr., T. Townend, H. Houldsworth, W.R. Whatton, R. Addison, Jo. Potter, George Hall, Thomas Potter, Joseph Heron H.S.

Moved by Mr. T. Townend. Seconded by Dr. J.P. Kay.

Resolved 1

    That a committee be appointed consisting of Colonel Shaw, Dr. Bardsley and Dr. Kay to draw up a memorial to the Lords of the Council for the purpose of obtaining (if practicable) the addition of the Boroughreeve and Constables and Churchwardens of the Town of Manchester for the time being as members of the Board of Health; and if that cannot be done under the general terms of Boroughreeve Constables and Churchwardens then to request the addition of the following names to the present list of gentlemen constituting the Board; viz:

Messrs. Benjamin Braidley Boroughreeve

    William Haynes
    H. Forth   Constables

    Rt. Ogden
    S. Fletcher
    William Crossley   Churchwardens

    J.C. Harter
    Evan Evans
    James Wood

    That the communication from the committee shall represent the desirableness of the above authorities forming part of the Board when a change shall take place in the present officers and that the committee be directed to make such further communication to the Council on this subject as may appear to them desirable.

    Moved by Dr. Bardsley. Seconded by Mr. Kenworthy.

Resolved 2

    That the Order in Council now read legally constituting this Board be entered on the Minutes.

    Moved by Dr. Hull. Seconded by Mr. Whatton.

Resolved 3

    That the proceedings of the former Board be adopted by this Board, and that the committees appointed by the former Board continue to act, and that they be constituted and have the same powers as conferred by the former Board.

    Moved by Dr. Bardsley. Seconded by the Revd. G. Dugard.

Resolved 4

    That a requisition to the Churchwardens be made by this Board requesting them to call a meeting of the Leypayers to be held as early as possible (for the purpose of obtaining their sanction to the expences which may be incurred by this Board) as directed by the Cholera Prevention Act; and that the following gentlemen be appointed a committee for drawing up the said requisition, and for making such arrangements as they think necessary and fit for bringing the subject before the consideration of the Leypayers, viz:

Colonel	Shaw	Messrs.	Thomas Potter
Drs.	Bardsley		P. Ewart junr.
	Kay		J. Woollam
Revd.	W. Marsden		

Moved by Dr. J.P. Kay. Seconded by Mr. T. Townend.

Resolved 5

That the Revd. George Dugard be allowed the use of the room in Harrison Street (rented by this Board as a Hospital) for the purposes of a Sunday school, with the understanding that the forms &c. placed therein by Mr. Dugard be removed every Sunday evening or Monday morning; it being also understood that Mr. Dugard shall immediately give up possession of the room when required by this Board on the same being made known to him through their secretary or otherwise.

Moved by Mr. Whatton. Seconded by Dr. Gaulter.

Resolved 6

That no document or tables of this Board shall be published or made use of by any Individual Member without the consent of the Board.

Moved by Dr. Johns. Seconded by Dr. Bardsley.

Resolved 7

That Dr. Kay be allowed if he think fit to make use of and print the Tables and other information obtained by this Board to which he has alluded in the paper read by him before the Philosophical Society.

J. Shaw (signature)

Board of Health, Manchester
March 31, 1832

Lieutenant Colonel Shaw, Chairman
Drs. S.A. Bardsley, H. Gaulter; Revd. James Crook; Messrs. T. Townend, W.R.Whatton, P. Ewart junr.

Resolved 1

That the proceedings of the Board on the 28th Inst. be confirmed.

Moved by Mr. T. Townend. Seconded by Dr. Bardsley.

Resolved 2

> That the memorial to the Privy Council of the 28th Inst. be entered on the minutes; as also the requisition to the Churchwardens to convene a meeting of the Leypayers. (See Appendix Nos. 1 & 2)

Resolved 3

> That the communication from the Central Board of the 20th Inst. be acknowledged by the Secretary and that it be entered on the minutes with the accompanying tables and the letter from the Central Board dated 23rd Inst. (See Appendix Nos. 3 & 4)

Moved by the Revd. J. Crook. Seconded by Mr. P. Ewart junr.

Resolved 4

> That the physicians and surgeons who are members of the Board shall form a Medical Committee and that they be requested whenever they may think fit, to call into consultation any other of the medical practitioners of this Town with whom they may deem it desirable to confer.

J. Shaw (signature)

Appendix No.1

To the Right Honourable
the Lords
of His Majesty's Privy Council
&c. &c. &c.

Board of Health
Town Hall, Manchester
March 28, 1832

My Lords,

> This Memorial humbly sheweth that in the constitution of the Board of Health for Manchester by an order of the Honourable the Lords of the Privy Council dated 23rd Inst. the present Boroughreeve and Constables and the present Churchwardens were not included as requested by the communication to the Lords of the Council of the 20th Inst. signed by Mr. W. Haynes.

> This Board takes the liberty to represent their opinion that it is very desirable that the Boroughreeve, Constables and Churchwardens for the time being shall form part of the Board and beg humbly to submit to the Honourable the Privy Council that if they cannot be included as forming part of the Board under the general designations of Boroughreeve, Constables, and Churchwardens that the following names be added to the list of those composing the Board of

Health for Manchester, viz:
Messrs. Benjamin Braidley Boroughreeve

W. Haynes
H.J. Forth   Constables

Robert Ogden
Samuel Fletcher
William Crossley   Churchwardens

Evan Evans
J.C. Harter
James Wood

The Churchwardens of course have the disposal of the parish rates but the Boroughreeve and Constables have no such control; the names above submitted included both the present Churchwardens and the Boroughreeve and Constables and it is thought proper to state this in case the Lords of the Council should see any objection to including the Churchwardens from their having the management of the funds of the Town.

Signed on behalf the Board
Joseph Heron
Honorary Secretary

Appendix No.2

Requisition &c.

To
The Churchwardens of Manchester &c. &c.

Gentlemen
In accordance with the order in that behalf made by the Lords and others of His Majesty's Most Honorable Privy Council, and dated the 6th day of the present month of March, I am directed by the Board of Health for the Township of Manchester, appointed by the said Privy Council, to request you will convene a public vestry meeting of the inhabitants of that Township, for the purpose of taking into their consideration the adoption of such precautionary measures as may be best calculated to prevent the introduction or spread of cholera; at which meeting the Board will come prepared to state the proceedings already taken under the sanction of a former meeting, and also to submit the propositions which as they conceive, now require the approbation of the inhabitants in vestry assembled.

I am
Gentlemen
Your obedient Servant
(Signed) Joseph Heron
Honorary Secretary to the Board

Town Hall, Manchester
28th March

Appendix No.3

Central Board of Health, Council Office
Whitehall, March 20, 1832

Sir,

It being desirable on many accounts that regular and correct information should be obtained as to the progress of cholera, and that a uniform system, as far as practicable, should be adopted in reporting cases of that disease, I am desired to transmit to you the enclosed Forms of Returns (Nos. 1 to 5), with the view of their being brought before your Board.

No.1 is the Form proposed to be used by Medical Practitioners for their Daily Numerical Returns to their respective Local Boards.

No.2 is a confidential Daily Nominal Return of New Cases and Deaths, on the back of No.1, by which Local Boards of Health will be enabled to apply, with due precision and despatch, such sanitary measures as they may judge necessary in each case.

No.3 is the Form of Daily Numerical Return to be furnished to the Central Board of Health by the Secretaries of Local Boards.

No.4 is a Form of Confidential Return (intended to serve also as a Register) to be furnished monthly, or whenever called on, by medical practitioners, to their Respective Boards.

No.5 The General Statistic Return of all cases of cholera that may have occurred in any Town, Parish or District, during one visitation, will be called for by the Central Board of Health, and be expected to be sent in by Local Boards, at the termination of the disease. This return is to be made up from the particulars contained in Nos. 1, 2, and 4, and is intended to afford to the Central Board the necessary data for a general report to His Majesty's Government upon the Progress of Cholera in the British Empire.

I am further desired to call your attention to the following extract of a circular addressed by this Board, with the form No.4 to the Local Boards of Health in the North of England, dated 7th January 1832: –

I am to add, that the necessity of keeping a correct register and the importance to the interests of humanity and of medical science that permanent sources of information as to the history and progress of cholera in this country should be established as soon as possible, will, it is hoped, induce all medical men to lend their aid to so useful an undertaking, and one so indispensable to the acquiring correct notions of the nature and treatment of this formidable disease.

You will please to acknowledge the receipt of this communication and of the accompanying forms of returns.

I have the Honour to be,
Sir,
your most obedient humble Servant,
(Signed) William Maclean
Secretary

To the
Chairman of the Board of Health
at Manchester

No. 1

To
The Secretary
Board of Health,
District

Daily Numerical Return of Cholera Cases under the Care of the undersigned in the Parish of ——————— 183 .

Date	Remaining at Last Report	New Cases	Dead	Recovered	Remaining this day at

From the Commencement of the Disease Under my Care		
No. of Cases	No. of Deaths	

(Signature)

No. 2

**Confidential Daily Return of New Cases and Deaths, to be furnished by
Medical Practitioners to their respective Local Boards of Health.**

New Cases

Name	Age	Residence
Deaths		

Date of Seizure	Remarks
Date of Death	

When there are objections to publicity initials
may be given without residence, but with all other particulars.

No. 3

Cholera – Daily Numerical Report of Cases for the Parish or District of

To be furnished to the Central Board of Health

Date	Remaining at Last Report	New Cases	Dead	Recovered	Remaining this day at

From the Commencement of the Disease on the		
Cases	Died	

No. 4

Monthly Confidential Return or Register of Cholera Ca‹
keep, and furnish to their respective <u>Local Board‹</u>
For the information <u>of the Lord‹</u>

Parish or District

No.	Name and Sex	Age	Residence	Employt of Patient; or of Parent or Husband in the case of unemployed Children or Females	Previous Health and Habits	Date of Seizure	Date ‹ Recov‹
1.							
2.							
3.							
4.							
5.							
6.							
7.							
8.							
9.							
10.							
11.							
12.							
13.							
14.							
15.							
16.							
17.							
18.							
19.							
20.							
21.							
22.							

Where there are objections to publicity, initials may be ‹

(Signed)

No. 4

ch Medical Practitioners are invited to
lth whenever called on.
Majesty's Most Honble. Privy Council.

|)ate) | From | to | 183 . |

ate of eath	Treated in Hospital	Treated in Patient's Dwelling	General Remarks on Precautionary Symptoms, Treatment, Appearance after Death, and apparent Origin, in any of the above Cases.

ut residence, but with all other particulars.

No. 5

Statistic Return of all Cases of Spasmodic Cholera wh
Districts during the

Name of Township Parish or District	Population according to Census of 1831		Date of first reported case	Date of Recovery or Death of last reported Case	Attacked since the Commencement			Total numbe attacked of Ages and both Sexes
						Adults		
	Males	Females			Children	Males	Females	

	Classes of Persons attacked										
Receiving Parochial Allowance		Labouring Classes		Persons in easy circumstances		Personal attendants on the sick		Washerwomen employed by the sick		Medical M	
Attacked	Dead	Attacked	Dead	Attacked	Dead	Attacked	Dead	Attacked	Dead	Attacked	D

N.B. –It is expected that a short Report will be subj
of the Weather and Winds immediately befor
symptoms in the different Classes, Ages, and Sexe
stance connected with the Origin and Progr

e occurred in the under-mentioned Townships, Parishes, or
valence of that Disease

d since the nmencement			Total Number died of all ages and both sexes	Treated in Hospitals		Treated in Patient's Dwelling		Greatest Number of Cases reported on any one Day with the Date of that Day	Greatest Number of Deaths reported on any one Day with the Date of that Day
	Adults								
dren	Male	Female		Dead	Recovered	Dead	Recovered		

rage Number of Hours een Attack & h in Cold Stage	Average Number of Days between Attack & Death in Fever Stage	Numbers of Families in which two or more Individuals have been attacked

above, noticing the state of the Public Health as to Man and
the Disease; the Localities and Floors of Houses attacked; the
nent; Post Mortem Appearances; and any remarkable Circum-
isease which may have been omitted in this Paper.

Appendix No. 4

Central Board of Health,
Council Office, Whitehall
23 March, 1832

Sir,

A supplement to the London Gazette of the 28th of February last containing an Order in Council issued in pursuance of the recent Act of Parliament relating to cholera is herewith transmitted for your information, and I beg to draw the particular attention of your Board to the last clause of such Order, by which they will find that the duty of calling upon the medical practitioners of their district for returns of all cases of cholera, or any disease anywise resembling cholera, and of appointing the time, place, manner and form of making such returns is imposed upon the Local Boards of Health, which the Central Board have to request no time may be lost in carrying into effect.

I am,
Sir,
Your most Obedient Servant
(Signed) W. Maclean, Secretary

To
The Chairman of the
Board of Health at Manchester

Board of Health, Manchester
April 4, 1832

Lieutenant Colonel Shaw, Chairman
Drs. S.A. Bardsley, H. Gaulter, C. Phillips, J.P. Kay, W. Johns; Revd. W. Marsden, James White, James Crook, George Dugard, H. Fielding; Messrs. T. Townend, F. Fincham, P. Ewart junr., Joseph Heron H.S.

Resolved 1

That the Order in Council of March the 30th adding the Boroughreeve, Constables and Churchwardens for the time being, to the Board of Health constituted March 23rd be entered on the minutes. (See Appendix)

Moved by Mr. Thomas Townend. Seconded by Dr. Bardsley.

Resolved 2

That the Boroughreeve for the time being be appointed Chairman and the Constables for the time being Deputy Chairmen of the Board of Health.

J. Shaw (signature)

Appendix

Sealed

At the Council Chamber, Whitehall
March 30, 1832
By the Lords of His Majesty's Most
Honorable Privy Council

It is this day ordered by their Lordships that the Boroughreeve, Constables and Churchwardens for the time being be added to the Board of Health constituted at Manchester on the 23rd Inst.

(Signed) C.C. Greville

Board of Health, Manchester
April 7, 1832

W. Haynes Esq., Chairman
Drs. J.P. Kay, S.A. Bardsley, H. Gaulter; Revd. G. Dugard; Messrs. E. Connell, P. Ewart junr., F. Fincham, T. Townend

Resolved 1

That the proceedings of the Board on March the 31st and on the 4th Inst. be now confirmed.

Resolved 2

That a copy of the resolutions passed at the public vestry meeting on the 6th Inst. be entered on the minutes. (See Appendix)

Moved by Colonel Shaw. Seconded by Dr. Bardsley.

Resolved 3

That the Secretary of the Board be directed to write by this day's post to Mr. Langford proposing to him immediately to undertake the superintendence of the three buildings now engaged by this Board as cholera hospitals, and the supervision of such boats as the Board may point out to him so far as he is capable of accomplishing the same, and that his engagement with the Board shall be monthly, with a salary of fifteen pounds per month; and four pounds per month for lodging and that Mr. Langford be not provided with board until he reside in the Hospital on the introduction of cholera.

Resolved 4

That circulars be issued to the members of the Board intimating that the Board continues to meet every Wednesday and Saturday at 11 o'clock precisely.

Moved by Mr. Townend. Seconded by Mr. Fincham.

Resolved 5

That owing to the extra business in preparing for the public meeting the Assistant Secretary whose terms of engagement ceases this day, be retained another week.

Moved by Dr. J.P. Kay. Seconded by Dr. Bardsley.

Resolved 6

That permission be given to Mr. P. Ewart junr. to make extracts from the returns of burials in Manchester obtained by the late Board.

Moved by Dr. J.P. Kay. Seconded by Mr. Ewart junr.

Resolved 7

That the Bills of Mortality from all places of interment in the boroughs of Manchester and Salford for the last four years be immediately obtained.

Moved by Mr. Fincham. Seconded by Dr. Gaulter.

Resolved 8

That a circular be immediately addressed by the Secretary to the various carriers by water connected with this Town, urging them to issue orders to the masters of boats to land at the place where they may be attacked any person who may fall sick on board the Boats and on no account to allow such persons to be brought forward to Manchester; and to inform them that it is in contemplation by the Board of Health to appoint a medical gentleman for the inspection of the boats as they arrive.

Resolved 9

That a list of names of the gentlemen constituting this Board be handed to each member of the Board.

William Haynes (signature)

Appendix

Town Hall, Manchester
April 6, 1832

At a Public Vestry Meeting of the inhabitants of Manchester, held here this day for the purpose of adopting such precautionary measures as may be best calculated to prevent the introduction or spread of cholera, and of receiving a report of the proceedings already taken under the sanction of a former meeting:

Robert Ogden, Esq., Senior Churchwarden
in the Chair.

Messrs. S.A. Bardsley, M.D.	Messrs. W. Crossley
D. Dockray	W. Haynes
P. Ewart junr.	Very Revd. Dr. Calvert
G.W. Wood	Revd. James Crook
S. Fletcher	J.E. Taylor
T. Townend	O. Milne
Rt. Garnett	Revd. W. Huntington
W.R. Whatton	J. Alexander, M.D.
F. Fincham	T. Harbottle
H. Gaulter, M.D.	Benjamin Braidley
G. Peel	N. Gardiner
Revd. James White	H. Beaver
Rd. Potter	J.P. Kay, M.D.
J. Hull, M.D.	E. Connell
Thomas Sharp	Hampson
E. Loyd	Revd. W. Marsden
J. Woollam	Joseph Heron
F. Walmsley	H. Smith
Sugden	Winder
Rowe	Miller

After a statement (made on the part of the late Board of Health for Manchester by Mr. Fincham) of the precautionary measures which have been already taken, and of the expences incurred in the execution thereof;

1. It was moved by Mr. G.W. Wood, seconded by Mr. Robert Garnett, and resolved unanimously, – That this meeting do now approve of the proceedings of the Special Board of Health, established in consequence of a resolution passed at a meeting of Leypayers, held on the 17th of November, 1831.

2. moved by Dr. Bardsley, seconded by Mr. E. Loyd, and resolved unanimously, – That, under the present circumstances, it is highly expedient, in this manufacturing and densely populous district, to adopt precautionary measures against the eventual introduction and spread of the disease called the cholera, or Spasmodic or Indian Cholera, and that the most salutary and approved mode will be to confide these measures wholly to the Board of Health, established for Manchester by his Majesty's Most Honourable Privy Council.

3. Moved by Mr. Thomas Sharp, seconded by Mr. Thomas Harbottle, and resolved unanimously, – That this Board be, therefore, requested and authorized to make such preparations, and exercise such of the conditional powers, in that behalf contained in an Order in Council of the 6th day of March last, and also to adopt such

other means as may appear to them best calculated to prevent the introduction and spread of the disease designated in the 2nd resolution; but so as not to occasion any charge upon the poor's rate beyond the limits to be now prescribed, without the consent of a subsequent meeting.

4. Moved by Mr. J.E. Taylor, Seconded by Mr. R. Potter, and resolved, –
That the means of precaution to be adopted by the Board will probably be attended with expense, requiring a provision for them of at least one thousand pounds, and that this sum be fixed and declared as the extent which the Board are at present empowered to claim against the Churchwardens when incurred, and a Magistrates order obtained.

5. Moved by Mr. T. Sharp, seconded by Mr. E. Loyd, and resolved unanimously, – That the best thanks of this meeting be given to the late Special Board of Health, for their zealous and effectual services and for the judicious measures of precaution which they have adopted.

Signed Robert Ogden, Chairman

6. Moved by the Very Revd. Dr. Calvert, Seconded by Mr. H. Beaver, and resolved unanimously, – That the thanks of the Leypayers be given to the Churchwardens for calling this meeting, and to Robert Ogden Esq., for his conduct in the Chair.

(Signed) Benjamin Braidley

Board of Health, Manchester
April 11, 1832

William Haynes Esq., Chairman
Drs. E. Lyon, J. Hull, S.A. Bardsley, W. Johns; Revd. George Dugard, W. Marsden; Colonel Shaw; Messrs H. Forth, F. Fincham, P. Ewart junr., W.R. Whatton, T. Townend, R. Addison

Resolved 1
    That the proceedings of the Board on the 7th Inst. be confirmed.

    Moved by Colonel Shaw. Seconded by Mr. Forth.

Resolved 2
    That the committees previously formed be now dissolved, with the exception of the Medical Committee the constitution of which will remain as directed by the 4th resolution of the Board on the 31st ultimo.

    Moved by Colonel Shaw. Seconded by Mr. Whatton.

Resolved 3
>That the following committees be now appointed, viz:

>>Accounts Committee
>>>Messrs. Benjamin Braidley
>>>S. Fletcher
>>>P. Ewart junr.

>>Committee for arranging the Placard
>>>Lieutenant Colonel Shaw
>>>Dr. S.A. Bardsley
>>>Dr. J.P. Kay
>>>Mr. Joseph Heron

>>Committee of Classification
>>and of Correspondence with Landlords
>>>Dr. J.P. Kay
>>>Revd. James Crook
>>>Revd. George Dugard
>>>Mr. Townend
>>>Mr. Fincham

>>Hospital and Reception House Committee
>>>Lieutenant Colonel Shaw
>>>Dr. J.D. Hulme
>>>Dr. J. L. Bardsley
>>>Mr. W.R. Whatton
>>>Mr. George Hall
>>>Mr. P. Ewart junr

>>General Correspondence Committee
>>>The Very Revd. Dr. Calvert
>>>Lieutenant Colonel Shaw
>>>Dr. E. Lyon
>>>Mr. Braidley

and that each committee be authorized to fix its own quorum.

Moved by Colonel Shaw. Seconded by Mr. Whatton.

Resolved 4
>That five members form a quorum at the meetings of this Board.

Moved by Colonel Shaw. Seconded by Mr. Whatton.

Resolved 5
> That the Chairman, or one of the Deputy Chairmen, or any three of the members may at any time call an extraordinary meeting of this Board; such previous notice being left at the residence of each member as to give him time to attend the meeting.

Moved by Colonel Shaw. Seconded by Mr. Whatton.

Resolved 6
> That the Chairman or either of the Deputy Chairmen of this Board, may at any time call an extraordinary meeting of any of the committees; and also that any two members of a committee may at any time call a meeting of the committee of which they are members; such previous notice being left at the residence of each member of the committee as to give him time to attend the meeting.

Moved by Mr. Forth. Seconded by Mr. Fincham.

Resolved 7
> That the Accounts Committee shall cause a monthly account to be made out of the whole of the expences of the Board. Each of those accounts to give in detail the expences incurred during the month up to the last day of the month, and the total of the previous expenditure, in one sum to be added. Those monthly accounts shall be presented at the Board's next meeting following the last day of each month and they shall after being approved of by the Board be kept amongst the records of the Board and a copy inserted in a book to be kept for that purpose. The first account to be for the period from the 7th Inst. to the 30th Inst. inclusive shall be presented to the Board at its first meeting after the 30th Inst. No expence whatever shall be allowed by this Board unless such as shall be directly authorized by future resolutions of this Board in which the particulars are specified and that a copy of this Resolution be transmitted by the Secretary to the Churchwardens, and Scavenging Committee.

Moved by Mr. Fincham. Seconded by Mr. Whatton.

Resolved 8
> That, it being important to Manchester that means should be adopted in the immediately adjoining Townships similar to those established by this Board; and it being farther the opinion of this Board that Manchester must be endangered and injuriously affected by the presence of cholera in the dense population of the surrounding districts; authorize and direct the General Correspondence Committee to enter into correspondence so far as they may see fit with the Authorities of the neighbouring Towns, or with the Boards of Health with the object of urging as far as they can the establishment of

Boards of Health where none exist and of offering the co-operation of this Board: and that the General Correspondence Committee may also as far as they may see fit enter into correspondence with the Central Board and with the Privy Council for the furtherance of these objects and that copies of the committee's correspondence on these points be kept by the Secretary for the information of the Board.

Moved by Colonel Shaw. Seconded by Dr. Bardsley.

Resolved 9
That Mr. Langford having attended this meeting of the Board as requested, his engagement with the Board be dated from Monday the 9th Inst.

Resolved 10
That Mr. Langford be informed that he will receive all his communications from the Chairman of the Hospital Committee or from some person appointed by that committee.

William Haynes (signature)

Board of Health, Manchester
April 14, 1832

Lieutenant Colonel Shaw, Chairman
Drs. Bardsley, Lyon, J. Hull; Revd. G. Dugard, H. Fielding, J. Crook; Messrs. Townend, Benjamin Braidley, Langford

Resolved 1
That the proceedings of the last meeting of the Board be now confirmed.

Moved by Dr. Bardsley. Seconded by Dr. Lyon.

Resolved 2
That the General Correspondence Committee be authorized to have printed 100 copies of the placard and of the circular prepared for transmission to the neighbouring Towns.

Moved by Dr. Lyon. Seconded by Mr. Townend.

Resolved 3
That £50 be placed at the disposal of the Hospital Committee for the objects mentioned in their proceedings of the 12th Inst. and that they be requested to submit as soon as possible an estimate of the sum required to complete the preparation of the hospital in Commercial Street.

Moved by Mr. Braidley

Resolved 4

That all orders incurring expence to this Board be given through the medium of the Secretary and that a book be kept in which those orders shall be entered.

Board of Health, Manchester
April 18, 1832

Henry Forth Esq., Chairman
Drs. S. Bardsley, E. Lyon, H. Gaulter, J. Hull; Revd. James Crook; Lieutenant Colonel Shaw; Messrs. T. Townend, P. Ewart junr., Joseph Heron, H.S., J. Langford

Resolved 1

That the proceedings of the last meeting of this Board be now confirmed.

Resolved 2

That the proceedings of the Medical Committee of the 16th Inst. be now confirmed excepting as to the rescinding the resolutions Nos. 2 & 3 passed by the Medical Sub-Committee and adopted by the General Medical Committee on the 27th of January last.
Moved by Colonel Shaw. Seconded by Mr. T. Townend.

Resolved 3

That the following gentlemen be added to the members already composing the Hospital and Reception House Committee, viz: W. Haynes Esq. to be appointed Chairman, the Revd. James Crook, Dr. Hull, Dr. C. Phillips, Dr. J.P. Kay, Messrs. F. Fincham, J. Woollam and J. Barker.

Resolved 4

That the Board recommend to the Hospital and Reception House to appoint a Sub-Committee of their body for the purpose of carrying into effect the necessary measures for removing persons from the dwellings in which cholera shall appear and for cleansing, whitewashing, and fumigating such dwellings; also for providing places of reception for persons so removed where their persons and clothes will be cleansed while their dwellings are being purified.

Resolved 5

That the sub-committee referred to in the preceding resolution be requested to report to the Board through the Chairman of their committee, the measures by which they may propose to effect the objects for which the sub-committee is appointed.

Resolved 6

That a committee consisting of the following three gentlemen be appointed for carrying into effect the arrangements for the conveyance of patients in slings to the various hospitals, viz: Mr. George Faulkner, Mr. Joseph Rooke and Dr. Henry Gaulter and that each member of the said committee shall take charge of one of the three great hospital divisions of the Town (See Placard Clause 4) and see that the necessary preparations are made at the factories, that slings are ready at the factories and at the hospitals, and that bearers are provisionally engaged and that the committee be requested to make a report of their arrangements to the Board as soon as completed.

Moved by Dr. Bardsley. Seconded by Dr. Hull.

Resolved 7
   That the proceedings of the Hospital and Reception House Committee at their meetings on the 16th & 17th Inst. now read be confirmed and receive the sanction of this Board.

Resolved 8
   That the proceedings of the Accounts Committee of the 16th Inst. be now confirmed and adopted as part of the proceedings of this Board.

Henry Forth (signature)

Board of Health, Manchester
April 21, 1832

Lieutenant Colonel Shaw, Chairman
Drs. Bardsley, H. Gaulter; Revd. W. Marsden; Messrs. W.R. Whatton, F. Fincham, J. Rooke, T. Townend, George Hall, J. Langford, D. Lynch junr.

Resolved 1
   That the proceedings of the Board on the 18th Inst. be now confirmed.

Moved by Dr. Gaulter. Seconded by Mr. Townend.

Resolved 2
   That the proceedings of the Hospital Committee on the 19th Inst. be confirmed and adopted as part of the proceedings of this Board.

Moved by Mr. Townend. Seconded by Dr. Bardsley.

Resolved 3
   That the resolutions Nos. 2 & 3 passed by the Medical Sub-Committee and adopted by the General Medical Committee on the 27th of January be now rescinded, due notice having been given.

Board of Health, Manchester
April 25, 1832

Benjamin Braidley Esq., Chairman
Drs J.P. Kay, Bardsley, Lyon; Revd. James Crook; Colonel Shaw; Messrs. W. Haynes, J. Woollam, F. Fincham, J. Langford

Resolved 1
> That there being a difference of opinion respecting the 3rd resolution passed at the last meeting of the Board, it be referred to the Medical Committee for their further consideration and that the other two resolutions of the last Board be confirmed.

Resolved 2
> That Dr. Gaulter having stated his inability to attend to the duties assigned him as a member of the Slings Committee that committee be requested to appoint a gentleman in his room.

Resolved 3
> That the communication from the Weekly Board of the Manchester Royal Infirmary complaining of the filthy state of Gibralter be referred to the Scavenging Committee with a request that they will immediately have it swept and cleansed and to send in an account of the expences as soon as completed.

Resolved 4
> That the Secretary be directed to acknowledge the receipt of the said communication and to inform the Weekly Board of the steps that have been taken by the Board of Health to remedy the evils complained of.

Moved by Mr. Fincham. Seconded by the Revd. J. Crook.

Resolved 5
> That the Scavenging Committee be requested to have Little Ireland thoroughly swept and cleansed, the dust and ashes removed and the privies emptied, the account of the expences to be sent in immediately it is completed.

Moved by Mr. Fincham. Seconded by the Revd. J. Crook.

Resolved 6th
> That the Paving and Soughing Committee be requested to furnish to the Board of Health an estimate for opening and cleansing the drains and sewers in Little Ireland.

Moved by Revd. W. Marsden. Seconded by Mr. Haynes.

Resolved 7
> That the following gentlemen be appointed members of the Board of Health for District No.11 in lieu of those of that Board who have declined acting viz:

Messrs. Paul Chappe
       J.G. Copley
       Crewdson (Dacca Twist Co.)
       John Fairweather
       John Ferneley
       John Glasgow
       William Glasgow
       Richard Hampson
       James Houtson
       Lionel Lloyd
       Lewis Magnus
       William Nuttall
       George Pickup
       John Pryce

Moved by Colonel Shaw. Seconded by Dr. Bardsley.

Resolved 8

That a list of the committees acting under this Board be placarded in the Board Room.

Moved by Colonel Shaw.

Resolved 9

That a committee consisting of the Revd. H. Fielding, Dr. W.C. Henry and Mr. John Potter be appointed for making such arrangements and taking such steps as may be necessary to ensure a medical inspection of boats arriving from places at which cholera exists.

The Board consider that Mr. Langford can inspect all the boats arriving from places at present affected with cholera and the committee are requested to arrange with him and with the proprietors of the boats as to the inspections, reports, & measures to be taken in the event of any suspicious case of disease occurring.

The committee are requested to make a report of their arrangements, when completed to the Board.

Moved by Colonel Shaw.

Resolved 10

That a Committee consisting of the Revd. C.D. Wray, Dr. Pendlebury and Mr. David Dockray be appointed for making all arrangements for effecting when it is thought necessary an inspection of the lodging houses.

It is not the intention of the Board that such inspection should take place unless the disease approaches nearer to Manchester; but the committee are requested to cause lists to be prepared of the lodging houses, to appoint inspectors provisionally and to take such measures as the committee may think fit for procuring the consent of the owners of the lodging houses that the inspectors may be allowed to make the inspection when it shall be deemed necessary.

Resolved 11
That the Board authorize the Hospital Committee (the Churchwardens consenting, to refund the sum charged for the iron bedsteads supplied to the Shudehill Hospital, on their being returned) to order 20 bedsteads with bedding to supply the deficiency.

Resolved 12
That the Board also authorize the Hospital Committee to have whitewashed and cleansed the whole of the buildings at Knott Mill and to have all the windows mended.

Board of Health, Manchester
April 28, 1832

Lieutenant Colonel Shaw, Chairman
Dr. Bardsley; Revd. G. Dugard, James Crook, W. Huntington, James White; Messrs. J. Rooke, F. Fincham, T. Townend, P. Ewart junr., Langford, Joseph Heron, H.S.

Resolved 1
That the proceedings of the last meeting of the Board be now confirmed.

Resolved 2
That the communication from the Surveyors of the Highways of the 27th Inst. be entered on the minutes (See Appendix) & be acknowledged by the Secretary expressing the thanks of this Board and that he intimate that the Hospital in Commercial Street, Knott Mill is now ready for the reception of the flags and that this Board are anxious to have them laid, if convenient to the Surveyors on Monday next.

Resolved 3
That the Revd. George Dugard be appointed a member of the Slings Committee in the room of Dr. Gaulter who has resigned in consequence of the severe illness of a relation requiring his close attention.

Resolved 4
That the proceedings of the Medical Committee of the 27th Inst. be confirmed.

Resolved 5
>   That the proceedings of the Hospital Committee on the 26th Inst. be now
>   confirmed.

Resolved 6
>   That a bath be procured for the hospital at Knott Mill as recommended by
>   the Hospital Committee, the expence of which shall not exceed £4.0.0.

Resolved 7
>   That the house for the residence of the medical officer at Knott Mill be paint-
>   ed and papered the expence not to exceed £4.0.0.

Resolved 8
>   That the Hospital Committee be authorized to purchase 2 loads of coals for
>   the use of the Knott Mill Hospital.

Resolved 9
>   That a letter be addressed to the Fire Engine Committee requesting the loan
>   of three horses (in the event of cholera appearing in Manchester) for the car-
>   riages which have been provided to convey patients to the hospitals: the hors-
>   es to be under the charge of the committee's own servants.

Appendix

Surveyor's Office, Minshull Street
April 27, 1832

Sir,
>   The Surveyors of the Highways request you will inform the Board of Health,
>   that they are willing to lend flags for the kitchen at the cholera hospital in
>   Commercial Street, and they will also find materials and send men to lay the
>   flags without any charge, at such a time as the Board of Health may require.
>   And attention will be given to any requests the Board of Health may make
>   to this establishment.

For the Surveyors of the Highways.
your Obedient Servant
(Signed) John Kenworthy
Deputy Chairman.

PS Your second letter has been received and will have the attention of the
Surveyors.

For the Secretary
To The Board of Health
Town Hall

Board of Health, Manchester
May 2, 1832

Lieutenant Colonel Shaw, Chairman
Dr. Bardsley; Revd. G. Dugard; Messrs. T. Townend, P. Ewart junr., George Hall, Langford

Resolved 1
   That the proceedings of the last meeting of this Board be now confirmed.

Resolved 2
   That the Revd. Mr Broadley be appointed chairman of No. 9 District Board.

   Moved by Mr Townend.

Resolved 3
   That in future this Board meet only once a week viz: on Thursdays at 11 o'clock and that due notice of this change be given to the members.

   Moved by Mr. Ewart.

Resolved 4
   That Mr. Loyd be appointed Treasurer of this Board.

Resolved 5
   That Mr. Langford be authorized to have the Shude Hill Hospital cleaned and to order a load of coals for the said hospital.

Board of Health Manchester
May 5, 1832

Lieutenant Colonel Shaw, Chairman
Drs. Bardsley, J. P. Kay; Revd. James Crook; Mr. T. Townend

Resolved 1
   That the proceedings of the last meeting of this Board be now confirmed.

   Moved by Mr. Townend. Seconded by Revd. James Crook.

Resolved 2
   That Mr. Braidley be requested to procure from one of the Magistrates an order on the Churchwardens for the sum of £300 to be placed in the hands of the Treasurer and that all accounts be paid by cheques on the Treasurer signed by the Chairman of the Board.

   Moved by Dr. Bardsley. Seconded by Revd. James Crook.

Resolved 3

That the nuisance complained of by Mr. Langford in the vicinity of the Knott Mill Hospital be reported by the Secretary to the Nuisance Committee with a request that they will immediately cause the same to be removed.

Resolved 4

That the Secretary be directed to write to the Chairman of the Board of Health at Goole informing him that cases of sickness have occurred on Board the boat Grocer – Marsden proprietor now on its passage to Goole and request that an inspection of that boat may be made on its arrival.

Memorandum 1

Mr. Langford reported that the Knott Mill Hospital was with the exception of a few articles in a complete state of preparation for the treatment of patients.

Memorandum 2

Notice of the two following motions was given by Dr. Kay.

That the resolution passed by the Medical Committee on the 27th. of April and adopted by the Board on the 28th. of April be rescinded.

That a general meeting of the Medical Gentlemen appointed to the various districts of the Town having recommended the plan of attendance on the cholera hospitals indicated in the resolutions adopted by the Board of Health on the 28th. of January, that the Board do readopt those resolutions.

Moved by Dr. Bardsley.

Resolved 5

That the Medical Committee be convened for 11 o'clock on Monday to consider the resolutions given notice of by Dr. Kay and to form such detailed arrangements as may be necessary for the medical attendance of the cholera hospitals.

Moved by Mr. Townend.

Resolved 6

That the return of burials in this and the adjoining Townships now presented be entered on the minutes. (See Appendix)

Moved by Dr. Bardsley. Seconded by Mr. Townend.

Resolved 7

That a copy of the same be furnished to Dr. Kay with permission to publish it if he should think fit.

Appendix

A General Return of the Number of Interments that have taken place in the Boroughs of Manchester and Salford in each year during the years 1828, 1829, 1830, 1831.

Manchester		**1828**	**1829**	**1830**	**1831**
Collegiate Church	Revd. H. Fielding	1083	1019	1118	1406
St. Georges	Revd. J. White	11	5	11	4
St. Johns	Revd. W. Huntington	239	228	224	238
St. James	Revd. J. Hollist	44	26	21	25
St. Anns	Revd. Dr. Smith	57	44	33	40
St. Peters	Revd. N. Germon	–	–	–	–
St. Marys	Revd. W. Hutchinson	76	63	69	78
St. Michaels	Revd. W. Marsden	17	10	16	13
St. Matthews	Revd. E.B. Shaw	–	–	–	–
St. Andrews	Revd. G. Dugard	–	–	–	1
Independent Chapel, Grosvenor Street		–	–	–	–
Baptist Chapel, St. Georges Road	Revd. W. Gadsby	–	–	–	–
Wesleyan Chapel, Gt. Bridgewater Street	Revd. Joseph Gill	63	54	55	82
New Jerusalem Temple, Peter Street	C. Bowker, J.Broadfield (Churchwardens)	76	54	54	82
Unitarian Chapel, Cross Street	Revd. J.G. Robberds	9	4	5	9
Unitarian Chapel, Mosley Street	Revd. J.J. Taylor	–	–	–	–

Christ Church, Every Street	Revd. J. Schofield	422	305	399	473
Catholic Chapel, Mulberry Street		–	–	–	–
Catholic Chapel, Granby Row	Revd. James Crook	422	474	577	606
Friends Burial Ground, Jacksons Row	T. King, Registrar	9	15	13	10
Friends Burial Ground Dickenson Street	T. King, Registrar	11	10	8	5
Bradford					
Chorlton Row All Saints	Revd. Dr. Burton	81	64	66	69
St. Lukes	Revd. A. Hepworth	39	43	29	34
General Burial Ground	Revd. W.M. Walker	1615	1409	1630	1814
Ardwick St. Thomas	Revd. N.W. Gibson	48	30	39	47
Beswick					
Hulme St. Georges	Revd. J. Lingard	–	20	35	109
Christ Church	Revd. Joseph Thompson	291	188	197	178
Cheetham St. Marks	Revd. F.G. Ethelstone	–	–	–	–
Newton		–	–	–	–
Harpurhey		–	–	–	–
		4613	4065	4599	4823
Salford Trinity Chapel		–	–	–	–

St. Stephens Church	Revd. R. Frost	67	51	86	105
Christ Church, Queen Street	Revd. Joseph Thompson	184	137	140	150
Unitarian Chapel	Revd. J.R. Beard	6	3	1	4
New Jerusalem, Bolton Street	Revd. D. Howarth	686	416	428	444
Wesleyan Chapel, Irwell Street	Revd. R. Wood	–	343	579	601
Christ Church, Acton Square		–	–	–	–
Pendleton St. Thomas	Revd. R. Keeling	46	34	38	38
Brunswick Chapel	Mr. Burgess, Steward	54	26	25	35
Jews Burial Ground	Revd. A. Abraham	4	4	3	4
Bethesda Chapel	Revd. R. Goodall	15	21	13	32
Broughton		–	–	–	–
In the Borough of Manchester		4613	4065	4599	5323
In the Borough of Salford		1062	1035	1313	1413
Total		5675	5100	5912	6736

Board of Health, Manchester
May 10, 1832

Drs. Kay, Divir, Holford, Lyon, Johns, Hull; Revd. J. Crook, James White; Lieutenant Colonel Shaw; Messrs. G. Hall, W. Whatton, P. Ewart junr., Townend, J. Potter, J. Woollam, Mr. Langford

Resolved 1
  That the resolutions passed at the last meeting of this Board be now confirmed.

Moved by Dr. Kay. Seconded by Dr. Lyon.

That the resolution passed by the Medical Committee on the 27[th.] April and adopted by the Board on the 28[th.] of April be now rescinded.

That a general meeting of the Medical Gentlemen appointed to the various districts of the Town having recommended the plan of attendance on the cholera hospitals indicated in the resolutions adopted by the Board of Health on the 28[th.] of January that the Board do readopt those resolutions.

Moved as an Amendment by Mr. Whatton. Seconded by Dr. Johns.

Resolved 2
That the Chairman do summon the Medical Committee, appointed by the Board constituted by an order of the Privy Council, to determine the appointment of the medical officers to the cholera hospitals.

Moved by Lieutenant Colonel Shaw. Seconded by Mr. Townend.

Resolved 3
That the Board not having power to add to their number Dr. Divir be allowed to attend the meetings of this Board and of the Medical Committee.

Board of Health, Manchester
May 17, 1832

Revd. William Marsden, Chairman
Drs. Johns, Divir; Revd. H. Fielding, W. Huntington; Messrs. Potter, G. Hall, Mr. Langford, Mr. Lynch junr.

Resolved 1
That the proceedings of the Board on the 10[th.] Inst. be now confirmed.

Resolved 2
That the proceedings of the Medical Committee on the 14[th.] Inst. be adopted as part of the proceedings of this Board.

Moved by Revd. H. Fielding. Seconded by Revd. W. Huntington.

Resolved 3
That Mr. D. Lynch Junr. be appointed to give his assistance in the inspection of the carriages arriving by the railway from Liverpool as recommended by the Committee for the Inspection of the Boats until the next meeting of the Board.

Moved by Mr. G. Hall. Seconded by Mr. J. Potter.

Resolved 4

That Mr. D. Lynch junr. and Mr. W.C. Begley be allowed to attend the meetings of this Board and of its Medical Committee.

Resolved 5

That the proceedings of the Correspondence Committee on the 17th. Inst. be approved and adopted as part of the proceedings of this Board.

Moved by Dr. Johns.

Resolved 6

That an application be made to the Chairman of the Board of Health at Liverpool requesting them to furnish this Board with correct information as to the existence of cholera in that Town and requesting a daily report in case that disease should unfortunately prevail.

Memorandum

Mr. Langford reported that he had received authentic information of the existence of cholera in Chester and that application had been made to the Secretary of State by the authorities of that Town for the appointment of a Board of Health.

Board of Health, Manchester
May 24, 1832

H. Forth Esq., Chairman
Drs Johns, Lyon, Divir; Revd. James Crook, H. Fielding, W. Huntington; Messrs. P. Ewart junr., F. Fincham, Townend, G. Hall, J. Woollam, Langford, Mr. D. Lynch junr.

Resolved 1

That the proceedings of the last meeting of this Board be now confirmed.

Moved by Mr. Fincham.

Resolved 2

That an answer be returned to the Board of Health of Salford respectfully informing them that it is out of the power of this Board to accede to their request, viz: that cases of cholera might be received into the hospital in Commercial Street on payment of a certain sum for each person until a meeting of the Trustees of the Dispensary could be convened.

Resolved 3

That the proceedings of the general meetings of the medical practitioners who have given their services to attend cholera patients on the 18th. and 23rd. of May be confirmed by this Board.

Resolved 4

That an extract from the Order in Council of the 29th. of February relating to the reports of cases of cholera or suspected cholera be furnished to the medical practitioners of Manchester with a copy of the communication of the 21st. of December.

Moved by Mr. Townend. Seconded by Dr. Johns.

Resolved 5

That the person at present resident at the Shude Hill Hospital be allowed two shillings and sixpence per week for the care of the premises and furniture to commence from the 19th. Instant.

Moved by Revd. W. Huntington. Seconded by Mr. Woollam.

Resolved 6

That Mr. Stephens be requested to furnish a correct statement of the case of James Palfreyman.

Moved by Mr. Townend. Seconded by Mr. G. Hall.

Resolved 7

That the services of Mr. D. Lynch junr. be continued until further notice.

Henry Forth (signed)

Special Meeting
Board of Health, Manchester
May 28, 1832

Lieutenant Colonel Shaw, Chairman
Drs. Bardsley, J.L. Bardsley, J.P. Kay, J. Pendlebury, E. Lyon, Charles Phillips, H. Gaulter; Revd. W. Huntington, H. Fielding, J. Crook, W. Marsden; Messrs J. Ainsworth, W.J. Wilson, J. A. Ransome, W. Haynes, H. Forth, J. Langford, Oswald Milne, J. Thorpe, T. Townend, George Hall, W.R. Whatton, P. Ewart junr., Benjamin Braidley, J. Heron, J. Rooke

Resolved 1

That the proceedings of the last meeting of this Board be now confirmed.

Moved by Dr. Bardsley. Seconded by Mr. Townend.

Resolved 2

That the Hospital and Reception House Sub-Committee be authorized to provide a house of reception and to take such other steps as may to them appear necessary for the separation of persons who may have been in contact who [*with*] persons who may have died of supposed cholera.

Moved by Dr. Bardsley. Seconded by Mr. P. Ewart junr.

Resolved 3

That a meeting of the Medical Committee be summoned for half past 8 o'clock precisely (Tuesday) morning to consider the several circumstances connected with the supposed case of cholera which has recently occurred in Ancoats and to report their opinion of the same at an early meeting of the General Board, and to offer any suggestions which may occur to them on the subject.

Moved by Dr. J.L. Bardsley.   Seconded by Revd. J. Crook.

Resolved 4

That the Hospital Committee be empowered to provide immediately twenty beds for the Harrison Street Cholera Hospital and all the other necessary articles required in the establishment on the same plan as was adopted at the Commercial Street Hospital.

Board of Health, Manchester
May 31, 1832

W. Haynes Esq., Deputy Chairman
Drs. J.P. Kay, C. Phillips, S.A. Bardsley, Divir, E. Carbutt, H. Gaulter, E. Lyon, Dr. Johns, Mr. Jeyes; Revd. George Dugard, James Crook, W. Marsden; Lieutenant Colonel Shaw; Messrs. T. Townend, Hunt, F. Fincham, Stephens, Peter Ewart junr., Mr. Langford

Resolved 1

That the proceedings of the last meeting of this Board be now confirmed.

Resolved 2

That the proceedings of the Medical Committee on the 29th. Inst. be confirmed and adopted as part of the proceedings of this Board.

Resolved 3

That a Special Meeting of the Medical Committee be convened for this evening 6 o'clock and that the report of the case of Mary Cavanagh now read by Dr. Kay be then referred to them for their consideration, and that the gentlemen who saw the patient during life and those who were present at the opening of the body be requested to attend.

Resolved 4

That a meeting of this Board be convened for 11 o'clock tomorrow morning to receive the opinion of the Medical Committee.

Resolved 5

> That Dr. Jeyes the Surgeon of the 15th. King's Hussars be allowed to attend the meetings of this Board and of the Medical Committee.

Resolved 6

> That the Hospital Sub-Committee be requested to meet as soon as possible to provide nurses and to make such further arrangements as may be necessary for the completion of the hospitals and in the mean time Mr. Langford be empowered to engage a nurse and make other arrangements for the present emergency.

Resolved 7

> That the Slings Committee be summoned to consider the propriety of making immediate arrangements for the conveyance of any case of cholera which may occur.

Resolved 8

> That further preparations at the Harrison Street Hospital be for the present suspended.

William Haynes (signature)

Special Meeting
Board of Health, Manchester
June 1, 1832

John Kennedy Esq., Chairman
Drs Johns, J.P. Kay, Lyon, C. Phillips, Divir; Revd. Calvert, J. White, J. Crook, W. Marsden, W. Huntington; Lieutenant Colonel Shaw; Messrs. J. Thorpe, F. Fincham, Heath, E. Connell, D. Lynch junr., J. Langford, Begley

Moved by Mr. E. Connell. Seconded by Mr. F. Fincham.

Resolved 1

> That the resolutions and minutes of the Medical Meeting of the 31st. Inst. be received by this Board.

Board of Health, Manchester
June 7, 1832

W. Haynes Esq., Deputy Chairman
Drs. S.A. Bardsley, J.L. Bardsley, Charles Phillips, J.P. Kay, Jeyes, Hull; Revd. J. Crook, W. Huntington, W. Marsden, George Dugard, H. Fielding; Messrs. E. Connell, Benjamin Braidley, T. Townend, P. Ewart junr., F. Fincham, J. Langford, D. Lynch junr.

Resolved 1
> That the proceedings of the Board on the 31st· of May and on the 1st· of June be now confirmed.

Memorandum 1
> Mr. Windsor reported that a fatal case of disease had fallen under his observation which he considered a case of suspicious cholera; Dr. Kay confirmed the opinion of Mr. Windsor. Mr Hunt and Mr. Stephens reported that they had attended the post-mortem examination and they considered the appearances coincided with those which had been reported as having occurred at Sunderland, London, and Paris.

> Moved by Mr. Townend. Seconded by Dr. Bardsley.

Resolved 2
> That the Medical Committee be requested to meet at 7 o'clock this evening to consider the case of Richard Bullock and that those gentlemen who saw the case during life and those who were present at the post-mortem examination be requested to attend.

> Moved by Mr. F. Fincham. Seconded by Dr. Phillips.

Resolved 3
> That a Special Meeting of the Board be called for 11 o'clock tomorrow to receive the report of the Medical Committee on the case of Richard Bullock.

> Moved by Dr. S.A. Bardsley. Seconded by Mr. Braidley.

Resolved 4
> That a letter be addressed to the editors of the Manchester papers respectfully requesting that they will not in future insert any particulars respecting any reported cases of cholera, without an express communication from the Board.

> Moved by Mr. Townend. Seconded by Dr. Bardsley.

Resolved 5
> That the Secretary be directed to furnish to Dr. Jeyes from time to time copies of the proceedings of the Medical Committee with regard to any cases of supposed cholera which may occur for the purpose of being forwarded to the head of the Army Medical Board.

> Moved by Dr. Bardsley. Seconded by Mr. Braidley.

Resolved 6
> That this Board consider it to be a breach of duty in any of its members communicating its proceedings in relation to any cases of cholera until they are officially published by the Board.

Resolved 7
> That Mr. Langford be empowered to procure for the Knott Mill Hospital an improved injecting apparatus – the expence not to exceed £3.

Resolved 8
> That the deceased Richard Bullock be interred as soon as possible.

Memorandum 2
> Mr. Langford reported that he had removed the wife and children of Richard Bullock to the hospital in Commercial Street.

William Haynes (signature)

**Special Meeting
Board of Health, Manchester
June 8, 1832**

H.H. Birley Esq., Chairman
Drs. Bardsley, J. L. Bardsley, Johns, Charles Phillips, Lyon, Henry, Gaulter, J.P. Kay; Revd.W. Huntington, W. Marsden; Messrs. Oswald Milne, J. Potter, T. Townend, P. Ewart junr., F. Fincham, Mr. Connell, J. Langford, J. Heron, Honorary Secretary

Moved by Mr. Townend. Seconded by Mr. Ewart junr.

Resolved 1
> That the report of the proceedings of the Medical Committee of the 7th. Inst. now read be received and adopted as part of the proceedings of this Board.

Resolved 2
> That Messrs. Fincham and Connell be requested to wait upon the editors of the Manchester papers to make such communication on the subject of cholera as they shall think fit.

**Special Meeting
Board of Health, Manchester
June 12, 1832**

Benjamin Braidley Esq., Chairman
Drs. J.P. Kay, Divir, Charles Phillips, Hulme, Henry, Lyon, Gaulter; Revd. J. Crook, George Dugard, C.D. Wray, W. Huntington; Lieutenant Colonel Shaw; Messrs. H.H. Birley, P. Ewart junr., J. Potter, W. Haynes, Joseph Rooke, J. Thorpe, T. Townend, R. T. Hunt, Miller, J. Walker, G. Hall, E. Connell, J. Langford, D. Lynch junr., W.C. Begley

Memorandum
> Dr. Kay reported on behalf of the medical staff of the hospital in Commercial Street that three deaths had occurred there viz: the wife and two children of Richard Bullock.

Moved by Mr. Townend.

Resolved 1
That the cases reported by Dr. Kay be referred to the Medical Committee for their opinion and the gentlemen who saw the cases during life and those who attended the post-mortem examinations be requested to attend – and that the Medical Committee be requested to report to a future Board to be specially summoned.

Resolved 2
That the Medical Committee be convened for 7 o'clock this Evening and that a special meeting of this Board be called for 11 o'clock tomorrow to receive their report and also the report of the Hospital Sub-Committee.

Moved by Lieutenant Colonel Shaw.

Resolved 3
That Mr. Dealey the Assistant Surgeon of the 15th. Hussars be allowed to attend the meetings of the Board and the Medical Committee.

Special Meeting
Board of Health, Manchester
June 13, 1832

Benjamin Braidley Esq., Chairman
Drs. J.P. Kay, Divir, Phillips, Hulme, C. Henry, Lyon, H. Gaulter; Revd. James White, W. Huntington, James Crook, C.D. Wray; Lieutenant Colonel Shaw; Messrs. J. Potter, T. Townend, P. Ewart junr., D. Dockray, G. Hall, Dealey, Joseph Rooke, F. Fincham, W.R. Whatton, Oswald Milne, Jonathan Mitchell, J. Langford, D. Lynch junr.

Resolved 1
That the proceedings of the last meeting of this Board be now confirmed.

Resolved 2
That the report of the Medical Committee be received and entered on the minutes.

Copy

Medical Committee
June 12, 1832

That the three cases which died in the Commercial Street Hospital on the 11th. and 12th. of June and have been reported to the Medical Committee resemble the four

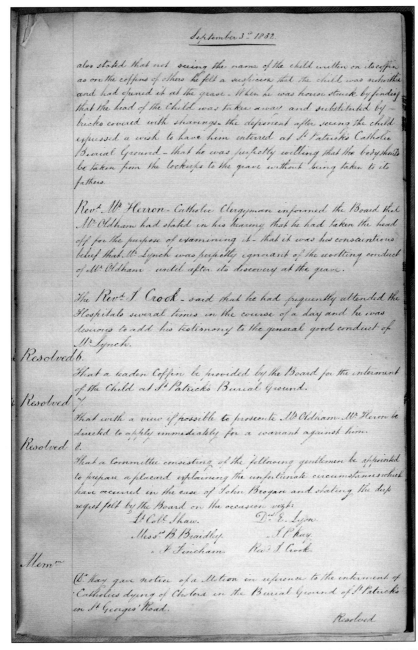

September 3rd 1832.

also stated that not seeing the name of the child written on its coffin as on the coffins of others he felt a suspicion that the child was not his and had opened it at the grave – When he was horror struck by finding that the head of the child was taken away and substituted by bricks covered with shavings – the deponent after seeing the child expressed a wish to have him interred at St Patrick's Catholic Burial Ground – that he was perfectly willing that the body should be taken from the lockups to the grave without being taken to its father.

Revd. Mr Herron – Catholic Clergyman informed the Board that Mr Oldham had stated in his hearing that he had taken the head off for the purpose of examining it – that it was his conscientious belief that Mr Lynch was perfectly ignorant of the wicked conduct of Mr Oldham until after its discovery at the grave.

The Revd J Crook – said that he had frequently attended the Hospitals several times in the course of a day and he was desirous to add his testimony to the general good conduct of Mr Lynch.

Resolved 6.
That a leaden Coffin be provided by the Board for the interment of the Child at St Patrick's Burial Ground.

Resolved 7.
That with a view if possible to prosecute Mr Oldham Mr Herron be directed to apply immediately for a warrant against him.

Resolved 8.
That a Committee consisting of the following gentlemen be appointed to prepare a placard explaining the unfortunate circumstances which have occurred in the case of John Brogan and stating the deep regret felt by the Board on the occasion viz:

Lt Coll Shaw.   Dr E. Lyon.
Messrs B. Braidley.   J P Kay
    J Fincham.   Revd J Crook

Memm
Mr Kay gave notice of a Motion in reference to the interment of Catholics dying of Cholera in the Burial Ground of St Patricks in St Georges' Road.

Resolved

A page from the Proceedings: the notorious Brogan case; see below, pp. 215–18

which have previously occurred (viz: Palfreyman's, Chorlton's, Cavanagh's and Bullock's) and are unequivocal examples of the cholera which has appeared in Sunderland and other parts of Great Britain.

(Signed) J.D. Hulme M.D., Chairman

Resolved 3

That the report of the Hospital Committee be received and adopted as part of the proceedings of the Board.

Moved by Mr. Townend. Seconded by Mr. F. Fincham.

Resolved 4

That the Hospital Committee be empowered to engage a porter and female nurse for the Swan Street Hospital and that that building be used as a Reception House until another building can be procured.

Moved by Mr. Fincham. Seconded by Mr. G. Hall.

Resolved 5

That Mr. Langford be authorized to engage 2 men at 10 shillings per week each for the purpose of placing the bodies of persons dying of cholera in their coffins and of superintending their interment.

Moved by Mr. P. Ewart junr.

Resolved 6

That a note be addressed to Messrs. Peel, Williams and Peel requesting that they will remove the family at present residing at the Swan Street Hospital.

Moved by Mr. Fincham. Seconded by Mr. P. Ewart junr.

Resolved 7

That the Medical Committee at its next meeting be requested to consider whether it be desirable to remove to the hospital patients of whose recovery there is little hope and of any means by which the objection of the people to the hospitals may be removed.

Resolved 8

That the Hospital Sub-Committee be requested to make enquiries for Houses of Reception and to report to this Board the terms on which they can engage such buildings.

Moved by Mr. T. Townend.

Resolved 9

That this Board do adjourn until Thursday the 21ˢᵗ· Inst. unless any special business occurs to require an earlier meeting.

Special Meeting
Board of Health, Manchester
June 18, 1832

Benjamin Braidley Esq., Chairman
Drs. E. Lyon, H. Gaulter, J.P. Kay, Divir, E. Holme, J. Pendlebury, J. Ferneley, S.A. Bardsley, Charles Phillips, Jonathan Hull; Revd. H. Fielding, George Dugard, J. Crook, W. Marsden; Lieutenant Colonel Shaw; Messrs. O. Milne, G. Greaves, P. Ewart junr., Dealey, W.R. Whatton, F. Fincham, W.J. Wilson, W. Haynes, J.C. Gordon, Joseph Rooke, J. Potter, J. Langford, D. Lynch junr.

Memorandum

Mr. Langford reported that 7 Cases of suspected cholera had been received into the hospital at Knott Mill, 5 had been taken from a house in Blakcly Street, 1 from Angel Meadow and 1 from Grove Street. 2 had died in the hospital.

Moved by Lieutenant Colonel Shaw.

Resolved 1

That this Board meet daily at 11 o'clock

Moved by Mr. Fincham.

Resolved 2

That in consequence of 7 cases of suspected cholera having been recently received into the Hospital at Knott Mill the Hospital Committee be requested to take instant measures to put the hospitals in Shude Hill and Knott Mill into a proper state for the reception of patients and to provide the requisite attendants.

Moved by Mr. Haynes. Seconded by Dr. J. Hall.

Resolved 3

That the following gentlemen be appointed a committee to prepare a placard advising the public to make early application for relief if attacked with cholera and warning them against pursuing the violent conduct that has been used in several towns towards the Medical Gentlemen, viz:

Mr. Braidley
Lieutenant Colonel Shaw
Mr. Fincham

Dr. Bardsley
Mr. O. Milne

Moved by Dr. Bardsley.

Resolved 4
That the Churchwardens be requested to have the pauper lodging houses inspected upon the plan suggested to their predecessors.

Moved by Dr. Bardsley.

Resolved 5
That a certain number of registers according to the forms furnished by the Central Board of Health be immediately printed and supplied to the different Medical Officers connected with the hospitals, and the practitioners of the various districts and that the Medical Officers be requested to fill up the columns and transmit the same to the Board.

Board of Health, Manchester
June 19, 1832

Benjamin Braidley Esq., Chairman
Drs. Kay, E. Lyon, C. Phillips, H. Gaulter; Messrs. T. Townend, G. Hall, J. Holford, P. Ewart junr., F. Fincham, J. Langford, D. Lynch junr.

Resolved 1
That the minutes of the preceding meeting of this Board be now confirmed.

Memorandum
Mr. Langford reported that no fresh cases had to his knowledge occurred.

Moved by Mr. Fincham. Seconded by Mr. T. Townend.

Resolved 2
That the publication of the placard be deferred until after the meeting of the Board tomorrow.

Board of Health, Manchester
June 20, 1832

H. Forth Esq., Deputy Chairman
Drs. S.A. Bardsley, E. Lyon, Charles Phillips, Henry Gaulter, J.L. Bardsley; Revd. J. Crook; Lieutenant Colonel Shaw; Messrs. F. Fincham, A.M. Heath, G. Faulkner, P. Ewart junr., H.H. Birley, T. Townend, R.J.J. Norreys, Oswald Milne, J. Langford, D. Lynch junr.

Resolved 1
   That the minutes of the preceding meeting of this Board be now confirmed.

Resolved 2
   That the report made to Mr. Shawcross by Mr. Reid of 111 Blakely Street stating that the men employed in whitewashing the house in Blakely Street from which patients had been removed had reported in the neighbourhood that out of eight persons who had died in the hospital in Knott Mill only two had been buried be referred to Mr. Fincham for investigation.

   Moved by Mr. Birley.

Resolved 3
   That a communication be addressed to the Churchwardens strongly recommending that the bodies of persons dying of suspected cholera may be buried not less than six feet deep and the graves covered immediately the coffins are deposited therein and also requesting that the coffins may be thoroughly pitched on the inside and made stronger 1/4 of an inch stouter than those which have been hitherto supplied.

   Moved by Mr. Fincham.

Resolved 4
   That a letter be addressed to the carriers by water requesting their scrupulous attention to the investigation of the boats as before recommended and that the slightest appearance of bowel complaint in any of the crew be immediately reported to the Medical Gentlemen at the hospital and that a similar letter be addressed to the owners of lodging houses and directing them to the Knott Mill or Shude Hill Hospitals or the police stations and that a list of the Medical Gentlemen within the district be sent to each police station.

Resolved 5
   That the letter from J. Satterthwaite and Thackery, J. Rogers, and T. Lees, Inspectors of No.3 District be referred to the Scavenging Committee with a request that immediate attention may be paid to it.

   Moved by Mr. F. Fincham.

Resolved 6
   That James Street and Edge Street are in so filthy a state that the Scavenging Committee be requested to have them cleared and the soughs unstopt.

   Moved by Mr. Fincham. Seconded by Mr. Townend.

Resolved 7
   That the publication of the placard prepared by the sub-committee be suspended for the present.

Resolved 8
> That the proceedings of the Hospital Sub-Committee on the 19[th.] Inst be now confirmed.

Resolved 9
> That the wages of the persons employed at the Knott Mill Hospital be raised to 16 shillings per week according to the recommendation of the Hospital Committee.

Resolved 10
> That this Board authorize the Hospital Sub-Committee to make arrangements with Mr. Langford for his accommodation (viz: board and lodging) at the hospital in Commercial Street.

Henry Forth (signature)

Board of Health, Manchester
June 21, 1832

H.H. Birley, Chairman
Drs. Divir, J.P. Kay, J. Hull, S.A. Bardsley, H. Gaulter, J.L. Bardsley, E. Lyon, W. Johns, Charles Phillips; Revd. W. Huntington, J. Crook; Lieutenant Colonel Shaw; Messrs. A.M. Heath, J. Holford, F. Fincham, T. Townend, J. Langford

Resolved 1
> That the minutes of the preceding meeting of this Board be now confirmed.

Memorandum
> Mr. Langford reported that a fresh case (viz: Lucy Pearson) had been received into the Hospital at Commercial Street from the Infirmary.

Resolved 2
> That the communications from the medical staff of the Commercial Street Hospital be received and entered on the minutes. (See Appendix)

> Moved by Mr. Townend. Seconded by Revd. W. Huntington.

Resolved 3
> That notice be given to the members of this Board urgently requesting their attendance at a special meeting of the Board at half past 3 o'clock this afternoon for the purpose of considering the propriety of publishing the placard prepared by the sub-committee and other business of importance.

Resolved 4
> That the placard be referred to the sub-committee for any addition or alteration which may appear to them desirable to be submitted to the Special General Meeting to be held this day at half past 3 o'clock.

Moved by Dr. J.L. Bardsley. Seconded by Dr. C. Phillips.

Resolved 5
That the committee be instructed to insert a clause in the placard declaring that no body will be opened at the hospitals without the consent of the friends.

Moved as an Amendment by Dr. Bardsley. Seconded by Dr. Carbutt.

That the committee be instructed to insert a clause in the placard declaring that no body will be opened at the hospitals.

The amendment was negatived and the original resolution carried.

Resolved 6
That any cases of death by cholera reported by the medical staffs of the hospitals be buried at the expence of the Board.

Resolved 7
That the Secretary be instructed to request Mr. Lavender to have two or three of the police stationed at the Knott Mill Hospital for the day.

Resolved 8
That the articles given in by Mr. Langford as the property of Jane Lewis (died at the hospital in Commercial Street) be sealed and ticketed and entrusted to the care of the secretary.

Appendix

To the Board of Health

As it is found necessary that a Resident Medical Officer should personally superintend the treatment of the patients both day and night and as it is impossible for one Resident Medical Officer to fulfil such arduous duties, the medical staff of the hospital in Commercial Street respectfully recommend to this Board the immediate appointment of as many as may be considered requisite. June 21st. 1832.

Signed   Joseph Jordan Esq., Chairman
Messrs.   R. T. Hunt   W.B. Stott.
              W. White   James Miller
              M. Sinclair   W. Owen
              E. Stephens   B.W. Booth
                                   J. Walker Esq.

To the Board of Health
In consequence of the frequent large collections of people about the gates of the hospital in Commercial Street and some acts of violence already committed, and

are evidently increasing hostility to the medical staff and attendants at this hospital, the undersigned respectfully suggest the propriety of submitting this statement of facts to the consideration of the Board of Health, that they may adopt such immediate measures as shall remedy the same.

	(Signed) Joseph Jordan Esq., Chairman	
Messrs	R.T. Hunt	W.B. Stott
	W. White	B.W. Booth
	James Miller	M. Sinclair
	W. Owen	E. Stephens
	J. Walker	J. Langford

Special Meeting
Board of Health, Manchester
1/2 past 3, June 21, 1832

H. Forth Esq., Deputy Chairman
Drs. S.A. Bardsley, E. Carbutt, C. Phillips, J.L. Bardsley, H. Gaulter, W. Johns, E. Lyon, J.P. Kay, J. Mitchell; Revd. J. Crook, W. Huntington, W. Marsden; Lieutenant Colonel Shaw; Messrs. F. Fincham, T. Townend, G. Faulkner, J. Holford, H.H. Birley, J. Heron, J. Langford, D. Lynch junr.

Moved by Mr. Birley.

Resolved 1
>   That the communication from the medical staff of the hospital at Commercial Street stating that additional resident medical officers are required be referred to the Hospital Committee for their consideration.

Moved by Mr. Birley. Seconded by Revd. W. Marsden.

Resolved 2
>   That the address to the public now presented by the sub-committee be placarded forthwith.

Moved as an amendment by Mr. Fincham. Seconded by Dr. Philips.
That the publication of the placard be suspended for the present.
The amendment was negatived and Mr. Birley's motion carried.

Moved by Mr. Fincham. Seconded by Mr. Townend.

Resolved 3
>   That the following paragraph be added to and form part of the placard – viz:
>   The Board of Health has the pleasure of assuring the public that only one case is at this moment under treatment at the hospital. 5 o'clock p.m.

Moved by Mr. Birley. Seconded by Mr. Fincham.

Resolved 4

That the address be printed and placarded under the direction of the sub-committee who prepared the same.

Resolved 5

That 500 copies of the placard be ordered from the printers.

Moved by Dr. J.L. Bardsley. Seconded by Mr. Birley.

Resolved 6

That the best thanks of this Board be given to the gentlemen composing the committee, who have so ably prepared the placard now presented and adopted by this meeting.

Moved by Mr. G. Faulkner. Seconded by Mr. Birley.

Resolved 7

That as there is too much reason to expect that the services of the Resident Medical Officers will be entirely required at their respective hospitals, their attendance will not be expected to present the daily report, nor will they be required to attend during the meetings of the Board but they will be requested to send the daily report and to communicate with the Board on any extraordinary circumstances which may occur.

Henry Forth (signature)

**Board of Health, Manchester
June 22, 1832**

H.H. Birley Esq., Chairman
Drs. S.A. Bardsley, E. Carbutt, J.P. Kay, E. Lyon, W. Johns, H. Gaulter; Revd. J. Crook, W. Marsden; Messrs. T. Townend, F. Fincham, J. Thorpe, W.R. Whatton, J. Woollam, Peter Ewart junr.

Resolved 1

That the minutes of the preceding meeting of this Board be now confirmed.

Resolved 2

That the nuisance in Jackson's Row, Deansgate complained of by Margaret Harrop be referred to the Nuisance Committee.

Moved by Mr. Townend. Seconded by Mr. Fincham.

Resolved 3
> That the propriety of affording assistance to the secretary be referred to the Accounts Committee for their consideration.

Board of Health, Manchester
June 23, 1832

Dr. S.A. Bardsley, Chairman
Drs. J.P. Kay, E. Lyon, W. Johns, E. Carbutt, H. Gaulter, C. Phillips; Revd. J. Crook, G. Dugard, W. Marsden; Messrs. F. Fincham, Benjamin Braidley, T. Townend, J. Potter, J. Rooke, J. Heron, R. J. J. Norreys, J. Thorpe

Resolved 1
> That the proceedings of the last Board be now confirmed.

Resolved 2
> That the Secretary be authorized to communicate to Dr. Divir (on his application) any information with regard to cholera he may require.

Moved by Mr. Fincham. Seconded by Dr. Lyon.

Resolved 3
> That the following printed notice be forthwith affixed to the gate of each hospital.

By Order of the
Board of Health

Patients received into this cholera hospital will be allowed to be attended by one relative or friend on the condition of such attendant not leaving the hospital without the permission of the Resident Medical Officer.

(Signed) Benjamin Braidley Boroughreeve
Chairman of the Board of Health.

Resolved 4
> That 1000 copies of the above notice be printed and placarded throughout the Town.

Resolved 5
> That the Secretary be directed to transmit the articles found on the person of Jane Lewis deceased to the Churchwardens with a request that it may be appropriated for the use of her child.

S.A. Bardsley (signed)

Board of Health, Manchester
June 25, 1832

H.H. Birley Esq., Chairman
Drs. E. Carbutt, E. Lyon, H. Gaulter, J.P. Kay, S.A. Bardsley, J.L. Bardsley, J. Hull; Revd. W. Huntington, James Crook; J. Holford, Dealey, Joseph Heron

Resolved 1
   That the minutes of the preceding meeting of this Board be now confirmed.

Resolved 2
   That the information required by Mr. Dealey of the 15th. Hussars respecting the present state of cholera in Manchester be furnished by the Secretary.

   No communication having been received from the Churchwardens in reply to the application made to them on June 18th. relative to the inspection of the pauper lodging houses it was *[sentence unfinished]*

Resolved 3
   That the Chairman be requested to apply at the Churchwardens Office and report at the next meeting of this Board.

Memorandum
   Half past 11. No report has been yet received from Swan Street Hospital.

Resolved 4
   That a messenger be sent to the hospitals each morning by 1/4 past 10 to receive the report of the Resident Medical Officers that they may be on the table at the hour appointed for the meeting of the Board.

Resolved 5
   That the above resolution be communicated to the Resident Medical Officers.

Resolved 6
   That this meeting do adjourn till tomorrow morning at the usual hour.

Board of Health, Manchester
June 26, 1832

Benjamin Braidley Esq., Chairman
Drs. E. Carbutt, H. Gaulter, E. Lyon, J.P. Kay, W. Johns, S.A. Bardsley, Divir; Revd. James Crook, W. Marsden, G. Dugard; Lieutenant Colonel Shaw; Messrs. J. Rooke, R.J.J. Norreys, W. Haynes, J. Holford, H.H. Birley, J. Heron

Resolved 1
   That the proceedings of the last meeting of this Board be now confirmed.

Resolved 2

That a copy of the communication from the Churchwardens Office dated June 25 be entered on the minutes.

(Copy)

Churchwardens Offices
Manchester 25 June 1832

Gentlemen

I am directed by the Churchwardens to state that they have taken measures to put into execution your recommendations of the 20th. Inst. respecting "visiting the pauper lodging houses" the burial of the bodies of persons dying of suspected cholera and the making of coffins for cholera cases".

Independently of the district Overseer's attention having been directed for Pauper Lodging Houses, the Churchwardens have selected an Overseer especially to visit and report daily upon them, and he is now engaged in that duty.

Directions have been given also by the Churchwardens that the bodies shall be buried in the way you recommend, as well as that the coffins shall be made on the plan suggested by your Board.

On another sheet I beg to hand you a list of the Visiting Overseers with their several districts and am,

Gentlemen,
your most obedient Servant
N. Gardiner
Directing Overseer

The Board of Health

P.S. I send you a small map to facilitate your business.

List of Overseers &c.

Mr. Butcher	Districts Nos. 1 & 4
Mr. Redman	Districts Nos. 2 & 4
Mr. Rose	Districts Nos. 5, 6, 9, 10, 11 & 14
Mr. Armitt	Districts Nos. 3, 7, 8, 12 & 13

Resolved 3

That the reports of cases sent in by Mr. Bamber, Mr. Lynch junr., Mr Langford and Dr. Johns be received.

Moved by Dr. Gaulter.

Resolved 4

That the filthy state of Woodward Court, Nicholas Street, Angel Street as well as the whole of the immediate neighbourhood be reported to the Scavenging Committee by the Secretary.

Resolved 5

That the lodging house No.67 Angel Street be referred to Mr. Redman for his immediate and special inspection.

Resolved 6

That the report of the proceedings of the Hospital Committee of this date be received and that the recommendations therein contained be adopted by this Board.

Resolved 7

That the subject of the best mode of providing board and accommodation for the Resident Medical Officers at the several hospitals be referred to the Hospital Committee for their consideration and that they be requested to report to this Board.

Resolved 8

That a book ruled according to the sheet now presented be ordered for the purpose of keeping a correct report of all cases of cholera reported to this Board.

Board of Health, Manchester
June 27, 1832

Benjamin Braidley Esq., Chairman
Drs. J.L. Bardsley, J.P. Kay, H. Gaulter, E. Lyon, J. Hull, E. Carbutt, S.A. Bardsley, W. Johns, Divir; Revd. W. Marsden, H. Fielding, James Crook; Lieutenant Colonel Shaw; Messrs. W.R. Whatton, J. Holford, J. Rooke, Peter Ewart junr., H.H. Birley, Joseph Heron

Resolved 1

That the proceedings of the last Board be now confirmed.

Moved by Mr. Birley.

Resolved 2

That the resolutions of the Accounts Committee of the 26th. of June be received and adopted as part of the proceedings of this Board.

Moved by Mr. Birley.

Resolved 3

That at the meetings of this Board the Chair be taken on all occasions punctually at 11 o'clock.

Resolved 4

That the report of the Hospital Committee be now received and adopted with the exception of the resolution relating to the removal of patients to the hospitals and that that resolution be adopted subject to the confirmation of the Board on Monday next.

Moved by Dr. J.L. Bardsley.

Resolved 5

That the decision of the Board as to the amount of salary to be paid to the Resident Medical Officers be delayed until information on this head be obtained from some of the towns where cholera has prevailed.

Resolved 6

That a communication be made to the Resident Medical Officers that the hour for funerals at the Parish Burial Ground being 5 o'clock in the afternoon; should it be necessary or advisable to have the funerals of persons dying of cholera at any other hour, a communication must in all instances be previously made to the officiating clergyman, that arrangements may be made for the performance of the funeral service.

Board of Health, Manchester
June 28, 1832

Benjamin Braidley Esq., Chairman
Drs. S.A. Bardsley, E. Carbutt, H. Gaulter, W. Johns, J.L. Bardsley, Divir; Revd. W. Huntington, W. Marsden, J. Crook; Lieutenant Colonel Shaw; Messrs. J. Barker, W. Haynes, H.H. Birley, J. Holford, H. Forth, G. Hall

Resolved 1

That the proceedings of the last meeting of this Board be now confirmed.

Memorandum

Mr. Langford reported that an attempt had been made to bury the body of Jane Wild (died of cholera) in the Parish Burial Ground in a grave only three *[feet]* in depth from the surface.

Moved by Mr. Birley.

Resolved 2

That the circumstances above stated by Mr. Langford be reported to the Churchwardens and that in future upon a similar occurrence the Resident

Officer be requested to report to the Town's Offices without waiting for the meeting of this Board.

Moved by Mr. Birley.

Resolved 3

That it be explained in the communication to the Churchwardens that it is the wish of the Board that at least four feet of earth should cover the last coffin deposited in each grave.

Resolved 4

That the child reported as recovered this morning in the Shude Hill Hospital be allowed to remain a day or two longer agreeably to the request of the mother.

Moved by Mr. Haynes.

Resolved 5

That the proceedings of the Medical Committee of the 27th. Inst. be received and adopted as part of the proceedings of this Board.

Moved by Dr. S.A. Bardsley. Seconded by Dr. E. Carbutt.

Resolved 6

That a communication be made to the clergy and ministers of all denominations requesting that they will take such immediate measures as well in their pulpits as in their Sunday schools as may appear to them best calculated to remove the present prejudices against the cholera hospitals from the minds of the poorer classes of the community.

Moved by Lieutenant Colonel Shaw. Seconded by Mr. George Hall.

Resolved 7

That the chairmen of the District Boards be requested to meet this Board at 11 o'clock on Saturday morning on business of urgent importance and that should they be unable to attend in person they will depute a member of their Board to attend for them.

Moved by Dr. S.A. Bardsley. Seconded by Mr. Haynes.

Resolved 8

That the Chairman be requested to transmit to the Central Board a statement containing the number of cases of cholera which have occurred in Manchester from the 18th. of May to the 28th. of June.

Moved by Dr. S.A. Bardsley. Seconded by Mr. W. Haynes.

Resolved 9

> That should the disease unfortunately continue a daily report signed by the chairman be transmitted to the Central Board.

Board of Health, Manchester
June 29, 1832

W. Haynes Esq., Deputy Chairman
Drs. S.A. Bardsley, E. Carbutt, H. Gaulter, J.P. Kay, E. Lyon, Divir; Lieutenant Colonel Shaw; Messrs. H. Forth, G. Hall, Peter Ewart junr., J. Barker, H.H. Birley

Resolved 1

> That the resolutions of the last meeting of this Board be now confirmed.

Moved Lieutenant Colonel Shaw. Seconded by Mr. H.H. Birley.

Resolved 2

> That the case in Little Pitt Street reported by Mr. Guest be referred to the Hospital Sub-Committee with a request that they will take such measures as they think requisite for the fumigating and whitewashing of the house on the first opportunity and that it be recommended to the sub-committee to appoint a superintendent of fumigating and whitewashing and to take such further measures as they may find effectual on the occurrence of all similar cases in which it may be necessary to remove families and to cleanse and fumigate their houses.

Moved by Mr. H.H. Birley. Seconded by Dr. E. Lyon.

Resolved 3

> That Mr. Sheldon's letter of this date complaining of dirty straw, clothing &c. being burnt in the yard of the Hospital be referred to the Hospital Sub-Committee with a request that it may be immediately attended to and that a copy of this resolution be transmitted to Mr. Sheldon.

Resolved 4

> That the letters from Mr. Hill and Mr. Johnson be referred to the Scavenging Committee with a request that immediate attention be paid to them.

Memorandum

> That the following gentlemen have offered themselves as candidates for the situation of Resident Medical Officers to the cholera hospitals.

Mr. F.H. Fazakerley, 7 Hunts Bank
Mr. S. Gaskell, 108 Portland Street

Resolved 5

That Mr. Gardiner's letter of the 28th Inst. reporting a list of filthy lodging houses be referred to the Hospital Sub-Committee.

William Haynes (signature)

Board of Health, Manchester
June 30, 1832

W. Haynes Esq., Deputy Chairman
Drs. J.P. Kay, W. Johns, E. Lyon, H. Gaulter; Revd. W. Huntington, H. Fielding, Broadley, George Dugard, J. Crook, William Hutchinson, W. Marsden, J. White, J. Hollist; Lieutenant Colonel Shaw; Messrs. R. Guest, P. Ewart junr., J. Barker, J. Thorpe, G. Hall, R.J.J. Norreys, J. Wood, J. Rooke, E. Evans, G. Withington

Resolved 1

That the proceedings of the last meeting of this Board be now confirmed.

Resolved 2

That the proceedings of the Hospital Sub-Committee of this date be received and adopted as part of the proceedings of this Board.

Moved by Revd. J. Crook. Seconded by Dr. E. Lyon.

Resolved 3

That the committee for arranging the placard be now directed to correct the placard and to publish it as soon as corrected in such numbers and forms as they may think fit.

Board of Health, Manchester
July 2, 1832

W. Haynes Esq., Deputy Chairman
Drs. S.A. Bardsley, C. Phillips, W. Johns, H. Gaulter, J.P. Kay, J. Hull, Divir, W.C. Henry; Revd. W. Marsden, H. Fielding, W. Huntington, C.D. Wray, J. Crook; Lieutenant Colonel Shaw; Messrs. J. Thorpe, G. Hall, Peter Ewart junr., J. Holford, J. Heron, J. Langford

Resolved 1

That the resolutions passed at the last meeting of this Board be now confirmed.

Resolved 2

That the resolution of this Board of the 27th ultimo respecting the means of conveyance of patients to the hospitals be now confirmed.

Moved by Lieutenant Colonel Shaw.

Resolved 3
> That the great placard as now received from the Placard Committee be adopted, and that the arrangements as now stated in that placard be carried fully into effect.

Moved by Lieutenant Colonel Shaw.

Resolved 4
> That a communication be made by the Slings Committee to the mill-owners who have been kind enough to allow that slings should be placed at their mills, stating that that measure will not be adopted by the Board at present, nor unless cholera should spread to a greater extent than at present and that should the measure become necessary due notice will be given to the mill-owners by the Slings Committee.

Memorandum
> A letter was read from the Central Board of Health stating that it is not their "intention to publish the cases of cholera now reported, unless the disease should materially increase".

Moved by Rev. C.D. Wray. Seconded by Dr. S.A. Bardsley.

Resolved 5
> That the report of the Hospital and Reception House Sub-Committee now read be received and the recommendations therein contained be adopted by this Board.

Resolved 6
> That in compliance with the recommendation made by the medical staff of the Shude Hill Hospital, that two assistants to Mr. Lynch be immediately appointed in consequence of the increased number of patients, Mr. Gaskell, and Mr. Fazarkerley be appointed such assistants by this Board and be requested immediately to attend at the hospital it being explained to them that the salary to be paid will be settled at the next meeting of the Board.

Resolved 7
> That Mr. Shoreland be requested to have 3 or 4 gas lights immediately put up in the Shude Hill Hospital and arrangements made for having the same lighted with gas – to have a pipe immediately laid for supplying the hospital with water and also to take measures for the better ventilation of the building.

Resolved 8
> That 30 bedsteads and 50 sets of bedding be immediately ordered by Mr. Langford for the use of the Hospitals and Reception House.

Resolved 9

That the communication from the conductors and teachers of the Angel Meadow Sunday School now read be received and submitted to the Nuisance Committee who be requested to return a written answer to the Board.

Resolved 10

That Mr. Langford be authorized by this Board to engage a conveyance for the interment of the dead until the carriage now altering be completed.

Board of Health, Manchester
July 3, 1832

Benjamin Braidley Esq., Chairman
Drs. S.A. Bardsley, J.P. Kay, C. Phillips, H. Gaulter, W. C. Henry, E. Lyon, W. Johns; Revd. W. Marsden, H. Fielding, J. White; Messrs. J. Holford, P. Ewart junr.

Resolved 1

That the proceedings of the last meeting of this Board be now confirmed.

Resolved 2

That the communication from Mr. Clough complaining of the dampness of a cellar in Wood Street be referred to the Board of Health for No.13 District with a request that they will communicate with the landlord for the purpose of having the same remedied.

Resolved 3

That Dr. Shaw be reinstated as one of the physicians to the Swan Street Hospital and that he be allowed to attend the meetings of the Board and its Medical Committee.

Resolved 4

That a Deputation consisting of Mr. P. Ewart junr. and the Revd. J. White accompanied by Mr. Langford be appointed to wait upon Messrs. Peel, Williams and Peel to engage another room of the building for the use of the nurses, and that these gentlemen be empowered to fit up the room for that purpose.

Resolved 5

That Mr. Woollam be requested to present Mr. Langford's application for 2 gas lights for the Commercial Street Hospital to the Lamp Committee.

Memorandum 1

Read a letter from T. Birtles stating that notice had been given to the owner of pig styes in Angel Meadow complained of by the conductors and teachers of the school in that neighbourhood to remove them within five days.

Memorandum 2

Read a letter from the Scavenging Committee in reply to the complaint made to them of the filthy state of Woodward Court, Nicholas Street, Angel Meadow and the whole neighbourhood. The committee reported that in this instance they had cleansed the streets reported but that they had *[neither]* legal authority, nor funds to apply to cleansing such streets and begged to refer the Board to the Churchwardens who have authority in such cases.

Resolved 6

That the Scavenging Committee be requested to have Woodward Court, Nicholas Street, Angel Street, immediately scavenged and cleansed and that when completed an account of the expences incurred be sent to the Board.

Resolved 7

That the Scavenging Committee be requested to appoint persons to visit and cleanse if necessary each locality from which cases of cholera have been taken to the hospitals.

Resolved 8

That a Special Meeting of this Board be called for Thursday Morning to receive the report of the Accounts Committee with a statement of the Weekly expences of this Board and that the Salaries to be paid to the Resident Medical Officers be then determined with other business of importance.

Board of Health, Manchester
July 4, 1832

Benjamin Braidley Esq., Chairman
Dr. H. Gaulter; Revd. W. Huntington, W. Marsden; Lieutenant Colonel Shaw; Messrs. H. Forth, O. Milne, R.J.J. Norreys, J. Woollam, J. Langford

Resolved 1

That the proceedings of the last meeting of the Board be now confirmed.

Moved by Mr. H. Forth. Seconded by Lieutenant Colonel Shaw.

Resolved 2

That a copy of the daily report of cholera cases be furnished to the Exchange Room and the Portico and also that one be placed at each of the hospitals, at the Town Hall and at New Cross.

Memorandum

Received a letter from Messrs. Peel, Williams and Peel expressing their will-ingness to let one of the rooms in the narrow building at Swan Street for the use of the nurses on condition that the windows looking to the back of the houses in Swan Street be bricked up and that no <u>cholera patients</u> should be received into it.

Resolved 3
That the letter from certain inhabitants of the Club Row complaining of a slaughter house be referred to the agent of the Lord of the Manor with a request that the nuisance complained of may be removed.

Special Meeting
Board of Health, Manchester
July 5, 1832

H.H. Birley Esq., Chairman
Drs. S.A. Bardsley, H. Gaulter, W. Johns, G. Shaw, H. Pendlebury, J.P. Kay; Revd. W. Huntington, J. Crook, G. Dugard; Messrs. J. Holford, J. Thorpe, P. Ewart junr., J. Kennedy, G.W. Wood

Resolved 1
That the proceedings of the last meeting of this Board be now confirmed.

Resolved 2
That the communication from Mr. Procter complaining of a nuisance in Tassle Alley be referred to the Nuisance Committee.

Resolved 3
That the letter from Patrick Flynn complaining of the dirty state of his cellar No.2 Ludgate Street, Angel Meadow be referred to the Board of Health for No.2 District and the letter from Mr. Conolly and I. Kelly complaining of the filthiness of the cellars 65 and 66 Shude Hill, to the Board for No.5 District and that they be requested to have the cellars visited and report to this Board.

Resolved 4
That the houses reported this day by the overseer as filthy be whitewashed as soon as possible.

Resolved 5
That the report of the Accounts Committee be read and adopted as part of the proceedings of this Board.

Moved by Mr. P. Ewart junr. Seconded by Mr. Holford.

Resolved 6
That the remuneration to each of the principal Resident Medical Officers (viz: Mr. Langford and Mr. Lynch) be £24 per month of 4 weeks including board

it being understood that they reside at the hospitals, this salary to commence from the date of their residence at the hospitals.

Moved by Dr. J.L. Bardsley. Seconded by Mr. P. Ewart junr.

Resolved 7
That the appointment of Mr. Gaskell as Medical Assistant, and of Mr. Fazakerley as Dispenser of Medicines, be confirmed by this Board.

Moved by Dr. J.P. Kay. Seconded by Dr. Gaulter.

Resolved 8
That the remuneration to the Dispenser of Medicines be £8 per month of 4 weeks including Board and that he reside at the hospital.

Resolved 9
That the remuneration to the Resident Medical Assistant be £15 per month of 4 weeks, including board it being understood that he resides at the hospital.

Resolved 10
That a special meeting of the Board be called for Monday to consider the necessity of applying for additional funds as well as other general business.

Resolved 11
That the Medical Committee be requested to consider the propriety of classifying the cases received into the hospitals.

Board of Health, Manchester
July 6, 1832

H.H. Birley, Esq., Chairman
Drs. E. Lyon, H. Gaulter; Revd. J. Crook; Messrs. O. Milne, P. Ewart junr.

Resolved 1
That the minutes of the preceding meeting of this Board be now confirmed.

Resolved 2
That the letter of Mr. S. Thompstone reporting a case of cholera at No.8 Jackson's Row be referred to Mr. J. Walker one of the Medical Officers for the District.

Resolved 3
That the letters now read from the Resident Medical Officers be referred to the Special Meeting of the Board on Monday next.

Memorandum

Mr. Langford enquired of the Board whether, when his services were no longer required, any and what notice would be given to him and also what notice would be required from him, should he wish to retire from the office.

Resolved 4

That Mr. James Wood be added to the Accounts Committee.

Resolved 5

That Dr. Lyon be requested to write to Mr. Bradshaw requesting that he will appoint a person to inspect the boats arriving by the canal at Preston Brooks.

Board of Health, Manchester
July 7, 1832

Lieutenant Colonel Shaw, Chairman
Dr. H. Gaulter; Revd. W. Marsden; Messrs. R.J.J. Norreys, P. Ewart junr.

Resolved 1

That the proceedings of the last meeting of this Board be now confirmed.

Memorandum

Received a letter from Mr. Walker, surgeon stating that he had visited the case in Jackson's Row reported by Mr. S. Thompstone – that the case had not hitherto presented any of the symptoms of malignant cholera but simply those of common cholera and that the patient was better but far from being well.

Resolved 2

That the letter from Samuel Hague junr. complaining of the filthy state of the cellars of an old building between Nos.32 and 36 Water Street be referred to the Board of Health for No.12 District with a request that they will endeavour to have the nuisance removed and that they be desired to report to this Board.

Resolved 3

That the letter from P. Malval D'Aquillion complaining of the pig styes at the back of his house (70 Thomas Street, Oldham Street) be referred to the Nuisance Committee.

Resolved 4

That the cellars 65 and 66 Shude Hill visited by Mr. R. Guest and Mr. D. Lynch junr. at the request of Mrs. Piccope be reported to the proprietor Mr. W. Lomas of Blackfriars Street.

Board of Health, Manchester
July 9, 1832

H.H. Birley, Esq., Chairman
Drs. E. Lyon, W. Johns, J. Hull, J.P. Kay, H. Gaulter; Revd. J. Crook; Messrs. James Wood, G. Hall, D. Dockray, P. Ewart junr.

Resolved 1
   That the proceedings of the last meeting of this Board be now confirmed.

Memorandum 1
   Read a letter from Mr. J.A. Smith stating that several of his patients had refused to employ him in consequence of knowing that his name is publicly posted on the walls as one of the surgeons to attend cholera patients and requesting that some other person may be appointed to the district to which his, Mr. Smith's name, is attached.

Memorandum 2
   Dr. Lyon stated that in answer to the letter which he addressed to Mr. Bradshaw, that gentleman had communicated his readiness to give every facility to the operations of the Board, but that he was not disposed to incur any extraordinary expence.

Resolved 2
   That the consideration of the necessity of applying for additional funds be deferred for the present.

   Moved by Mr. P. Ewart junr. Seconded by Dr. E. Lyon.

Resolved 3
   That £24 per month of 4 weeks (the remuneration to the principal Resident Medical Officers proposed on July 6th) is in the opinion of this Board the utmost which they feel themselves justified in offering.

   Moved by Dr. J.P. Kay. Seconded by Dr. W. Johns.

Resolved 4
   That the Board had contemplated that 4 Weeks notice should be given to and required from the Resident Officers on relinquishing their duties but that if a fortnight would be preferred the Board beg that the Resident Officers will immediately intimate the same.

   Moved by Dr. E. Lyon. Seconded by Dr. Gaulter.

Resolved 5
   That the remuneration to the Resident Medical Assistant be £10 per month of 4 weeks including Board it being understood that he resides at the hospital.

   Moved by Mr. P. Ewart junr. Seconded by Dr. Lyon.

Resolved 6
> That the Revd. James Crook and Dr. Gaulter be requested in conjunction with such of the medical staff of the Swan Street Hospital as may be present to confer with Mr. Fazarkerley as to the remuneration to be made to him as Dispenser of Medicines and that they report to this Board at its next meeting.

Resolved 7
> That while there are no patients in the hospital at Knott Mill Mr. Langford be requested to give his assistance at the Swan Street Hospital.

Resolved 8
> That the letter from Samuel Ward of Sharp Street, St. George's Road complaining of the filthy state of that neighbourhood be referred to the Nuisance Committee.

Resolved 9
> That a copy of the daily report of cases of cholera be transmitted to the Churchwardens Office.

Board of Health, Manchester
July 10, 1832
15 minutes past 11

Drs. E. Lyon, H. Gaulter; Revd. W. Marsden; Mr. H. H. Birley

Adjourned for want of sufficient attendance at the hour of meeting.

Memorandum
> Mr. Langford reported that he had taken measures to have the two flats in which cases had occurred fumigated.

Board of Health, Manchester
July 11, 1832
20 minutes past 11

Drs. E. Lyon, J.P. Kay, H. Gaulter; Mr. P. Ewart junr.

Attendance insufficient to form a quorum.

Board of Health, Manchester
July 12, 1832

H.H. Birley Esq., Chairman
Drs. S.A. Bardsley, H. Gaulter, J.P. Kay, W. Johns; Messrs. J. Woollam, P. Ewart junr.

Resolved 1

That the proceedings of this Board on the 9th Instant be now confirmed.

Memorandum

Read a communication from the Scavenging Committee stating their willingness to cleanse such localities as the Board may require (the cost being charged to the Board) and requesting that Mr. Thorpe may be informed by note of the places to be cleansed.

Resolved 2

That on receiving a proper certificate that the offered services of the Scavenging Committee are necessary the Secretary immediately make the required communication to Mr. Thorpe & report to the Board.

Resolved 3

That the medical staff of the Swan Street Hospital be requested to consider and report to the Board what permanent medical establishment may appear to them at present necessary.

Moved by Mr. P. Ewart junr. Seconded by Dr. Gaulter.

Resolved 4

That the men, car and horse for burying the dead be removed for the present to the Swan Street Hospital but that Mr. Langford be authorized to send for the nurse if his services should be required at the Hospital in Commercial Street.

Board of Health, Manchester
July 13, 1832

H. Forth Esq., Deputy Chairman
Drs. S.A. Bardsley, E. Lyon, H. Gaulter; Revd W. Huntington; Messr H.H. Birley, P. Ewart junr., J. Woollam

Resolved 1

That the minutes of the proceedings of the last meeting of the Board be now confirmed.

Henry Forth (signature)

Board of Health, Manchester
July 14, 1832

J.J. Norreys Esq., Chairman
Drs. W. Johns, H. Gaulter, G. Shaw, J.P. Kay, S.A. Bardsley; Revd. W. Marsden, J. Crook; Messrs P. Ewart junr., G. Hall, J. Woollam

Resolved 1

That the Secretary be instructed to send to Messrs. Satterthwaite and other inspectors of No.3 District a copy of the resolution passed June 20th referring their complaint to the Scavenging Committee and that they be requested to furnish a further report with a list of the streets complained of.

Resolved 2

That when the report is obtained a further communication be addressed to the Scavenging Committee stating that a complaint has been made that no attention has been paid to the letter sent them on June 20th.

Resolved 3

That the letter from Mr. George Harding of No.147 Gt. Ancoats Street complaining of a slaughter house at the back of his house be referred to the Nuisance Committee with a request that immediate attention may be paid to it.

Resolved 4

That the filthy state of Lower Blakeley Street be reported to the Scavenging Committee and that they be requested to have it thoroughly swept and cleansed.

Board of Health, Manchester
July 16, 1832

H. Forth Esq., Deputy Chairman
Drs. S.A. Bardsley, H. Gaulter, J.P. Kay, W. Johns; Revd. W. Marsden, J. Crook; Messrs W.R. Whatton, P. Ewart junr., James Wood, George Hall

Resolved 1

That the proceedings of the preceding meeting of the Board be now confirmed.

Memorandum 1

Read a letter from Mr. Langford stating that a case of cholera had occurred in Little Ireland which has not been reported to the Board.

Resolved 2

That it being understood that the case alluded to was under the treatment of Mr. Howard of the Infirmary, a letter be addressed to him requesting him to send in a report of the case if he consider it necessary.

Memorandum 2

Mr. Bailey the Deputy Constable of Cheetham attended to enquire whether cases of cholera occurring in that Township would be received into the

Manchester hospitals – Mr. Bailey was informed that the Board had deemed it necessary to refuse that privilege to other Townships and that the same answer would apply to the Township of Cheetham.

Memorandum 3

The Secretary reported that after the meeting of the Board on Saturday he had received a communication from Mr. D. Clark, Surgeon,12 Oak Street complaining of a pig stye – heaps of night soil and other dirt in the back yard of Nos. 43, 45 & 47 George Leigh Street: which he had referred to the Inspectors of Nuisances.

Memorandum 4

Messrs. G. Hall and P. Ewart junr. reported that the Reception House in Harrison Street was ready for the admission of the families of persons seized with cholera.

Memorandum 5

Read a communication from the medical staff of the Swan Street Hospital – stating that Mr. Lynch would attend on their part to point out the medical assistance required at that hospital. Mr. Lynch stated that at present himself and the two assistants were able to perform the duties of the hospital but that should the number of cases increase a compounder of medicines would also be required.

Resolved 3

That the remuneration to Mr. Fazakerley be £12 for the current month of 4 weeks.

Henry Forth (signature)

Board of Health, Manchester
July 17, 1832

Drs. S.A. Bardsley, H. Gaulter; Messrs. George Hall, J. Woollam

Attendance insufficient to form a quorum.

Board of Health, Manchester
July 18, 1832

Dr. S.A. Bardsley, Chairman
Dr. E. Lyon; Revd. W. Huntington, J. Crook; Messrs. J. Barker; P. Ewart junr.

Resolved 1

That the proceedings of the Board on the 16th Inst. be now confirmed.

Resolved 2
> That the Hospital Committee be requested to take into consideration the complaint of the medical staff of the *[left blank]*

Resolved 3
> That convalescent patients at the hospital *[at]* Swan Street be removed at the discretion of the medical staff to the hospital at Commercial Street until perfectly recovered and that this practice be continued until further orders.

Resolved 4
> That it having appeared that the cholera has been communicated to several persons in consequence of the bodies of those who have died of the disease at their own houses having been kept too long, the Board of Health desire to know whether they have the power to compel the immediate interment of those who die under such circumstances.

Resolved 5
> That the Secretary communicate the above resolution to the Central Board of Health.

S.A. Bardsley (signature)

Board of Health, Manchester
July 19, 1832

W. Haynes Esq., Deputy Chairman
Drs. H. Gaulter, J.P. Kay, S.A. Bardsley, G. Shaw; Revd. J. Crook; Lieutenant Colonel Shaw; Messrs. J. Barker, J. Woollam, G. Hall, P. Ewart junr., J. Langford

Resolved 1
> That the minutes of the proceedings of the Board on the 18th Inst. be now confirmed.

Resolved 2
> That the Churchwardens be particularly requested to attend the meeting of this Board tomorrow for the purpose of taking into consideration the best means for furnishing clothing to poor convalescents whose clothes have been destroyed by order of the Board.

Moved by Mr. P. Ewart junr.

Resolved 3
> That when the carriage or slings are sent out for patients, a man be sent (in addition to the driver or the bearers) whose duty it shall be to prevent bystanders approaching the patients.

Moved by Lieutenant Colonel Shaw.

Resolved 4
>That the Board of Health at Warrington be requested to furnish a daily report of the state of the cholera at that Town and that this Board will furnish the daily report for Manchester if required.

Board of Health, Manchester
July 20, 1832

W. Haynes Esq., Deputy Chairman
Drs. S.A. Bardsley, H. Gaulter, W. Johns; Revd. W. Marsden, J. Crook; Lieutenant Colonel Shaw; Messrs. J. Barker, P. Ewart junr., J. Heron, W.R. Whatton

Resolved 1
>That the proceedings of the Board on the 19th Inst. be now confirmed.

Resolved 2
>That a special meeting of the Board be called for Wednesday next to take into consideration the propriety of convening an early meeting of the Leypayers for the purpose of making an application for additional funds with other business of importance.

Board of Health, Manchester
July 21, 1832

Dr. S.A. Bardsley, Chairman
Drs. H. Gaulter, J.P. Kay; Revd. J. Crook; Messrs. G. Hall, P. Ewart junr.

Resolved 1
>That the proceedings of the Board on the 20th Inst. be now confirmed.

Resolved 2
>That the filthy state of Well Street, Back Street and Garden Street be reported to the Scavenging Committee and that they be requested to have them immediately and thoroughly cleansed – an account of the expense to be sent in to the Board.

Resolved 3
>That the above resolution be communicated to the Inspectors of No. 3 District and that they be informed that the Board are at present instituting an enquiry as to the powers which they possess to force the removal of nuisances arising from unhealthy and filthy occupations or from other causes likely to engender disease.

S.A. Bardsley (signature)

**Board of Health Manchester
July 24, 1832**

Benjamin Braidley Esq., Chairman
Drs. S.A. Bardsley, J.P. Kay; Revd. J. Crook; Messrs. George Hall, H.H. Birley, P. Ewart junr.

Resolved 1
  That the proceedings of the last Board be now confirmed.

Resolved 2
  That the Order in Council be referred to Mr. Milne for his consideration and that he be requested to make an abstract thereof shewing the powers thereby given to the Board ready for the meeting of the Board tomorrow.

**Board of Health Manchester
July 25, 1832**

H. Forth Esq., Deputy Chairman
Drs. S.A. Bardsley, J.L. Bardsley, J. Hull, E. Lyon, J.P. Kay, J. Pendlebury; Revd. W. Marsden; Messrs. F. Fincham, J. Heron, J. Wood, J. Thorpe, J. Holford, G. Hall, H.H. Birley, W. Haynes, P. Ewart junr., E. Connell, E. Evans

Resolved 1
  That the proceedings of the last meeting of the Board be now confirmed.
  The Order in Council having been read.

Moved by Dr. S.A. Bardsley.

Resolved 2
  That a request be made to the Churchwardens to call a meeting of the Leypayers to be held on the 2nd of August for the purpose of obtaining their sanction to the expenses which may be incurred by this Board as directed by the Cholera Prevention Act and the subsequent Orders in Council and that the following Gentlemen be appointed a committee for drawing up the said requisition and for making such arrangements as they shall think necessary and fit for bringing this subject before the consideration of the Leypayers.

Lieutenant Colonel Shaw
  Drs. S.A. Bardsley
        E. Lyon
        J.P. Kay

Revd. W. Marsden
Messrs. Thomas Potter
        P. Ewart junr.
        J. Woollam

Resolved 3
  That the Nuisance Committee be requested to report to the sub-committee just appointed such sewers or drains not within the jurisdiction of the

Commissioners of Sewers as shall appear to them most to require the interference of the Board.

Resolved 4

That in all future reports of new cases instances of strangers coming into the
Town in a state of disease or falling ill after their arrival be distinguished
from patients who are inhabitants.

Resolved 5

That a copy of the above resolution be sent to the Resident Medical Officers
and that it be also posted at the entrance to the hospitals for the information
of the medical practitioners.

Henry Forth (signature)

Board of Health, Manchester
July 26, 1832

W. Haynes Esq., Deputy Chairman
Drs. S.A. Bardsley, E. Lyon, H. Gaulter; Revd. J. Crook; Messrs. J. Woollam, J.
Barker

Resolved 1

That the proceedings of the last meeting of the Board be now confirmed.

Resolved 2

That the following requisition be transmitted to the Churchwardens.

To the Churchwardens of Manchester &c. &c.

Gentlemen

In accordance with the orders in that behalf made by the Lords and others of His Majesty's Most Honorable Privy Council and dated the 6th day of
the month of March last and the 20th day of the present month of July – I
am directed by the Board of Health for the Township of Manchester,
appointed by said Privy Council to request you will at the earliest possible
opportunity convene a Public Vestry Meeting of the inhabitants of that
Township for the purpose of taking into their consideration the adoption of
such measures as are recommended and authorized by the before mentioned
Orders in Council – at which meeting the Board will come prepared to state
the proceedings already taken under the sanction of a former meeting, and
also to submit the proposition which as they conceive now require the approbation of the inhabitants in Vestry assembled including a proposal for a further grant of money from the poor's rates for the purposes of the Board.

I am, Gentlemen
your most Obedient Servant

Joseph Heron
Honorary Secretary

Board of Health, Manchester
July 26, 1832

Board of Health, Manchester
July 27, 1832

W. Haynes Esq., Deputy Chairman
Dr. S.A. Bardsley; Revd. James Crook; Messrs. J. Barker, P. Ewart junr.

Resolved 1
That the proceedings of the last meeting of the Board be now confirmed.

Board of Health, Manchester
July 28, 1832

W. Haynes Esq., Deputy Chairman
Drs. S.A. Bardsley, H. Gaulter; Messrs. P. Ewart junr., G. Hall, J. Heron, W. R. Whatton

Resolved 1
That the number of attendants at the hospitals appearing to this Board greater than at present necessary – It be suggested to the medical staff at such hospitals whether they could not dismiss some of them, to be reengaged should the number of cases increase so as to render their services necessary.

Board of Health, Manchester
July 30, 1832

H. Forth Esq. Deputy Chairman
Drs. S.A. Bardsley, E. Lyon, J.P. Kay, H. Gaulter; Revd. J. Crook; Lieutenant Colonel Shaw; Messrs. W. Haynes, P. Ewart junr., G. Hall, J. Rooke

Resolved 1
That the proceedings of the last meeting of the Board be now confirmed.

Resolved 2
That Mr. Winder, Ashley Lane be written to directing his attention to the extract from the Order in Council enforcing the necessity of reporting cases of cholera to the local Boards of Health.

Resolved 3
That the following form of placard informing persons attacked with cholera where to apply for medical assistance be adopted and printed viz:

District No. ____
Board of Health, Town Hall, Manchester
July 30 1832

Persons residing in this neighbourhood who are attacked with cholera or looseness of the bowels, requiring gratuitous medical assistance will immediately apply to any of the gentlemen whose names & addresses are subjoined, viz: ____ ____

Resolved 4

That 100 copies of the same be circulated in each district by posting on the walls and placing them as publicly as possible in the shops of the districts.

Resolved 5

That it be recommended to the Medical Committee to prepare a plan of diet for the inmates of the Reception House and also for the nurses of the hospitals.

Resolved 6

That the Hospital and Reception House Committee be authorized to have a wooden railing made across Harrison Street to prevent the inmates from communicating with the neighbourhood and to provide such articles as they may consider necessary for the accommodation of persons taken there.

Resolved 7

That notice be given to the medical staff of the hospitals at Swan Street and Commercial Street that the Reception House is in a complete state for the admission of the families of persons attacked with cholera.

Resolved 8

That the following note be subjoined to the daily report.

"Fourteen of the cases reported this day and on Saturday occurred in a court in No.3 District and six in another in No.2 District.
Thirty-five persons chiefly removed from these courts are at present secluded in the Reception House."

Henry Forth (signature)

Board of Health, Manchester
July 31, 1832

William Haynes Esq., Deputy Chairman
Drs E. Lyon, H. Gaulter; Revd. W. Huntington; Lieutenant Colonel Shaw; Messrs.
J. Thorpe, E. Connell, W.R. Whatton, P. Ewart junr., J. Heron (Honorary Secretary)

Resolved 1

That the proceedings of the last Board be now confirmed.

Resolved 2

That the resolutions now read of the committee appointed for preparing resolutions for the meeting of Leypayers be approved & adopted by this Board.

Resolved 3

That Mr. Shoreland be immediately requested to board up the windows complained of in the letter now read from Messrs. Peel, Williams & Peel.

Resolved 4

That a communication be made to the medical staff at the Commercial Street Hospital requesting them to inform the Board whether or not any and how many of the attendants there refuse to attend at the Shude Hill Hospital when required and that such of them as shall so refuse be immediately dismissed: and also to request in case the whole number at present employed consent to the above terms that 2 of them be forthwith sent to give their assistance at the Shude Hill Hospital, to be recalled when the medical staff of the Commercial Street Hospital shall think it necessary.

Resolved 5

That a letter be sent to Messrs. Peel & Co. to request their consent to a fire place being put up in each of the nurses wards in the Shude Hill Hospitals and also to inform them that their letter received this morning (requesting that the windows of the Swan Street Hospital looking into Mason Street may be boarded up) has been attended to.

Board of Health, Manchester
August 1, 1832

William Haynes Esq., Deputy Chairman
Drs. J.L. Bardsley, H. Gaulter, E. Lyon, J.P. Kay, W. Johns; Revd. W. Marsden; Lieutenant Colonel Shaw; Messrs. J. Thorpe, P. Ewart junr., J. Heron

Resolved 1

That the proceedings of the last meeting of this Board be now confirmed.

Resolved 2

That Mr. Langford be directed to send one of the men from Commercial Street to the Reception House in Harrison Street with directions to him to prevent the inmates leaving the premises and that he be recalled when the medical staff of the Commercial Street Hospital require his services.

Board of Health, Manchester
August 2, 1832

In consequence of the Public Vestry Meeting held this day on the requisition of the Board to make a further grant of £1000 the meeting of the Board adjourned till 11 o'clock, August 3rd.

Board of Health, Manchester
August 3, 1832

Benjamin Braidley Esq., Chairman
Drs. E. Lyon, H. Gaulter, J.P. Kay; Revd. W. Marsden; Messrs. H. Forth, W. Haynes, P. Ewart junr.

Resolved 1
    That the proceedings of the Board on the 1st. Inst. be now confirmed.

Resolved 2
    That the resolutions of the medical staff of the Commercial Street Hospital of the 1st. Inst. now read be entered on the minutes. (See Appendix)

Memorandum 1
    Read a letter from the Revd. J Schofield complaining of a pig stye at the back of the house No.35 Boardman Street belonging to Mr. Deane.

Resolved 3
    That a letter be addressed to Mr. Deane directing the immediate removal of the pigs under the authority vested in the Board by the Order in Council of July 20th.

Resolved 4
    That the proceedings of the Medical Committee of the 1st. Inst. be received and adopted as part of the proceedings of the Board.

Resolved 5
    That the persons taken from Allen's Court be allowed to remove such of their goods as Mr. Ewart and Dr. Kay may think it unnecessary to destroy.

Resolved 6
    That a communication be addressed to the Treasurer of the House of Recovery stating that this Board is desirous that a deputation of their members should have a conference with the committee of the Fever Ward with respect to the erection of a disinfecting apparatus.

Memorandum 2
    Mr. Wood 68 Long Millgate called to state that a man in the employ of this Board has brought to his shop for sale some old clothes and rags from the cellar of Martha Barker in Hanover Street.

Resolved 7

That Mr. Ewart be requested to investigate the above complaint and take such measures as he may consider necessary and report to the Board at its next meeting.

Appendix

Cholera Hospital, Commercial Street
August 1, 1832

Resolved 1

That two nurses be permitted to serve at the Swan Street Hospital, it being understood that on the admission of fresh cases or if any other sufficient reason arise rendering their services at Commercial Street requisite they shall immediately return thither, on the receipt of a letter signed by the physician of the day and one surgeon of the week and addressed to the Resident Medical Officer at the Swan Street Hospital.

Resolved 2

That the Board be informed that when the foregoing resolution is carried into effect, two nurses only will remain at Commercial Street Hospital, one of whom must also act as porter. That there are at present two cases in the hospital, one of which requires minute attention; and that should other cases occur in the neighbourhood, the Hospital is not supplied with bearers of slings, or with a carriage, or with a messenger to summon the medical attendants or to convey notices of meetings of the Staff.

Resolved 3

That a copy of these resolutions be forthwith transmitted to the Board.

Minutes of Staff August 1, 1832.

Dr. J.P. Kay in the Chair.
Mr. Mann
Mr. Owen
Mr. Stott
Mr. Walker

J. Langford
Resident Medical Officer.

Daily Report

August 3rd.

Remaining at last Report	New Cases	Dead	Recovered	Remaining this day 11 o'clock
17	2	4	3	12

From the commencement of the disease on the 18[th.] June [sic] 1832.

Cases   Died   Recovered
149   93   44

Board of Health, Manchester
August 4, 1832

Benjamin Braidley Esq., Chairman
Drs. E. Lyon, J.P. Kay, H. Gaulter; Revd. J. Crook; Lieutenant Colonel Shaw;
Messrs. W. Haynes, G. Hall, P. Ewart junr.

Resolved 1
   That the proceedings of the last meeting of the Board be now confirmed.

Memorandum 1
   Read a letter from Mr. N. Gardiner dated August 1st offering a mill in
   Walker's Croft, Mill Brow for the purpose of a hospital at 50 shillings per
   week. The building consists of 5 rooms, 72 feet long by 21 wide.

Resolved 2
   That Mr. Shoreland be requested to inspect the rooms at the Swan Street
   Hospital requiring the erection of fire places and report to the Board the prob-
   able expence of such erection.

Memorandum 2
   Read a letter from Messrs. Peel, Williams and Peel dated August – consenting to the erection of fire places in the nurses wards on condition that they
   are made perfectly secure and that should any accident arise from fire the
   damage be made good by the Board of Health.

Resolved 3
   That a communication be addressed to Mr. Coxon, coach proprietor of
   Portland Street, directing the immediate removal of the pigs complained of
   at the back of No.70 Thomas Street, Oldham Street.

Resolved 4
   That the Secretary be directed to ascertain the name of the owner of the pig
   styes opposite the Lord Cornwallis in Hanover Street, also of those at the
   back of No.26 Garden Street and to address to them a similar letter.

Resolved 5
   That the Hospital and Reception House Committee be requested to state to
   the Board what alteration they consider it necessary to make in the wages of
   the hospital attendants in consequence of their being placed on a plan of diet.

Resolved 6
> That a letter be addressed to any gentlemen concerning whom it may be com-
> municated that he has not <u>immediately</u> reported any case of cholera to the
> Board or that any case in his care has not been <u>immediately</u> sent to the hos-
> pital requesting that his reports may be prompt and punctual and that he will
> in every case exert his influence as much as possible to obtain the immedi-
> ate removal to the hospital of every patient which he may visit.

Resolved 7
> That a copy of the preceding resolution be transmitted to Mr. Harrison.

Daily Report

August 4th

Remaining at last Report	New Cases	Dead	Recovered	Remaining this day 11 o'clock
12	4	1	-	15

From the commencement of the disease on the 18th. of May 1832.

Cases	Died	Recovered
153	94	44

Board of Health, Manchester
August 6, 1832

W. Haynes Esq., Chairman
Drs. E. Lyon, J. Hull, J.P. Kay; Revd. W. Marsden, J. Crook; Messrs. George
Hall, P. Ewart junr.

Resolved 1
> That the proceedings of the Board on the 4th. Instant be now confirmed.

Resolved 2
> That the Secretary be directed to transmit a copy of the 6th. resolution passed
> on August 4 to Messrs. J. Garside, R.T. Hunt & J. Windsor.

Resolved 3
> That the proceedings of the Hospital and Reception House Committee of the
> 4th Inst. be received and adopted as part of the proceedings of this Board.

Resolved 4
> That the Scavenging Committee be requested to cleanse the streets named in
> the reports of the Nuisance Inspectors at the expence of the Board and that
> a copy of the Inspector's Reports be furnished to the Scavenging Committee.

Resolved 5
>   That all destitute persons dismissed from the Reception House be furnished with a note to the Churchwardens stating these circumstances and that the Secretary be directed to prepare and have printed a form of circular for that purpose.

Resolved 6
>   That a circular be addressed to all the District Medical Officers in the Town informing them:
>   1. That the Board has prepared a house in Harrison Street, North Street, Pollard Street, for the reception of the families of persons who have been affected with cholera.
>
>   2. That the Board is desirous that medical gentlemen should in all cases where the inmates of any house in which cholera has occurred are liable to receive the infection immediately persuade them to be removed to the Reception House at the same time furnishing them with an order of admission.

Daily Report

August 5 & 6th.

Remaining at last Report	New Cases	Dead	Recovered	Remaining this day 11 o'clock
15	12	5	-	22

From the commencement of the disease on the 18th. of May 1832.

Cases	Died	Recovered
165	99	44

Board of Health Manchester
August 7, 1832

William Haynes Esq., Deputy Chairman
Drs. H. Gaulter, J.P. Kay; Revd. G. Dugard, J. Crook; Messrs. G. Hall, J. Woollam, P. Ewart junr., D. Lynch junr.

Resolved 1.
>   That the minutes of the last meeting of the Board be now confirmed.

Memorandum 1
>   The Secretary reported that he had written to Mr. James Bullen of 24 Garden Street and Mr. Tunbridge of Market Street directing the immediate removal of the pigs at the Back of 26 Garden Street and also to Mr. Hyde respecting those opposite the Lord Cornwallis in Hanover Street.

Memorandum 2

Read a letter from Dr. William Henry dated the 6th Inst. enclosing £50 for the erection of a disinfecting apparatus.

Resolved 2

That the above mentioned letter be entered on the minutes and that the thanks of this Board be given to Dr. Henry. (See Appendix)

Resolved 3

That the Board do erect a disinfecting apparatus on the proposed by Dr. Henry the situation to be determined at a future meeting.

Resolved 4

That a letter be addressed to the Scavenging Committee requesting them immediately to cleanse and scavenge Back Hart Street & to remove the refuse and filth from the said street.

Resolved 5

That a communication be addressed to the owner and occupiers of the pig styes at the corner of Little John Street and Quay Street directing the immediate removal of the pigs complained of.

Resolved 6

That a communication be addressed to the Churchwardens requesting that they will continue to whitewash the habitations of the poor, the Board of Health cleansing only those in which cases of cholera have occurred.

Resolved 7

That the reports of houses in a filthy state presented this day by the Overseer be returned to the Churchwardens with the letter from Mr. Willis of 28 Sackville Street complaining of the filthy state of the cellar No. 30 Sackville Street and of the destitute condition of the occupant to which the attention of the Churchwardens be invited.

Resolved 8

That 500 copies of the following placard be printed and posted.
viz:

Reform Celebration Holiday

The Board of Health owing to the existence of cholera in many districts of the Town are very <u>anxious</u> to <u>caution</u> the inhabitants against taking intoxicating liquor on the Reform Celebration Day.

<u>Drunkenness</u> has often been followed by cholera and the disease has almost always been fatal in a few hours.

Benjamin Braidley Boroughreeve
Chairman of the Board of Health

Town Hall, Manchester
August 7th.

Memorandum 3

A deputation of the inhabitant householders from Swan Street and vicinity waited on the Board with a memorial complaining of a smell stated to proceed from the Swan Street Hospital and which the memorialists considered highly prejudicial to the health of themselves and families.

It having been explained that the smell complained of arose from the burning of a feather bed of a person who had died of cholera the deputation retired after expressing themselves satisfied with the reply of the Board.

Daily Report

August 7th.

Remaining at last Report	New Cases	Dead	Recovered	Remaining this day 11 o'clock
22	12	4	5	25

From the commencement of the disease on the 18th. of May 1832.

Cases	Dead	Recovered
177	103	49

Appendix

To the Chairman of the Manchester Board of Health.

Sir,

Having understood, from an active member of the Board of Health, that the plan of disinfection, which I suggested to the public some time ago, is now under the consideration of the Board with a view to its adoption, I beg leave to address to you what, I trust is a fair and impartial estimate of its probable advantages.

That a temperature, raised to a few degrees below the boiling point of water, without exposing the articles to be disinfected, however costly and delicate, to the risk of the slightest injury, is still sufficient *[for]* <u>one</u> kind of contagion (that of scarlet-fever) I consider as established, by the experiments which I published several months ago.

But that the same means will be effectual in destroying the contagion of cholera, supposing that disease to be propagated by contagion (which is every day becoming more probable) is, as yet, matter of inference only. The analogy, however, in which that inference rests, seems to me in itself so strong, and to be so supported by a legitimate train of reasoning on known chemical laws and phenomena, as fully to justify an experiment (for such it must still be) on a large scale; more especially as the experiment, if it should fail, will not increase the spread of infection, and if it succeed, will effectually tend to limit it. It is from analogy, that almost all the most important improvements in medicine have hitherto been derived; and if we are to reject such reasonings, there must be an end to all attempts in future to prove that Act by borrowing aid from the collateral sciences.

Still, it would be unreasonable in me, to expect the same degree of conviction, that I feel, in the minds of others, who have not considered the subject with the same anxious and long continued attention. I shall, therefore, have no right to complain, if some members of the Board should be less sanguine than myself, in their expectation of benefit from adopting the plan. I respect also, and entirely approve of, the exercise of the greatest caution, and most rigid economy, in the expenditure of the public funds of the Town, raised as these funds necessarily are, by demands upon many hundreds of persons, who can ill afford to answer such claims. I request, therefore, if the Board should decide to carry the proposed method of disinfection into effect, that I may be allowed to contribute to that purpose the inclosed sum, which will cover the cost of the apparatus, according to the estimate of a practical engineer.

> I have the honour to be,
> Sir,
> your most Obedient Servant
> (Signed) William Henry

Cornbrook
Monday, 6[th.] August 1832

Board of Health, Manchester
August 8, 1832

W. Haynes Esq., Deputy Chairman
Drs. E. Lyon, H. Gaulter, J.P. Kay; Revd. J. Crook; Messrs. E. Connell, H. Forth, P. Ewart junr.

Resolved 1
That the proceedings of the Board on the 7th Inst. be now confirmed.

Resolved 2
>That the Scavenging Committee be requested to cleanse and scavenge Bow Lane.

Resolved 3
>That permission be given for the interment of Mrs. Dalton deceased at the Rusholme General Burial Ground on condition that she be buried not less than 14 feet below the surface of the earth with three pounds of chloride of lime in the coffin.

Daily Report

August 8th

Remaining at last Report	New Cases	Dead	Recovered	Remaining this day 11 o'clock
25	10	6	5	24

From the commencement of the disease on the 18th of May 1832.

Cases	Dead	Recovered
187	109	54

August 9, 1832

Reform Celebration Holiday – no meeting of the Board.

Daily Report

August 9th

Remaining at last Report	New Cases	Dead	Recovered	Remaining this day at 11 o'clock
24	8	2	3	27

From the Commencement of the disease on the 18th of May 1832.

Cases	Dead	Recovered
195	111	57

Board of Health, Manchester
August 10, 1832

W. Haynes Esq., Deputy Chairman
Drs. S.A. Bardsley, J. Hull, J.P. Kay, H. Gaulter; Revd. J. Crook; Messrs. J. Wood, E. Connell, G. Hall, P. Ewart junr.

Resolved 1
> That the proceedings of the Board on the 8th Inst. be confirmed.

Resolved 2
> That a note be sent to Mr. Lynch directing him to send the van with two men and a coffin for the interment of Sarah Street of No.2 Court, near No.8 Hart Street as early as possible.

Resolved 3
> That a note be addressed to the friends of Mrs. Brown, 95 Water Street, deceased requesting that they will have the body interred as speedily as possible.

> Mr. Hall having reported that a man has died of cholera in Pollard Street it was [left blank]

Resolved 4
> That Mr. Lynch be requested forthwith to make enquiry with a view to ascertain whether this was an unequivocal case of cholera and by whom it was attended and to order the immediate interment of the body if it should prove to be cholera and that he report to the Board tomorrow.

Resolved 5
> That a circular be addressed to all the medical practitioners of Manchester informing them that an Order has been issued by the Privy Council requiring that all persons dying of cholera shall be interred within twenty four hours after death and that they shall also be buried in the ground provided by the Board of Health for the interment of persons who have been the victims of cholera (unless special leave be granted by the Board for their interment elsewhere upon grave reasons being adduced to establish the exception) and requesting that they will not permit any person whatsoever who may be under their care to remain in ignorance of the Order in Council requiring that they will immediately report all deaths to the Board and desiring them to use every exertion to procure obedience to those orders of the Privy Council.

> That the extract from the Order in Council of February 29th already transmitted to the medical practitioners be added to the circular also an intimation that the ground attached to the Parish Burial Ground is provided for the interment of persons dying of cholera.

Resolved 6
> That the postages of all letters addressed to the members of the Board and the medical practitioners be paid.

Resolved 7
> That a Special Meeting of the Board be convened for Monday next to consider the propriety of establishing convalescent wards.

Resolved 8

That Mr. Langford be authorized to engage a cook to provide and cook the diet for the hospital.

Resolved 9

That the bedsteads, tables, crockery and pans from the house of Elizabeth Edge, 17 Back Hart Street be taken to the hospital Commercial Street and that the bedding &c. be destroyed and that Alfred Heslop be directed to have this resolution carried into effect.

Resolved 10

That a copy of the 6th resolution passed on the 30th of July be transmitted to Mr. Stewart.

Daily Report

August 10th

Remaining at last Report	New cases	Dead	Recovered	Remaining this day at 11 o'clock
27	7	4	5	25

From the commencement of the disease on the 18th day of May 1832.

Cases	Dead	Recovered
202	115	62

Town Hall, Manchester
August 2, 1832

At a Public Vestry Meeting of the inhabitants of Manchester, held here this day for the purpose of adopting such further precautionary measures as may be best calculated to prevent the spread of cholera and of receiving a report of the proceedings already taken under the sanction of a former meeting:

George Withington Esq. Senior Churchwarden in the Chair

Messrs.	J.E. Taylor	Messrs.	Revd. C.D. Wray
	Thomas Harbottle		G.H. Winder
	F. Fincham		Thomas Sharp
	J.P. Kay, M.D.		J. Potter
	W. Haynes		R. Potter
	Crewe		E. Connell
	S. Phillips		H. Forth
	H. Gaulter, M.D.		D. Lynch

E. Evans	P. Ewart junr.
E. Lyon, M.D.	W.R. Whatton
Benjamin Braidley	J. Railton
S. Fletcher	J. Walker
Revd. W. Marsden	G. Peel
Messrs. George Faulkner	Joseph Heron
J. Woollam	George Hall
O. Milne	J. Barker
J.L. Bardsley, M.D.	R. Ogden
Revd. H. Fielding	A. Prentice

After a statement (made on the part of the Board of Health by Dr. J.P. Kay) of the precautionary measures which had been already adopted and of the expences incurred in the execution thereof.

1st. It was moved by Mr. Crewe. Seconded by Mr. J. Railton and resolved unanimously

That this meeting do now approve of the proceedings of the Board of Health appointed by the Lords of His Majesty's Privy Council, and authorized by a Public Vestry Meeting held on the 6th of April last.

2nd. Moved by Mr. Shakespeare Phillips. Seconded by Mr. Thomas Harbottle and resolved unanimously

That it having appeared by the reports of the Board that 147 cases of cholera have occurred in this Town, and it being highly expedient that further precautionary measures should be adopted in order to mitigate the severity, and if possible to arrest the progress of the disease, the Board of Health be requested and authorized to make such further preparations, and exercise according to their discretion, such of the conditional powers as are contained in the Orders in Council of the 6th day of March, and the 20th of July last; and also, to adopt such other means as may appear to them best calculated to prevent the spread of the said disease.

3rd. Moved by Mr. Thomas Sharp. Seconded by Mr. Fletcher and resolved unanimously

That the Board of Health be authorized to expend a sum not exceeding fifty pounds for the purpose of draining that part of the Town generally known by the name of Little Ireland.

4th. Moved by Mr. J.E. Taylor. Seconded by Mr. R. Potter and resolved unanimously

That the Nuisance Committee of the Commissioners of Police be requested to take immediate measures to abate the nuisance which is reported to arise from the existence of a weir on the River Medlock near Little Ireland if it be found that the same is an illegal encroachment, and that this resolution be forthwith communicated to that committee.

5th. Moved by Mr. R. Potter. Seconded by Mr. S. Phillips and resolved unanimously
That for the support of the hospitals already established for the reception of persons afflicted with cholera, and for the further precautionary measures to be adopted by the Board, the sum of at least one thousand pounds will be required, and that this sum be now declared as the extent to which the Churchwardens are empowered to allow from the Poor's Rates for the use of the Board of Health.

6th. Moved by Mr. J.E. Taylor. Seconded by Mr. Neden and resolved unanimously
That the best thanks of this meeting be given to the Board of Health and to the Medical Gentlemen connected with it for their zealous and effectual services and for the judicious measures which they have adopted.

(Signed) George Withington, Chairman
Mr. Braidley having taken the Chair.
It was moved, seconded and resolved unanimously

That the thanks of this meeting be given to George Withington Esq. for his services in the chair.

(Signed) Benjamin Braidley

Board of Health, Manchester
August 11, 1832

W. Haynes Esq. Deputy Chairman
Drs. S.A. Bardsley, H. Gaulter, J.P. Kay; Revd. J. Crook; Lieutenant Colonel Shaw; Messrs G. Hall, P. Ewart junr.

Resolved 1
   That the minutes of the preceding meeting of the Board be now confirmed.

Resolved 2
   That Mr. Lynch be requested to wait upon Mr. Boyer and request him to give a certificate of the case of Daniel Kemp, 121 Pollard Street and also that Mr. Lynch attend at the New Bailey to take a warrant against the person who offered obstruction to the removal of the body.

Resolved 3
   That a letter be addressed to Mr. Ferneley enquiring his reason for not reporting the case of Rayner in Hart Street and informing him of the

determination of the Board to take steps to enforce the penalty annexed to the concealment of cases of cholera from the Board.

Resolved 4

That the friends of Ann Birch, deceased be allowed to inter the body in the burial ground at Bridgewater Street on condition of the grave being 14 feet in depth and three pounds of chloride of lime being put in the coffin.

Resolved 5

That a similar letter to that sent to Mr. Ferneley be also transmitted to Mr. Butterworth respecting the case which is stated to have occurred at the Duke of Orleans, Oldham Street.

Resolved 6

That a letter be sent to Mr. Clough requesting to know whether he can certify that the case of Sarah Street in No.2 Court, Hart Street was an unequivocal case of cholera and enquiring if he can inform the Board what Medical Gentleman treated the case.

Resolved 7

That the Medical Committee be requested to take into their consideration the kind and degree of disinfection required for the clothing, bedding &c. with which cholera patients have been in contact and what portion should be destroyed and that they report to the Board at an early meeting.

Memorandum

Read a letter from Mr. E. Norris of Hanover Mill, Long Millgate complaining of a nuisance occasioned by a man boiling bones in Bedford Court at the back of his factory and stating that the stench was occasionally so great as to drive his hands from their work.

Resolved 8

That Mr. Norris be informed that if he will furnish the Board with a certificate signed by two Medical Gentlemen of the existence of the nuisance the Board will take measures for its immediate removal.

Resolved 9

That a similar letter be addressed to Mr. Beale of St. Mary's Gate respecting the nuisance occasioned by the sausage maker in Riding's Court.

Resolved 10

That Mr. Langford and Mr. Lynch be authorized to procure such utensils as may be necessary for carrying into effect the resolution ordering the attendants at the hospitals to be put on a plan of diet. The account of the expence incurred in so doing to be furnished to the Board in the ensuing week.

Resolved 11

> That Dr. S.A. Bardsley and Dr. E. Lyon be appointed a deputation for the purpose of conferring with the Committee of the House of Recovery on the erection of a disinfecting apparatus.

Resolved 12

> That the account from Mr. Prichard for drugs supplied in No. 3 District be referred to the Medical Committee for their examination and that they be requested to report to the Board what plan they consider most advisable for the dispensing of medicines.

Resolved 13

> That Mr. Lynch be requested to attend the meeting of the Medical Committee to furnish such information on the subject as may be required.

Resolved 14

> That the druggists be directed to send in their accounts for drugs supplied to the orders of the District Medical Officers if possible on Monday next and to continue to send in their accounts weekly until further orders.

Daily Report

August 11th

Remaining at last report	New Cases	Dead	Recovered	Remaining this day at 11 o'clock
25	17	12	4	26

From the commencement of the disease on the 18th of May 1832.

Cases	Dead	Recovered
219	127	66

Board of Health, Manchester
August 13, 1832

H. Forth Esq., Deputy Chairman
Drs. S.A. Bardsley, E. Lyon; Revd. H. Fielding, W. Huntington, G. Dugard, J. Crook; Lieutenant Colonel Shaw; Messrs. P. Ewart junr., W. Haynes, J. Wood, E. Evans, G. Hall, W.R. Whatton

Resolved 1

> That the proceedings of the Board on the 11th Inst. be now confirmed.

Memorandum 1

Answers were received from Mr. G. Ferneley and Mr. Butterworth explaining in a satisfactory manner the reason they had not reported the cases of cholera which they had visited.

Resolved 2

That copies of the 6th resolution passed on August 4th and of the 3rd resolution passed on the 11th August be addressed to Mr. Haigh, Mr. Jesse and Mr. Windsor.

Memorandum 2

Mr. Langford communicated to the Board that additional Resident Medical Officers are required at the Commercial Street Hospital.

Resolved 3

That the Resident Medical Officers be informed that the Officiating Minister will attend at the burial ground at 9 o'clock in the morning at quarter past 12 and quarter before 5 in the afternoon for the interment of persons dying of cholera and that all bodies to be buried be at the ground precisely at those hours.

Resolved 4

That the Resident Medical Officers be directed to placard a copy of this resolution at their respective hospitals.

Moved by Lieutenant Colonel Shaw.

Resolved 5

That an additional carriage be obtained for the conveyance to the burial ground of the bodies of persons dying of cholera and that one be stationed at each hospital. That Mr. Ewart junr. be requested to procure such an one as he may think fit.

Moved by Mr. James Wood. Seconded by Revd. W. Huntington.

Resolved 6

That a convalescent ward be provided for patients discharged from the cholera hospitals.

Resolved 7

That Mr. Whatton's offer to visit the Reception House daily and order the discharge of such of the inmates as he may consider advisable until a further arrangement can be made be accepted by the Board.

Resolved 8

> That the Hospital and Reception House Sub-Committee be requested to undertake the arrangement of the convalescent wards and that they meet for this purpose as soon as possible.

Daily Report

August 12 & 13

Remaining at last Report	New Cases	Dead	Recovered	Remaining this day at 11 o'clock
26	34	17	8	35

From the commencement of the disease on the 18th of May 1832.

Cases	Dead	Recovered
253	144	74

Henry Forth (signature)

Board of Health Manchester
August 14, 1832

W. Haynes Esq. Deputy Chairman
Drs. S.A. Bardsley, J.P. Kay, H. Gaulter; Revd. J. Crook, Revd. H. Fielding; Lieutenant Colonel Shaw; Messrs. E. Connell, W.R. Whatton, J. Barker

Resolved 1

> That the proceedings of the last meeting of the Board be now confirmed.

Memorandum 1

> An application having been made by Messrs. Hadfield and Grave desiring that the Board would have whatever portion of the furniture of Susannah Hall destroyed that they consider necessary, Dr. Kay stated that he would call at Messrs. Hadfield and Grave's and leave directions in writing as to what furniture should be destroyed.

Resolved 2

> That Mr. P. Ewart junr. be requested to see Messrs. Peel, Williams and Peel and obtain their consent to the erection of a disinfecting apparatus on the premises at Swan Street.

> Mr. Forth as Chairman of the Scavenging Committee having stated that Waddington the superintendent of the Scavengers might by employed in carrying into effect the Orders of this Board in abating and removing all nuisances and Mr. Forth having been good enough to mention that he will for the present undertake the superintendence of Waddington in this duty it was resolved.

Resolved 3

That the Board authorize Mr. Forth to empower Waddington to employ persons to assist in carrying this duty into effect and that an account of the expence incurred in so doing be furnished weekly to the Board and defrayed accordingly. That a copy of this resolution be transmitted to Mr. Forth.

Memorandum 2

Read a letter from the Scavenging Committee stating that their carters object to being employed in carting furniture from houses where cholera has existed and that as such employment materially interferes with the business of the committee they respectfully decline to allow their carts or carters to be so employed in future.

Resolved 4

That the same be referred to the Hospital and Reception House Sub-Committee and that they be requested to procure some other means for the purposes in question.

Resolved 5

That the resolution of the Board allowing patients at the hospitals to be attended by one of their friends be now rescinded.

Resolved 6

That owing to the great increase of patients at the Knott Mill Hospital, the Board wish that Mr. Lynch should allow Mr. Fazackerley to go to that hospital immediately as an Assistant and that if Mr. Lynch requires a substitute for Mr. Fazackerley he be requested to recommend one to the Board.

Resolved 7

That a letter be addressed to the ministers of the several burial grounds requesting that before any person is interred by them a certificate from a medical practitioner be required as to whether the deceased died of cholera and if so to direct the body to be taken for interment to the Parish Burial Ground in accordance with the order in that behalf made by the Lords of the Privy Council.

Resolved 8

That the report presented by Mr. Whatton of the state of the Reception House at Ancoats dated August 13th be received.

Memorandum 3

The Watch Committee made application requesting the Board of Health would favour them with their opinion as to the best mode of purifying the air in the Watch Offices – which are very ill ventilated, damp and offensive.

Resolved 9

That this subject be referred to the Medical Committee for their opinion.

Resolved 10

That the Medical Committee be requested to give their opinion as to the time which should elapse before the interment of persons dying of cholera.

Board of Health, Manchester
August 15, 1832

W. Haynes Esq., Deputy Chairman
Drs. S.A. Bardsley, J.P. Kay, H. Gaulter; Lieutenant Colonel Shaw; Messrs. G. Hall, P. Ewart junr., H. Forth, H.H. Birley, J. Thorpe, J. Heron

Resolved 1

That the proceedings of the Board on the 14th Inst. be now confirmed.

Memorandum 1

Mr. Haynes reported that he had ordered two police officers to attend at the cholera burial ground to keep off the populace.

Resolved 2

That a weekly tabular report be made to the Privy Council of all cases in which interments have taken place with the permission of the Board contrary to the provisions of the Order in Council.

Resolved 3

That the Medical Committee be requested to consider the propriety of disinterring the body of Richard Elliston improperly buried yesterday at St. James's Church Yard or what other course they would recommend. There are other coffins beneath this one and no other grave in the churchyard to which it could be removed.

Resolved 4

That Mr. Fazackerley be permanently appointed Resident Medical Assistant at the Knott Mill Hospital at the advanced salary of £18 per Month.

Resolved 5

That a Dispenser of Medicines be appointed for each hospital and that the medical staff of the respective hospitals be requested to engage such an assistant at the salary of £12 per month.

Resolved 6

That John Jones, Tripe Dresser of Barret's Court be paid £1.10s.0d. in compensation for the inconvenience he has sustained by the measures of the Board.

Resolved 7
> That Edward Bentley be paid £2.0.0 on account for the bedding &c. which has been destroyed by the order of the Board and that the actual value be ascertained by Heslop.

Memorandum 2
> Received a letter from Mr. Barrett, Mr. Greaves, and other inhabitants of the vicinity of St. James's Churchyard complaining of the interment of the body of Richard Elliston in that ground reported by Mr. Crossdale of Portland Street having died of cholera.

Resolved 8
> That Mr. Heron be requested to take measures for the prosecution of Joshua Wainwright, 32 Portland Street who caused the interment of Richard Elliston in opposition to the Order in Council directing the interment in the ground appropriated by the Board of Health for that purpose.

Resolved 9
> That the superintendent of fumigating &c. be directed to have an order in writing signed by a Medical Gentleman before he destroys any bedding or clothing and that an agreement be made by him with the owner of the clothing as to what compensation shall be made for them which agreement shall be signed by the parties and that the superintendent keep an account of the same and report to the Board.

Resolved 10
> That the Churchwardens be informed that difficulties have occurred in providing clothing for convalescent patients when in a fit state to be sent out of the hospitals in consequence of its having been thought necessary to burn what they have worn, and that this Board venture to hope the Churchwardens will allow the necessary clothing to be furnished from their stores at the expense of the Board on the application in writing of the Resident Medical Officers. That a copy of this resolution be transmitted to the Churchwardens.

Resolved 11
> That the proceedings of the Hospital and Reception House Sub-Committee of the 14th Inst. be received and adopted as part of the proceedings of this Board.

Resolved 12
> That a washing apparatus on Dr. Henry's plan be affixed to the disinfecting apparatus.

Resolved 13
> That Mr. Kay, the Agent to Sir O. Mosley, be requested to allow a portion of the stone quarries at Collyhurst for the purpose of burying the beds, clothing &c. with which cholera patients have been in contact.

Resolved 14

That the 1st resolution of the meeting of the medical staff at Knott Mill Hospital on August 14 be referred to the Medical Committee for their consideration.

Resolved 15

That it be recommended to the Board tomorrow to appoint a medical gentleman who shall inspect the houses of persons attacked with cholera and point out such persons as shall be secluded in the Reception House and select such of the clothes and bedding as it may be necessary to destroy and to make a valuation of the same.

Resolved 16

That the report of the present state of the Reception House be received and that Mr. Whatton be requested to continue discharging the inmates when he may consider it proper to do so.

Memorandum 3

Read letters from Mr. Windsor and Mr. Haigh stating that they had reported every case which had occurred in their practice and that they knew nothing of the cases referred to in the communication of the Board.

Read a letter from Mr. Clough stating that the case of Sarah Street in No.2 Court, Hart Street had been attended by Mr. Catlow who informed Mr. Clough that he had reported the same to the Board.

Board of Health, Manchester
August 16, 1832

W. Haynes Esq., Deputy Chairman
Drs. S.A. Bardsley, J.P. Kay; Revd. W. Marsden, H. Fielding, W. Huntington, J. Crook; Lieutenant Colonel Shaw; Messrs. E. Connell, J. Kennedy, H.H. Birley, P. Ewart junr., J. Barker, J. Thorpe, J. Heron

Resolved 1

That the proceedings of the last meeting of the Board be now confirmed.

Resolved 2

That the daily report of the new cases &c. be not in future posted at either of the hospitals.

Memorandum 1

Application having been made by the friends of Mary Lewis (deceased at the hospital Swan Street) for permission to inter the body at the burial ground in Every Street, Ancoats it was:

Resolved 3

That permission be given upon condition that the grave be not less than 14 feet in depth and that 3 lbs of chloride of lime be put in the coffin.

Resolved 4

That the letter from the Churchwardens of this date now read be entered on the minutes and that a copy be sent to each of the Resident Medical Officers. (See Appendix)

Resolved 5

That this Board are of opinion that they are bound to stand between Messrs. Peel, Williams and Peel and any parties who may as intimated in the letter now read from Messrs. Peel & Co., commence any proceedings against them, in consequence of their premises being occupied by the Board as a cholera hospital and to protect Messrs. Peel & Co from any injury to be sustained by such proceedings.

Resolved 6

That the report of the Hospital and Reception House Sub-Committee on the 15th Inst. be received and adopted as part of the proceedings of the Board.

Resolved 7

That a medical deputation consisting of Drs. E. Lyon, W.C. Henry, & C. Phillips be appointed to visit the premises used as a barrack in Dyche Street and to report whether any part could safely be occupied by convalescents while the other part is used as a Reception House and that they be requested to make their report as early as possible to the Board.

Resolved 8

That the communication from Mr. Clough complaining of a nuisance occasioned by pig styes and a dunghill in a court in Cable Street be transmitted to the Chairman of the Scavenging Committee.

That in future all communications of a similar nature be referred forthwith to the Chairman of the Scavenging Committee.

Resolved 9

That a medical gentleman be employed at a salary of twelve pounds per month to perform the following duties.

1st. He will inspect the houses where cases of cholera have occurred and will determine what persons from them shall be sent to the Reception House; he will communicate with the Reception House Committee as to the number of persons they are prepared to receive and give a ticket to each person whom he orders to the Reception House shewing that they are to be placed there by his authority.

2nd. He will give directions to the whitewashers and fumigators what cleansing and purifying each house is to undergo in which the disease has appeared, and he will determine what articles are to be destroyed and what only cleansed or disinfected: in every case in which actual burning of any body-clothes or bedding or other articles is necessary the nearest relative whom he finds upon the premises must be consulted as to the value of the things to be destroyed, and sign a list of them with the value at which such relative agrees to their destruction; but should the medical gentleman not be able to agree with the persons as to the value of the articles to be destroyed they must be removed to the hospital to which the patient has been sent there to be valued by a person appointed by this Board.

3rd. He will make a written report daily to this Board stating to what number of persons he has given tickets for entrance into the Reception House, mentioning the numbers of houses he has visited in the twenty-four hours, enclosing the lists of property signed to the nearest relative and with the prices affixed to each article of the property he has ordered to be destroyed, stating and specifying if any property of disputed value has been sent to the hospitals, and adding to his report any observations which he may deem useful for the information of the Board.

Resolved 10

That slings and bearers be stationed in or near Back Parliament Street and Bank Top and that the neighbourhood be placarded with directions where the slings and bearers are to be found – the bearers being directed to obtain the certificate of a medical gentleman concerning the nature of the case.

Resolved 11

That the Slings Committee be requested to have this resolution carried into effect as early as possible.

Resolved 12

That Mr. Shoreland be requested to prepare a plan and estimate for the erection of a wooden building for the accommodation of at least 15 nurses at the Knott Mill Hospital.

Resolved 13

That the Honorary Secretary be requested to submit Messrs. Peel, Williams and Peel's letter to Mr. Foster for his opinion on the case.

Resolved 14

That Mr. Shoreland be requested to give in a plan and estimate for the extension of the accommodation at the Swan Street Hospital by fitting up the large room formerly used as a foundry.

Appendix

To the Board of Health

Churchwardens Offices Manchester
August 16, 1832

Gentlemen

In reply to yours of yesterday, I am directed by the Churchwardens respectfully to state that they "will allow the necessary clothing to be furnished from
their stores at the expense of the Board on the application in writing, of the
Resident Medical Officers."

I am, Gentlemen, your Obedient Servant
N. Gardiner, Directing Overseer

Board of Health Manchester
August 17, 1832

Dr. S.A. Bardsley, Chairman
Drs. E. Lyon, J.P. Kay, J.L. Bardsley; Revd. W. Marsden, H. Huntington, H.
Fielding, J. Crook, – Broadley; Messrs. H. Forth, F. Fincham, J. Barker, P. Ewart
junr., J. Woollam, H.H. Birley, E. Evans, R. Ogden

Resolved 1

That the proceedings of the last meeting of the Board be now confirmed.

Resolved 2

That the proceedings of the Medical Committee of the 16th Inst. be received.

Resolved 3

That the 1st resolution of those proceedings be now adopted.

Resolved 4

That the 2nd resolution be adopted and that Mr. Pritchard's account be set-
tled as soon as possible.

Resolved 5

That the 3rd and 4th resolutions be adopted.

Resolved 6

That the 5th resolution be adopted.

Resolved 7

That the 6th resolution be adopted.

Resolved 8

That the 7th resolution be adopted with the following addition that an account
be kept of the time of burial of each person dying of cholera.

Resolved 9
That the 8th resolution be adopted.

Resolved 10
That the 9th resolution be adopted.

Resolved 11
That a circular containing the 3rd, 4th and 5th resolutions of the Medical Committee be addressed to all the District Medical Officers of the town.

Resolved 12
That the following advertisement be inserted in the Manchester papers tomorrow.

The Board of Health exceedingly regrets that the meritorious exertions of the Clergy of the Collegiate Church should have been subjected to an ill founded aspersion it having been reported that they have neglected to read the burial service over the graves of patients who have died of cholera.

The Board of Health is desirous of contradicting this report at the earliest period the clergy having in the most disinterested and devoted manner attended at the Parish Burial Ground the interment of the bodies of all those who have been the victims of cholera and have read the burial service over all with one exception which resulted from the neglect of the friends. The Board is anxious to express the high estimation in which they hold the humane exertions of the clergy. The public are informed that the hours of nine in the morning, quarter past 12 at noon and quarter to five in the evening are appointed for the burial of persons who have died of cholera at all which hours the clergy are in attendance to read the burial service at the graves and the Board hopes that the utmost exertion will be made to secure punctuality in the attendance of those who are desirous of being present at the interment of such of their friends as may have been the victims of cholera.

Resolved 13
That a copy of the 6th Resolution of the Medical Committee be furnished to the Watch Committee.

Resolved 14
That copies of the 7th resolution of the Medical Committee with the addition adopted in the 7th resolution be furnished to the Resident Medical Officer of each hospital.

Resolved
The following report was presented by Dr. E. Lyon on the part of the deputation appointed to examine the premises in Dyche Street at present used as a barrack viz: Drs. E. Lyon, Charles Henry and C. Phillips have inspected the

premises in Dyche Street lately used as barracks, and are of opinion that the building would easily admit of being converted into a Reception House, and Convalescent Wards, with a distinct entrance to each; but, that in point of situation, some spot less crowded with population would be more eligible.

On behalf of the Deputation
(Signed) Edmund Lyon

It having been stated by several members of the Hospital Committee that they have in vain exerted themselves to find a more eligible site.

Resolved 15
That the necessary applications be immediately made with the view of converting the premises in Dyche Street into a Reception House and Convalescent Wards.

Resolved 16
That the Parochial Officers be authorized to remove into the cholera hospitals any patients (having a legal settlement in Manchester) who may be attacked with cholera in adjoining Townships until an arrangement is made respectively with the Boards of Health in Salford and other Townships visited by the Manchester Overseers on the subject of such patients belonging to the respective Townships.

Resolved 17
That it appears desirable to this Board that an application be made to the benevolent inhabitants of this Town for such articles of cast off apparel or raiment in general as may be useful to persons of each sex, children as well as adults who may have been infected with cholera.

Resolved 18
That Dr. J.L. Bardsley and Revd. W. Huntington be requested to prepare an advertisement to this effect for insertion in the Manchester papers of tomorrow – and also for distribution in the form of a circular.

Resolved 19
That those cases which are admitted into the hospitals in collapse be distinguished in the reports from the hospitals from all others.

Resolved 20
[left blank]

Resolved 21
That the friends of Mary Lewis not having complied with the regulations of the Board upon which they were allowed to bury her body in Every Street

Burial Ground – and Smith, druggist having been stated not to have reported a case of cholera – Mr. Heron be requested to enquire into the cases and proceed against one or both according to his judgement.

Resolved 22

That the required accommodation for attendants at the hospital, Commercial Street be provided under the direction of such of the medical staff as may be in attendance this week and of Mr. Ewart.

Resolved 23

That the following advertisement prepared by Dr. J.L. Bardsley and Revd. W. Huntington be inserted in the Manchester papers, viz:

Board of Health, Manchester
August 17, 1832

Owing to the distressed state of many of the cholera patients on their recovery from the disease, in consequence of the destruction of their wearing apparel, linen and bedding, in order to prevent all risk of infection; and as often happens from their want of these articles, the Board of Health consider it their duty to make an application both generally and specially to the wealthier inhabitants of Manchester and the neighbourhood, for contributions of every kind of cast-off apparel, suitable to each sex (including children as well as adults) and likewise bed clothes of every description.

The Board feel assured that at a time like the present when Malignant Cholera is committing destructive ravages amongst the families of the poor, this appeal to the benevolence of the rich, will be met with a most hearty concurrence and support.

The Board request that each contribution of clothes or bedding will transmit the same in a proper parcel, with a ticket containing the name of the donor and an inventory of the articles, directed to Mr. Heron, the Honorary Secretary of the Board of Health, at the Town Hall, King Street.

Resolved 24

That the following advertisement be also inserted in the Manchester papers of tomorrow viz:

The Board of Health is desirous of obtaining the services of three Medical Gentlemen. One as an Inspector and two as Dispensers of Medicine to the Hospitals – Salary £12. per Month – Candidates for these appointments are requested to apply to the Secretary of the Board at the Town Hall, King Street.

Resolved 25

That Mr. Lynch be empowered to order the requisite number of bedsteads, beds and bedding for Swan Street Hospital.

S.A. Bardsley (signature)

Board of Health
August 18, 1832

H.H. Birley Esq., Chairman
Drs. H. Gaulter, J. P. Kay; Revd. W. Marsden, G. Dugard, J. Crook; Lieutenant
Colonel Shaw; Messrs. J. Heron, P. Ewart junr., E. Evans, G. Hall

Resolved 1
    That the proceedings of the last meeting of this Board be confirmed.

Resolved 2
    That the communication from Mr. Lessey, druggist of Piccadilly be referred
    to the Medical Committee.

Memorandum 1
    Read a letter from Mr. Radford, surgeon requesting to withdraw his name
    from the list of surgeons attending pauper cholera patients.

Resolved 3
    That Mr. D. Lynch junr. be directed to have the present situation of the dead
    house of the Swan Street Hospital removed to some part of the building where
    the surrounding inhabitants can not see the dead bodies and to avoid as much
    as possible whatever may be offensive to them.

Resolved 4
    That Dr. J.P. Kay be requested to revise the document prepared by the Medical
    Committee on the 11th of February in reply to a petition from the inhabi-
    tants of Swan Street and vicinity for the purpose of being distributed as a
    circular in that neighbourhood.

Resolved 5
    That Mr. G.W. Wood be requested to attend the meetings of this Board.

Memorandum 2
    A communication was made by Mr. Langford that he had sent yesterday
    evening (August 17th) to remove for interment two children in a cellar No.
    27 Parliament Street, and that refusal was made and the servant of the hos-
    pital threatened if he entered the house.

Resolved 6
    That the said communication be referred to Mr. Heron with directions to him
    to take proceedings against the parties.

Board of Health, Manchester
August 20, 1832

Lieutenant Colonel Shaw, Chairman
Drs. J.P. Kay, J.L. Bardsley, H. Gaulter; Revd. G. Dugard, J. Crook; Messrs.
J. Holford, W. Haynes, J. Barker, G. Hall, J. Woollam, R. Ogden, R. Thorpe, W.R.
Whatton

Resolved 1
   That the proceedings of the last meeting of this Board be now confirmed.

   Moved by Mr. Whatton.   Seconded by Mr. Haynes.

Resolved 2
   That Mr. Francis Walmsley be appointed inspector according to the terms of
   the 9th resolution passed on the 16th Inst. and that he be required to enter
   upon the duties of that office forthwith.

Resolved 3
   That permission be granted to inter the body of Mrs. Higginbottom of No.
   32 Major Street at Bollington in Cheshire on condition that the grave be made
   as deep as possible, enclosed in a leaden coffin with 3 lbs. of chloride of
   lime: and that a notice be given with the address of the party to the Secretary
   that an Inspector from this Board may see that the above regulations have
   been complied with as regards the coffin; and that a copy of this resolution
   be forwarded to the clergyman at Bollington by the parties interring who must
   bring to this Board a certificate from the clergyman of his having received
   the copy of a resolution and also of the depth of the grave.

Resolved 4
   That Mr. Walmsley be directed to pay an immediate visit to Brook's Court
   opposite Messrs. Ogden's factory and to report the state of the patients sick
   in some of the houses in that court; and if found to be cases of cholera, to
   secure their speedy removal to the cholera hospital and to direct the whitewashing of the houses from which the patients have been removed.

Resolved 5
   That a communication be made to Mr. Ashton requesting to know his reason for not reporting to the Board the case of John Pratt, 15 Byrom Street.

Resolved 6
   That full authority be given to Mr. Ewart by this Board to obtain the use of
   such further horses and men as also of carriages as shall appear to him to be
   necessary for rendering efficient the regulations made by this Board for the
   conveyance of patients to the hospitals.

Resolved 7
   That Dr. J.P. Kay and the Honorary Secretary be requested to prepare an
   advertisement for insertion in the papers as also for placarding on the walls
   of the Town informing the public of the regulations made by the Orders of
   the Privy Council both as it respects the reports to be made to the Board on
   the part of the medical men of all cases of cholera which they may attend;
   as also with respect to the interment of the bodies of all parties dying of

cholera in the burial ground appointed for that purpose by the Board and that they be requested to submit the same to the Board at their meeting tomorrow.

Resolved 8

That permission be given for the interment of James Ormrod of Minshull Street at the Rusholme Lane Burial Ground (the clergyman consenting) on condition that the grave be not less than about 9 feet deep and it being understood that such grave will not again be opened and that the body be enclosed in a leaden coffin with 3 lbs. of chloride of lime and that notice be given to the Board in order that an Inspector may see the regulations as to the coffin carried into effect and that a copy of this resolution be forwarded to the clergyman with a request that he will send this Board a certificate of the depth of the grave and also that such grave will not be allowed to be again opened.

Resolved 9

That Mr. Hunt be informed that it was not the intention of the Board of Health to convert the Surgeon-Apothecaries who have kindly offered their gratuitous attendance upon the poor labouring under cholera in their respective districts, into druggists, but in order to meet the wishes of several of the Surgeon-Apothecaries, the Board adopted the resolution which seems to have met with Mr. Hunt's disapprobation. The Board beg to inform Mr. Hunt that it was not meant to be imperative on all Surgeon-Apothecaries to compound the medicines deemed proper, but merely that those gentlemen who were desirous of supplying the necessary remedies might meet their own convenience by so doing, at the same charges as the druggists. The Board also state that the word "privilege" mentioned in the resolution was not in the least degree used in a disrespectful sense to the Surgeon-Apothecaries.

Resolved 10

That the cast off apparel and other articles received at this office be verbally acknowledged to the donors by the secretary and that the articles be registered in a book to be kept for that purpose as also the time received, the name of the donor, and how disposed of and that Mr. Woollam be requested to undertake the distribution of the clothing.

Resolved 11

That the Medical Committee be summoned for the purpose of reconsidering the resolution passed at their meeting on the 17th Instant concerning the dispensing of the drugs – and also the propriety of meeting the District Medical Officers on the subject.

Resolved 12

That Mr. Shoreland be desired immediately to carry into effect his estimate for increasing the wards at the Swan Street Hospital.

Resolved 13
>   That Mr. Langford be requested immediately to furnish the Knott Mill Hospital with bedsteads and bedding as also Mr. Lynch to completely furnish the Swan Street Hospital.

Board of Health, Manchester
August 21, 1832

Lieutenant Colonel Shaw, Chairman
Dr. J.P. Kay; Revd. G. Dugard; Messrs. J. Thorpe, G. Faulkner, J. Woollam, W. Haynes, J. Rooke, G. Hall, R. Ogden, P. Ewart junr., J. Heron, H.S.

Resolved 1
>   That the proceedings of the last meeting of the Board be confirmed.

Resolved 2
>   That Mr. Lynch junr. be directed to make enquiries into the particulars of the case of George Ashworth, cellar, 65 Chapel Street, Bank Top reported by Mr. Schofield for the purpose of ascertaining whether or not the same was a case of genuine cholera.

Resolved 3
>   That the Resident Medical Officers of each hospital and Mr. Walmsley be requested to furnish Mr. Woollam on each morning with a list of such cast off clothes as they may require with the name and age of the individuals and also if bedding be required in any particular case.

Resolved 4
>   That the Board having received information that Mr. Crossdale had treated a case of strangulated hernia as a case of cholera and knowing the fatal consequences likely to ensue from such conduct, and also being informed that Mr. Crossdale is not a legally authorized practitioner of medicine, a letter be addressed to him by the secretary reminding him of the penalties to which by law he is liable for so practising as a Surgeon Apothecary for the guidance of his future conduct.

Resolved 5
>   That the secretary draw out a list of all subscriptions in money and in clothing with the names and places of abode of the donors in aid of the unfortunate distressed persons whose furniture and clothing may have been destroyed in cholera cases and that the same be laid before the Board at its meeting on Fridays for publication in the Saturday's papers.

Resolved 6
>   That Mr. Braidley be requested to act as a Treasurer to the Clothing and Bedding Fund at the disposal of the Board of Health and that Mr. Ogden be requested to act in Mr. Braidley's absence.

Resolved 7

That the Secretary be requested to acknowledge with the best thanks of the Board Mr. Heywood's liberal donation of £50 placed at the disposal of the Board.

Resolved 8

That the donation of £10 received from E.A.P. of Hulme be placed in the hands of the Treasurer and acknowledged as directed in the 5th resolution.

Resolved 9

That Mr. Wilde be allowed 10 shillings as remuneration for his property which was buried.

Resolved 10

That the appointment of Mr. Handforth as Dispenser of Medicines by the Medical Staff of the Knott Mill Hospital be confirmed by this Board.

Board of Health, Manchester
August 22, 1832

George Hall Esq., Chairman
Drs. H. Gaulter, J.L. Bardsley; Revd. W. Marsden, G. Dugard; Messrs. R. Ogden, P. Ewart junr., J. Woollam, G.W. Wood, G. Faulkner

Resolved 1

That the proceedings of the Board on the 21st Inst. be now confirmed.

Resolved 2

That permission be given for the interment of Martha Harrison at the Northenden Burial Ground (the Clergyman consenting) on condition that the grave be not less than 9 feet deep and it being understood that such grave will not again be opened and that the body be enclosed in a leaden coffin with 3 lbs of chloride of lime and that a note be addressed to the clergyman requesting him to furnish a certificate that this regulation has been complied with. That permission be also given for the interment of Mrs. Smith at the Rusholme Lane Burial Ground upon the same conditions.

Resolved 3

That Dr. Kay and Mr. Heron be requested to draw up a placard which may tend to remove or at any rate diminish as far as possible the prejudices existing amongst the lower orders against being removed to the Hospitals and to have the same placarded as soon as possible.

Moved by Mr. R. Ogden.   Seconded by Mr. G. Faulkner.

Resolved 4

That the Board finding that Mr. Schofield continues to bury parties dying of cholera in his burial ground in spite of the Orders in Council – Mr. Heron be requested to summon Mr. Schofield before the Magistrates for disobeying the orders with respect to the interment of cholera patients and also for neglecting to make a daily report of the cases of cholera that have been attended by him.

Resolved 5

That the circulars ordered to be printed on the 17th Inst. be delivered by a messenger appointed for the purpose at the houses of the wealthier inhabitants and shop-keepers and that he report as soon as possible the names of the parties to whom they are delivered and that Mr. Thorpe be requested to name a suitable messenger for the purpose.

Board of Health, Manchester
August 23, 1832

R. Ogden Esq. in the Chair
Drs. E. Lyon, J.P. Kay, H. Gaulter; Revd. W. Huntington, G. Dugard, J. Crook; Messrs. H. Forth, G. Faulkner, W. Haynes, J. Woollam

Resolved 1

That the proceedings of the last meeting of this Board be confirmed.

Resolved 2

That permission be given for the interment of Mr. Zephania Fletcher at St. Mary's upon condition that the grave be not less than 14 feet deep and that the clergyman be requested to furnish a certificate that this regulation has been complied with.

Resolved 3

That a letter be addressed by the secretary to Dr. Alexander Murray informing him that the Cholera Act requires him to report to the Board of Health immediately and without loss of time each case of cholera that may come under his treatment and that it is highly important that the residence of the patients should be included in the return unless there are very strong reasons to the contrary in order that it may be visited by the inspector and properly fumigated and cleansed. The Board is induced to take this notice of Dr. Murray's report, from having observed on it that 4 of the cases occurred in an ill-ventilated cellar in Oldham Street, the number of which is concealed.

Resolved 4

That power be given to Mr. Woollam to distribute clothes to any persons who may have been discharged from the hospitals or Reception House on the recommendation of any member of this board; the age, sex and amount of loss sustained by or the necessities of the distressed parties being distinctly stated by such member.

Resolved 5
>That a meeting of the Medical Committee and of the District Surgeons be summoned for August 24th 7 p.m. to confer on the fourth, and fifth resolutions of the Medical Committee of the 16th Inst.

Resolved 6
>That the Slings Committee be authorized to make application to the Board of the House of Recovery in order to ascertain upon what terms the carriage of the Fever Hospital can be obtained for the use of the Board of Health.

Resolved 7
>That the present entrance to the Swan Street Hospital be closed & that another entrance be made from Cable Street.

Resolved 8
>That the gate in Mason Street be raised sufficiently high to prevent the yard being overlooked from the houses in Mason Street.

Memorandum
>Received a notice from Mr. Chew, solicitor on the part of some of the inhabitants of Swan Street stating that unless the hospital be removed within 7 days an injunction will be forthwith applied for.

Resolved 9
>That the same be referred to Mr. Heron and that he be requested to take such measures as he may consider necessary.

Board of Health, Manchester
August 24, 1832

W. Haynes Esq., Deputy Chairman
Drs. J.L. Bardsley, J.P. Kay; Revd. W. Marsden, J. Crook; Lieutenant Colonel Shaw; Messrs. J. Woollam, P. Ewart junr., H. Forth, F. Fincham, E. Connell, R. Ogden, J. Barker, J. Heron

Resolved 1
>That the proceedings of the last meeting of this Board be now confirmed.

Resolved 2
>That Mr. Walmsley be directed to take with him some other medical practitioner to inspect the cellar of W. Dearden, Henry Street used for storing

old rags and bones and be requested to certify to the Board their opinion thereon.

Resolved 3

That a circular be addressed to all the medical practitioners of the Town requesting that they will in filling up their reports of cholera cases, introduce into the column of remarks as many of the leading characteristic symptoms of each cases as is possible.

Resolved 4

That permission be given for the interment of Samuel Harton, 71 Primrose Street at the Every Street Burial Ground on condition that the grave be not less than 14 feet in depth and that 3 lbs of chloride of lime be put in the coffin.

Resolved 5

That in all cases in which the remarks do not state the leading characteristic symptoms that they be returned to the reporter to be filled up.

Resolved 6

That Mr. Woollam be authorized to provide bedding and clothing for convalescent patients and such others as have had their bedding and clothing destroyed by order of the Board and that the accounts be referred to the Treasurer for payment.

Resolved 6

That the recommendation of the Hospital Committee of this date that the floor of the new ward at the Swan Street Hospital be boarded instead of laid with brick be adopted.

Board of Health, Manchester
August 25, 1832

W. Haynes Esq., Deputy Chairman
Dr. J.P. Kay; Revd. W. Marsden, G. Dugard, J. Crook; Lieutenant Colonel Shaw; Messrs. O. Milne, J. Barker, J. Heron

Resolved 1

That the proceedings of the last meeting of this Board be confirmed.

Memorandum

Mrs. Richard Walker, Bloomsbury, presented a donation of one pound in aid of the cloathing account.

Resolved 2

That a special meeting of this Board be summoned for Saturday next the 30th Inst. at 11 o'clock to take into consideration the very important subject of engaging or not as a Reception House and Convalescent Ward, the building in Dyche Street now occupied as a barrack. This question involving a subject of great importance both as to expense and as to the management of the disease. The Board will also proceed with its ordinary business.

Resolved 3

That the secretary address a letter to Mr. Braybrooke, the Barrack Master, enclosing a list of the articles in the building in Dyche Street which would be required by the Board and requesting him to furnish the same to the Board of Ordnance.

Board of Health, Manchester
August 27, 1832

H. Forth Esq., Deputy Chairman
Drs. J. Hull, E. Lyon, J.P. Kay; Lieutenant Colonel Shaw; Messrs. W. Haynes, R. Ogden, J. Woollam, P. Ewart junr.

Resolved 1

That the proceedings of the last meeting of this Board be now confirmed.

Resolved 2

That the Honorary Secretary be requested to acknowledge the receipt of Lord Stamford's donation of £30 to be applied for the purchase of bedding and clothing for the cholera patients and to return to his Lordship the best thanks of this Board for the same.

Resolved 3

That the Honorary Secretary be requested to prepare a communication to be forwarded to the Privy Council on the subject of the doubt whether as the burial ground appointed by the Board for the interment of cholera patients is not without the limits of the Town, the Magistrates have power to fine those parties who inter cholera patients in any other ground and to submit the same if possible to the Board at their next meeting.

Moved by Lieutenant Colonel Shaw.   Seconded by Mr. Haynes.

Resolved 4

That Mr. Woollam be authorized to engage such assistance as he may consider necessary to enable him to fulfil the duties he has so kindly undertaken in distributing the clothing &c.

Board of Health, Manchester
August 28, 1832

W. Haynes Esq., Deputy Chairman
Revd. W. Marsden, J. Crook; Lieutenant Colonel Shaw; Messrs. P. Ewart junr.,
J. Barker, J. Heron

Resolved 1
> That the proceedings of the last meeting of this Board be now confirmed.

Resolved 2
> That the letter now read by Mr. Heron be adopted and entered on the minutes and that a copy be transmitted forthwith to the Privy Council. (See Appendix)

Resolved 3
> That the appointment of Mr. Oldham by the medical staff of the Swan Street Hospital as Dispenser of Medicines to that hospital be confirmed.

Resolved 4
> That the secretary be directed to send per post as desired by the Board of Health in Stockport in letter now read a copy of the daily report of cases occurring in this Town.

Resolved 5
> That the donation of £20 "on account of the fund for supplying clothing to patients recovering from cholera" from Mrs. Heywood of Acresfield be acknowledged by the Honorary Secretary with the best thanks of this Board.

Resolved 6
> That the Hospital Sub-Committee be authorized to make such compensation to the men who superintend the burning of the clothes during the night as they shall think proper.

Resolved 7
> That the Secretary write to the practitioners who attended the four cases as reported by Mr. Lynch on the 27th of August requesting to know their reason for not reporting the said cases to the Board.

Appendix

Board of Health, Manchester
August 28, 1832

Sir,

The Board of Health of Manchester immediately after its constitution by order of His Majesty's Privy Council, made arrangements with the proper authorities for the appropriation of a part of the burial ground attached to the Manchester Workhouse for the exclusive interment of persons dying of cholera; and have made all the necessary provisions and arrangements for the interment of the bodies of parties so dying therein.

This burial ground though within the <u>Township</u> of Manchester is situated quite on the outskirts <u>of the Town itself</u> and in a more advantageous situation than any other site which the Board of Health could procure for the purpose; and where, as the Board is advised by the medical gentlemen connected with it, there is no danger of any prejudicial influence being had on the surrounding neighbourhood by its being used for such purpose.

The Board anxious that the regulations made by the Privy Council for the prevention of the spread of cholera should as far as possible be carried into effect, have summoned before His Majesty's Justices of the Peace for the County of Lancaster one or two individuals for having buried or caused to be buried cholera patients in other places than that appointed by the Board and without obtaining the consent of the Board in the manner prescribed by the order.

The Magistrates have however felt considerable doubt whether or not under existing circumstances they have the power to convict: for as the order (for disobeying which the parties were summoned being of the 20th of July last) only states "that <u>when and so soon</u> as any such Board of Health so authorized and empowered as aforesaid shall have procured any such burying grounds <u>without the Walls, Limits, or bounds of any City, or Town but within a reasonable and convenient distance of the same</u>" &c. that then the interment elsewhere is strictly forbidden, they fear that as they can only look at the words of the Order, and, as the ground appointed by the Board of Health can not be said to have complied with the direction contained in the Order and it is only when and as soon as the Board shall have done this, that the prohibition to bury elsewhere takes effect, and the parties dis-obeying become liable to a penalty.

It may be stated that if the Board be compelled before the regulation as to the interment of cholera patients can be rendered effectual, to procure a burial ground without the <u>Township</u> of Manchester, it will entail upon the Board a very considerable, and as it appears, unnecessary expence. The Township of Manchester is so very extensive in itself and surrounded by districts so populous, that the Board would be compelled to go many miles before it would be able (if at all) to procure a piece of ground suitable for the purpose, and which when procured would not in all probability be in any respect so desirable as the one already set apart for the purpose; and would thereby incur a great expence in the first place in the <u>purchase</u> of the ground as well as in the subsequent removal of the bodies to so great and inconvenient a distance.

The Board of Health think it proper that the doubt which has arisen in the minds of the Magistrates as to the power of conviction as also the difficulties attendant upon the removal of the cause, if that doubt be well founded, should be thus fully stated to his Majesty's Most Honourable Privy Council, that they may take the matter into their consideration and make such Order as may appear to them necessary.

The question is one of great importance in this neighbourhood as the Board are informed that the Boards of Health both for the Townships of Pendleton and Hulme, have made arrangements for the interment of cholera patients in church yards in their respective <u>Townships</u>, so that as the matter now stands the arm of the Magistrates will be completely paralysed so far as regards the enforcing the penalty for disobeying the Order of His Majesty's Privy Council relating to the interment of cholera patients.

Board of Health, Manchester
August 29, 1832

Lieutenant Colonel Shaw, Chairman
Dr. J.L. Bardsley; Revd. W. Marsden, J. Crook; Messrs. P. Ewart junr., J. Barker, W. Haynes, J. Woollam, G.W. Wood

Resolved 1
That the proceedings of the last meeting of the Board be now confirmed.

Resolved 2
That permission be given for the interment of Mary Ann Robinson, Oldham Road at St. Augustine's, Granby Row Burial Ground, on condition that the body be enclosed in a leaden coffin with 3 lbs of chloride of lime and that a copy of this resolution be forwarded to the officiating clergyman with a request that he will send this Board a certificate of these instructions being complied with.

Resolved 3
That permission be given for the interment of Jonathan Waddington at the Cheetham Hill Burial Ground (the clergyman consenting) on condition that the grave be not again opened and that the body be enclosed in a leaden coffin with 3 lbs of chloride of lime and that the clergyman be requested to furnish a certificate to the Board that these regulations have been complied with.

Board of Health, Manchester
August 30, 1832

W. Haynes Esq., Deputy Chairman
Drs. E. Lyon, J. Pendlebury, J. P. Kay; Revd. W. Marsden, W. Huntington, G. Dugard; Messrs J.J. Norreys, J. Heron, J. Woollam, R. Ogden, J. Barker

Resolved 1

That the proceedings of the last meeting of the Board be now confirmed.

Resolved 2

That permission be given upon the usual conditions for the interment of Margaret Smith, No.3 Little Pitt Street, Port Street at Ardwick.

Resolved 3

That it is considered advisable in consequence of the diminution in the number of cases to decline at present engaging the building in Dyche Street for the purposes of a Convalescent Ward and Reception House.

Resolved 4

That a copy of the preceding resolution be furnished to Mr. Brooks and also to the Barrack Master.

Board of Health, Manchester
August 31, 1832

E. Connell Esq., Chairman
Drs. J.L. Bardsley, H. Gaulter, J.P. Kay; Revd. J. Crook; Lieutenant Colonel Shaw; Messrs. P. Ewart junr., J. Woollam, J. Potter, R. Ogden, G.W. Wood

Resolved 1

That the proceedings of the last meeting of this Board be now confirmed.

Memorandum

A donation was received from Mrs. Marshall of Ardwick of £20 which was acknowledged by the Secretary.

Resolved 2

That permission be given for the interment of Thomas Mellor at the Cheetham Hill Burial Ground upon condition that the usual arrangements in such cases are complied with.

Resolved 3

That the Superintendants of Whitewashing be directed to report every Morning to Mr. Walmsley the work done on the preceding day by the whitewashers and fumigators and that Mr. Walmsley be requested to make a daily report to the Board showing the number of men employed and the work done by each man or set of men daily; as also of the number of houses still remaining to be whitewashed. That Heslop superintend the work to be done in the Swan Street Hospital District and Binyon the Knott Mill Hospital District, and that they be directed to keep separate books of the work done in their respective districts. That when additional men are required they report the same to Mr. Walmsley who will make a written communication to Mr. Gardiner.

Board of Health, Manchester
September 1, 1832

W. Haynes Esq., Deputy Chairman
Drs. J.P. Kay, H. Gaulter; Revd. W. Marsden, J. Crook; Messrs. R. Ogden, J. Woollam

Resolved 1
That the proceedings of the last meeting of this Board be now confirmed.

Resolved 2
That the Revd. H. Fielding and Mr. Evans Churchwarden be respectfully requested to attend the Board on Monday next relative to the present indecent and improper mode of interring the bodies of cholera cases in the Parish Burial Ground, as reported to this Board by Mr. Robinson, Governor of the Workhouse.

Resolved 3
That a Special Board be called for Wednesday next to take into consideration the memorial of the Medical Officers for a remuneration for their services in attending cholera patients.

Board of Health, Manchester
September 3, 1832

Benjamin Braidley Esq., Chairman
Drs. G. Shaw, E. Carbutt, J.L. Bardsley, J.P. Kay, E. Lyon, W. Johns; Revd. W. Marsden, J. White, H. Fielding, W. Huntington, J. Hollist, J. Crook; Lieutenant Colonel Shaw; Messrs. H. Forth, F. Fincham, J. Holford, J. Potter, D. Dockray, O. Milne, R. Ogden, E. Connell, P. Ewart junr., J. Barker, W. Haynes, G.W. Wood, J. Rooke, W.R. Whatton, J. Heron

Resolved 1
That the proceedings of the last meeting of this Board be confirmed.

Memorandum
Read a communication from Mr. Edward Loyd enclosing a cheque for £30 for the purchase of clothing &c ordered to be acknowledged by the Secretary.

Resolved 2
That Mr. Shoreland be requested to make an estimate of the damage done at the Swan Street Hospital and that the Hospital Committee be requested to take measures for immediately repairing the same.

Moved by Mr. Haynes. Seconded by Mr. Whatton.

Resolved 3
    That the reporters to the public press be admitted to hear the proceedings of the Board of this particular case of John Brogan.

Resolved 4
    That the communication from the Knott Mill Hospital be received and entered on the minutes. (See Appendix)

Resolved 5
    That in consequence of there having been several incorrect reports of the state of cholera in Manchester the Board of Health established in that Town fearing that the trade of the Town may suffer from the exaggerated reports made think it necessary to publish a statement of the cases which have occurred from August 18th to September 3rd.

    The Board is also desirous that when reports are in future made the days on which cases occurred should be enumerated and that the preceding Resolution be advertised in the Times, Morning Chronicle, Morning Herald, Courier and standard newspapers with the list of cases.

Mr. D. Lynch junr. – Resident Medical Officer of the Swan St. Hospital.
Stated – that John Brogan was admitted into that hospital on the forenoon of Friday August 31st and died on the same afternoon. That the grandfather saw the child previous to his being placed in the coffin on the Saturday. The coffin provided being too small another was sent for – which was not delivered until 7 o'clock on Saturday evening. That Mr. Robert Oldham was appointed Dispenser of Medicines to the Swan Street Hospital on the 21st of August. That on Saturday night it was Mr. Oldham's turn to sit up with the patients. Mr. Oldham admitted that he had severed the head from the body of John Brogan during the night – which had been found where it had been secreted by Mr. Oldham but not at the hospital. It was the impression on his (Mr. Lynch's) mind that no laudanum had been administered to the boy. That he had undergone the same treatment which other patients of a similar age had been subjected to.

John Hayes – the grandfather of John Brogan stated that he saw his grandchild on the Saturday afternoon after his death and expressed himself perfectly satisfied that he had died a natural death viz: of cholera. He also stated that not seeing the name of the child written on its coffin as on the coffins of others he felt a suspicion that the child was not within and had opened it at the grave. When he was horror struck by finding that the head of the child was taken away and substituted by bricks covered with shavings – the deponent after seeing the child expressed a wish to have him interred at St. Patrick's Catholic Burial Ground – that he was perfectly willing that the body should be taken from the lockups to the grave without being taken to its fathers.

Revd. Mr. Herron *[Hearne]* – Catholic clergyman informed the Board that Mr. Oldham had stated in his hearing that he had taken the head off for the purpose of examining it – that it was his conscientious belief that Mr. Lynch was perfectly ignorant of the revolting conduct of Mr. Oldham – until after its discovery at the grave.

The Revd. J. Crook – said that he had frequently attended the hospitals several times in the course of a day and he was desirous to add his testimony to the general good conduct of Mr. Lynch.

Resolved 6
That a leaden coffin be provided by the Board for the interment of the child at St. Patrick's Burial Ground.

Resolved 7
That with a view if possible to prosecute Mr. Oldham, Mr. Heron be directed to apply immediately for a warrant against him.

Resolved 8
That a committee consisting of the following gentlemen be appointed to prepare a placard explaining the unfortunate circumstances which have occurred in the case of John Brogan and stating the deep regret felt by the Board on the occasion viz:

Lieutenant Colonel Shaw	Dr. E. Lyon
Benjamin Braidley	Dr. J.P. Kay
Frederick Fincham	Revd. J. Crook

Memorandum
Dr. Kay gave notice of a motion in reference to the interment of Catholics dying of cholera in the burial ground of St. Patrick's in St. George's Road.

Resolved 9
That the Hospital Committee be authorized to purchase the van offered by the Board of the House of Recovery to replace that destroyed on yester evening.

Appendix

To the Chairman of the
Board of Health

Sir:
The Medical Officers of the Commercial Street Hospital having heard with regret and indignation, the gross violation of the orders of the Board, which

has been committed by the "Dispenser of Medicines" of the Swan Street Hospital; and knowing that this offence must be regarded with similar feelings by the Medical Officers of the Swan Street Hospital, conceived it desirable that a Special Meeting of the Staff of the Knott Mill Hospital should be summoned, for the purpose of addressing the Board on this subject.

Having the greatest reliance in the Resident Medical Officers of the Commercial Street Hospital, they have nevertheless conceived it to be their duty to make special inquiry, and can most confidently assure the Board, that since the regulation was made, requiring that the consent of the friends of the deceased should precede the inspection of bodies, not even the slightest incision has been made in any subject in this hospital. The medical staff beg also to express their wish, that no feeling of courtesy to the medical profession may prevent the Board from taking such measures in prosecution of the Offender as may appear desirable.

(Signed)	Robert Mann, Chairman	
	J.P. Kay, M.D.	W.B. Stott
	M. Sinclair	R.T. Hunt
	J. Walker	B.W. Booth

Commercial Street Hospital
September 3rd 1832

Board of Health, Manchester
September 4, 1832

Benjamin Braidley Esq., Chairman
Drs J.P. Kay, H. Gaulter, E. Carbutt; Revd. W. Marsden, H. Fielding, G. Dugard, J. Crook; Lieutenant Colonel Shaw; Messrs. J. Holford, J. Woollam, E. Connell, O. Milne, D. Dockray, W. Haynes, J. Potter, J. Heron H.S.

Resolved 1
    That the proceedings of the last meeting of this Board be now confirmed.

Resolved 2
    That a copy of the placard (detailing the occurrences of Sunday last) be transmitted to the Central Board of Health in London suggested the probable prejudices likely to arise in the minds of the public against cholera hospitals in other parts of the kingdom and the propriety of publishing the same in the London papers that the correct statement of the facts may be known.

Resolved 3
    That permission be given after the inspection of the body of Mary McCormick that the body may be removed for interment in St. Patrick's Burial Ground the usual regulations of the Board being complied with.

Memorandum

> Received £10 from A.F. to be applied to the purchase of clothing for cholera patients.

Resolved 4

> That the communication from the staff of the Swan Street Hospital now read be received and entered on the minutes and that a copy be sent to each of the papers to be included in their report of the proceedings of the Board in relation to the case of Brogan.

Appendix

Town Hall
September 3rd 1832

At a meeting of the medical staff of the Swan Street Hospital held this evening –

It was resolved unanimously.

"That this meeting feel called upon to express in the strongest terms of reprehension their censure of the unprecedented and most dangerous misconduct of the Resident Dispenser Mr. Oldham. In the excited tone of public feeling, which cholera has roused in this and other large towns, the Officers of the Swan Street Hospital had systematically forborne the <u>customary inspection</u> of all those dying under their care. It is therefore with feelings of the most painful regret as well as of just indignation that they have learned, that a person recently appointed to a subordinate office in the hospital has ventured to violate rules, which his superior officers have uniformly and faithfully respected. At the same time that they feel compelled to visit the flagrant offence of Mr. Oldham with their strongest censure, it becomes their duty and their pleasure to exculpate Mr. Lynch and Mr. Gaskell from all participation in this most unprofessional transaction and to testify their continued approbation of the zealous, active and judicious services of these meritorious Officers."

It was resolved unanimously

"That the present meeting feeling strongly the necessity of exonerating the whole of the medical staff of the hospital and especially the two Senior Resident Medical Officers from any part of the blame which must attach to the transaction in question, respectfully suggest to the Board the necessity of immediately publishing the Declaration to which this meeting has agreed."

(Signed)   G. Shaw M.D., Chairman
           C. Phillips M.D.   W.C. Henry M.D.
           John Thorpe   James Bent
           J.C. Gordon   G. Greaves

C. Clough	G. Haigh
L.H. Nathan	J. Owen

Board of Health, Manchester
September 5, 1832

W. Haynes Esq., Deputy Chairman
Drs. E. Lyon, G. Shaw, H. Gaulter, W. Johns; Revd. W. Marsden, W. Huntington,
G. Dugard; Lieutenant Colonel Shaw; Messrs. J. Heron, D. Dockray, T. Townend,
W.R. Whatton, R. Ogden, J. Holford, F. Fincham, J. Potter

Resolved 1
  That the proceedings of the last meeting of this Board be now confirmed.

Resolved 2
  That the memorial presented to this Board by the Medical Officers be referred
  to the consideration of a sub-committee with power to receive information
  from such gentlemen as are desirous of communicating on the subject –
  that the Boroughreeve, Lieutenant Colonel Shaw, Mr. F. Fincham and
  Mr. Thomas Townend be appointed such sub-committee and to report to this
  Board accordingly.

Memorandum
  Mr. Holroyde stated his necessity of resigning the office of surgeon for No.
  3 District in consequence of indisposition.

Board of Health, Manchester
September 6, 1832

H. Forth Esq., Deputy Chairman
Drs. J.L. Bardsley, Jeyes; Revd. J. Crook; Lieutenant Colonel Shaw; Messrs. W.
Haynes, G.W. Wood, T. Townend

Resolved 1
  That the proceedings of the last meeting of this Board be now confirmed.

Resolved 2
  That the report from the sub-committee be received and entered on the minutes. (See Appendix)

Resolved 3
  That a copy of the same be transmitted to Mr. Whatton to be laid before a
  meeting of the District Medical Officers.

Resolved 4
  That in accordance with the recommendation of the sub-committee the medical staff of the Swan Street Hospital be requested to appoint a dispenser of

medicines in the room of Mr. Oldham and that the applications and testimonials now before the Board be referred to the Medical Staff.

Resolved 5

That an application be made by the Secretary to the Trustees of the Ancoats Dispensary respectfully soliciting them to inform the Board of Health if they will allow medicines to be dispensed at that institution on the understanding that the whole of the expences connected with this proposal be defrayed by the Board of Health.

Resolved 6

That the accounts for drugs be referred to a Medical Sub-Committee consisting of Drs. E. Lyon, J.P. Kay and Mr. Whatton with the assistance of Mr. Lynch, any two of whom shall form a quorum.

Appendix

The committee appointed to take into consideration the memorial from the District Medical Officers beg to state to the Board that it will be requisite the committee should be furnished with the names of the medical gentlemen who are willing to continue their gratuitous services in attending on cholera patients and of those who are not.

The committee recommend that from and after Monday next the 10th of September no medicine be dispensed at the expence of the Board except at the cholera hospitals and that with this view one of the medical gentlemen whose recommendation is now before the Board be appointed dispenser of medicines at the Swan Street Hospital and if necessary the medical staff of each hospital be authorized to engage an additional porter for each hospital to carry the order for medicine to the dispensers and to take the medicine to the bearers of the orders so that the bearers of such orders should remain at the gates and not enter the enclosure of the hospital also that an application be made to the Ancoats Dispensary for permission to dispense medicines on account of the Board should it become necessary to increase the number of stations where medicines are dispensed.

That the medical staff at each hospital be allowed to order medicines to be dispensed to any person who may apply to them whilst labouring under bowel complaint which in their opinion may lead to or terminate in cholera. That all orders for dispensing medicines signed by one of the District Medical Officers whose services have been accepted by the Board, be received at the before mentioned stations.

Board of Health, Manchester
September 7, 1832

Benjamin Braidley Esq., Chairman

Drs. S.A. Bardsley, J.L. Bardsley, H. Gaulter, G. Shaw; Lieutenant Colonel Shaw; Messrs. W. Haynes, T. Townend, R. Ogden

Resolved 1

That the proceedings of the last meeting of this Board be confirmed.

Resolved 2

That permission be given for the interment of William Harker at St. Luke's the usual regulations of the Board being complied with and that a copy of the regulations be transmitted to the Revd. A. Hepworth.

Resolved 3

That the donation of £10 per the Revd. H. Fielding from the Very Revd. Dr. Calvert towards the fund for providing clothing for convalescent patients be acknowledged by the Secretary – with the best thanks of the Board to Dr. Calvert; also the receipt of £5 for the same fund from the Revd. Henry Fielding.

Resolved 4

That permission be given for the interment of Jonathan Crowther in the Bridgewater Street Burial Ground the usual regulations of the Board being complied with.

Resolved 5

That the appointment of Mr. Bennett in the place of Mr. Oldham as dispenser of medicines to the Swan Street Hospital under the new arrangement be confirmed by this Board.

Resolved 6

That an answer be transmitted to the application from the gentlemen in the neighbourhood of Ancoats stating that no other gentlemen than those named in the placards having offered their services for that district, the Board cannot obviate the difficulties arising from that fact unless the gentlemen signing the letter can procure other medical gentlemen residing in the immediate neighbourhood to offer their services and also stating the arrangements about to be made for dispensing medicines at each of the cholera hospitals: as also those proposed to the Trustees of the Ancoats Dispensary – for arranging that medicines be dispensed on account of the Board there also to the order of any of the District Medical Officers as also stating that placards relating to the District No.1 have already been issued and posted by the Board.

Resolved 7

That the Secretary be directed to write to the Secretary of the Ancoats Dispensary stating that the Board are particularly desirous that the answer to the application made by this Board should be received by the Board at the meeting tomorrow.

Memorandum

Mr. Haynes reported that he had given permission for the interment of James Woolfenden at the All Saints' Burial Ground on condition of the usual regulations being complied with.

**Board of Health, Manchester
September 8, 1832**

Lieutenant Colonel Shaw, Chairman
Drs. S.A. Bardsley, E. Lyon, H. Gaulter: Revd. G. Dugard; Messrs. Benjamin Braidley, T. Townend, R. Ogden, J. Heron

Resolved 1

That the proceedings of the last meeting of this Board be confirmed.

Resolved 2

That the donation of £10 from the Miss Holfords be acknowledged with the best thanks of this Board.

Resolved 3

That permission be given for the interment of Richard Woolfenden in All Saints' Burial Ground, the usual regulations being complied with.

Resolved 4

That on receiving the information promised the Secretary be instructed to write to Mr. James Bent to know why, having offered his gratuitous services to the Board in attending upon poor patients, he required payment for visiting a patient in the neighbourhood of Swan Street Hospital in order to his giving a certificate for the removal of the party into the hospital.

Resolved 5

That a copy of the following communication be sent to each of the District Medical Officers as also to the druggists. (See Appendix)

Resolved 6

That 500 Copies of the following placard be ordered and 300 of them immediately posted about the Town, and at a subsequent time the remaining 200. (See Appendix)

Resolved 7

That a Special Meeting of the Board be summoned for Wednesday next for the purpose of taking into consideration the propriety of certain regulations being made if practicable for limiting the hours during which the public houses and dram Shops should be allowed to remain open on the Sunday as well as other days, it is considered that the excess of drinking too common has a most material influence in increasing the number of cases of cholera and that the attendance of the Magistrates of the district be urgently and respectfully requested.

Appendix No.1

Board of Health
Town Hall, Manchester
September 8, 1832

From and after Monday next, the 10th instant, medicines for cholera patients, or for those whose complaints seem to have a tendency to terminate in cholera, who require aid from the Board, will be dispensed at the Swan Street Hospital, Shudehill, and the Commercial Street Hospital, Knott Mill, on the orders of the medical gentlemen whose gratuitous services are accepted by the Board.
The Board will not sanction any payments for medicines dispensed after the 10th Instant, otherwise than at the cholera hospitals and under the restrictions now stated.

F.A. Walsh
Secretary

Appendix No.2

Cholera

Board of Health
Town Hall, Manchester
September 8, 1832

From and after Monday the 10th September, advice and medicine to the poor, in cases of bowel complaints having a tendency to cholera, will be given gratuitously at all hours, at the cholera hospitals; and advice will also be afforded, as usual, by the District Medical Officers whose prescriptions will be made up at the Hospitals.

Benjamin Braidley, Boroughreeve
and Chairman of the Board of Health

**Board of Health, Manchester
September 11, *[sic]* 1832**

Lieutenant Colonel Shaw in the Chair
Dr. H. Gaulter; Revd. W. Marsden; Messrs. Benjamin Braidley, T. Townend, J. Heron, H.S.

Resolved 1

That the proceedings of the last meeting of this Board be now confirmed.

Resolved 2

That permission be given for the interment of Mary Evans of Red Bank in St. John's Churchyard the usual regulations of the Board being complied with.

Memorandum 1

The letter from the Miss Atherton's enclosing a donation of £10 read as having already been acknowledged by the Board.

Memorandum 2

The answer from the District Medical Officers to a communication from this Board having been read – it was

Resolved 3

That a communication be forwarded to the Medical Officers stating, that the Board had no intention whatever to hurt the feelings of the Medical Officers by the question proposed to them, and that their valuable and gratuitous services hitherto given to the Board, are duly appreciated by all its members and that the Board deeply regret that the medical gentlemen should, (through the want of sufficient explicitness on the part of the Board) have misconceived the object of the Board and considered the communication made to them as an answer to their memorial, rather than, as was the intention and wish of the Board, have provided the Board with the information required, that information being absolutely necessary before the Board can give any Answer to the Memorialists on the subjects alluded to in such memorial.

Board of Health, Manchester
September 10, *[sic]* 1832

Lieutenant Colonel Shaw, Chairman
Drs. S.A. Bardsley, E. Lyon, H. Gaulter, W. Johns; Revd. W. Marsden, W. Huntington; Messrs. T. Townend, R. Ogden, W.R. Whatton

Resolved 1

That the proceedings of the last meeting of this Board be confirmed.

Resolved 2

That the whitewashers who have been attacked with cholera during the time they have been employed by the Board be paid for the time they were ill in the hospital.

Resolved 3

That a copy of the circular to the District Medical Officers be transmitted by the Secretary to Mr. Winder as an answer to his letter read to the Board.

A donation of £5.0s.0d. was received from Mr. Richard Hole, Daisy Bank to be applied to the purchase of bedding and clothing. Ordered to be acknowledged by the Secretary with the best thanks of the Board.

Resolved 4

That the Secretary be directed to defray the accounts of the surgeons and druggists as corrected by the committee.

Board of Health, Manchester
September 12, 1832

Benjamin Braidley Esq., Chairman
Drs. S.A. Bardsley, J.L. Bardsley, H. Gaulter, W. Johns; Revd. W. Marsden, C.D. Wray, W. Huntington, J.White; Lieutenant Colonel Shaw; Messrs. W.R. Whatton, T. Townend, J. Barker, Joseph Heron. E. Evans, O. Milne, F. Fincham, H. Forth, R. Addison

Resolved 1

That the proceedings of the last meeting of this Board be confirmed.

Resolved 2

That the Secretary be directed to acknowledge the receipt of Mrs. J.C. Dyer's donation of £10 as also the packet of clothing with the best thanks of the Board.

Resolved 3

That the case of Jon. Hinds be referred to Mr. J. Woollam to make such allowance as he may think fit.

Resolved 4

That a letter be addressed to the Boroughreeve and Constables of Manchester requesting them to enforce with the utmost rigour the provision of the Beer Act and if in their power to appoint officers or Inspectors to each district for this express purpose.

Resolved 5

That a letter be addressed to the Watch Committee requesting they will pass a bye law making it imperative on each watchman on pain of being discharged for neglect of this duty to report any beer shop which may be open or entertain company out of the legal hours.

Moved by Revd. W. Huntington.   Seconded by Mr. Townend.

Resolved 6

That as in the opinion of this Board a considerable increase of the number of cases of cholera is to be apprehended from the too prevalent dissipation and drunkenness consequent on the opening of the public houses and beer shops during the greater part of the Sunday and late on all other evenings the Magistrates of the division be respectfully requested to take the subject into their consideration and to make such order as may appear to them most desirable for preventing if practicable the opening of all public houses and beer shops until 1/2 past 4 o'clock on Sundays, and also for securing the closing of all such houses at 10 o'clock on Sunday and all other evenings excepting Saturday.

Board of Health, Manchester
September 13, 1832

Dr. S.A. Bardsley in the Chair
Revd. J. Crook; Dr. E. Lyon; Messrs. H. Forth, W.R. Whatton, Mr. T. Townend

Resolved 1
   That the proceedings of the last meeting of the Board be confirmed.

Resolved 2
   That a copy of the tables and queries now read from the Central Board be sent to each hospital to be filled up by the Resident Medical Officer and returned to this Board.

S.A. Bardsley

Board of Health, Manchester
September 14, 1832

H. Forth Esq., Deputy Chairman
Drs. S.A. Bardsley, J.L. Bardsley, H. Gaulter; Revd. W. Marsden; Messrs. W.R. Whatton, T. Townend

Resolved 1
   That the proceedings of the last meeting of this Board be confirmed.

Resolved 2
   That the donation of £5 from Miss Brotherton of Deansgate to be applied to the purchase of clothing &c. be acknowledged by the Secretary and that he express the best thanks of the Board, as also to Mrs. Byrom of Quay Street for her donation of £20 to be applied to the same purpose.

Resolved 3
   That Mr. Walmsley be requested to enquire into the truth of the statement that several fatal cases of cholera have occurred in Silk Street which have

not been reported to the Board and whether they had been attended by any
and what medical practitioner.

Resolved 3
    That the report of the proceedings of the District Medical Officers on the
    13th Inst. be received and entered on the minutes. (See Appendix)

Appendix

Meeting of District Medical Officers
September 13, 1832

W.R. Whatton Esq., Chairman
Dr. H. Gaulter; Messrs. J. Whitelegg, G. Greaves, R.T. Hunt, B.W. Booth, W.B.
Stott, J. Walker, W. Owen, J.N. Joynson, R. Mann, B. Roberts, W. White, J.P.
Catlow

A resolution passed at the meeting of the Board of Health on September 11th
in reply to a communication from the District Medical Officers on the 8th
Inst. having been read, it was

Moved by Dr. Gaulter.   Seconded by Mr. J.P. Catlow.
and resolved

That the District Medical Officers, not perceiving any disposition in the Board
of Health to view their representation of the necessity of granting a remuneration for their losses in attendance on cholera patients with the consideration they think it merits, and anxious to avoid an invidious distinction
between the gentlemen who might return opposite answers to the question
proposed to them, (a question which the meeting is of opinion ought not to
have been put to it,) at once declare their determination to continue their gratuitous services to the poor patients as heretofore.
                                    (Signed) W.R. Whatton, Chairman.

Dr. Gaulter having taken the Chair, It was

Moved by Mr. J.P. Catlow.   Seconded by Mr. R.T. Hunt.
and resolved unanimously
That the thanks of this meeting be given to Mr. Whatton for his very able,
gentlemanly, and impartial conduct in the chair.

**Board of Health, Manchester
September 15, 1832**

Dr. J.P. Kay, Chairman
Messrs. W.R. Whatton, R. Addison, T. Townend

At 1/2 past 11 o'clock the attendance being insufficient to form a quorum the meeting adjourned till Monday at 11 o'clock.

Memorandum

A donation of £5.0.0. was received from Mr. S. Taylor Chorlton Row Brewery also £10.0.0. from —— *[left blank]* of Down's Cottage to be applied to the purchase of bedding and clothing for convalescent cholera patients – both of which have *[been]* acknowledged in the advertisement of this day.

Board of Health, Manchester
September 17, 1832

Dr. S.A. Bardsley, Chairman
Drs. E. Lyon, J.L. Bardsley, J.P. Kay; Revd. J. Crook; Messrs. W.R. Whatton, T. Townend, Mr. G. Hall, D. Lynch junr.

Resolved 1

That the proceedings of the last meeting of this Board be confirmed.

Resolved 2

That permission be given for the interment of Ann Slater at the New Jerusalem Burial Ground on condition that the regulations are complied with.

Resolved 3

That in future the Board meet only three times a week viz: on Mondays, Wednesdays and Saturdays.

Resolved 4

That a meeting of the Board be specially called for Wednesday next to take into consideration the urgent necessity of an immediate application for a further grant of money from the Leypayers.

Memorandum

A communication was read from the Trustees of the Ardwick and Ancoats Dispensary stating their compliance with the request of the Board, that medicines might be dispensed from thence to the orders of the District Surgeons.

S.A. Bardsley (signature)

Board of Health, Manchester
September 19, 1832

Dr. S.A. Bardsley, Chairman
Drs. E. Lyon, J.L Bardsley, J.P. Kay, H. Gaulter; Revd. J. White; Messrs. W.R. Whatton, T. Townend, J. Heron, J. Barker, J. Wood, G. Hall, T. Potter

Resolved 1
   That the proceedings of the last meeting of this Board be now confirmed.

Resolved 2
   That the proceedings of the Medical Committee of the 17th Inst. be confirmed and that the letter from Mr. Stott alluded in the 2nd resolution be entered on the minutes. (See Appendix)

   Moved by Dr. J.P. Kay.   Seconded by Mr. Townend.

Resolved 3
   That the Churchwardens be requested to summon a public meeting of the Leypayers for Wednesday the 26th of September in order that application may be made for £1500 to meet the current expences of the Board of Health.

                                     S.A. Bardsley (signature)

Appendix

Sir,
   It was my intention to have brought before the meeting of District Medical Officers assembled last evening at the Town Hall a motion to the following effect – "That this Meeting strongly urge upon the Board of Health, the propriety of their immediate consideration of the subject of attendance upon the patients who positively refuse to go to Hospital; the District Medical Officers feeling themselves very unpleasantly circumstanced with respect to these patients" – believing, however, that this might be considered somewhat contradictory to the resolution passed at that meeting, I determined to withdraw it and to address the Board on the subject with the view if possible of its applying a remedy. To shew the necessity of the proceeding I need only state that I have been called to two cases in Ryton Street, one upon Saturday last, the other yesterday afternoon, neither of them could I by any possibility induce to go to Hospital, and thus have I been compelled to pay five or six visits daily to one of these patients for the last six days rather than a solitary one as required by the Board of Health and thus leave the patient to the fate that inevitably awaited him.
   I am most willing to admit the difficulty of applying a suitable remedy, but at the same time I consider it hard that the District Medical Officers to whom such cases fall, should have such an onerous duty forced upon them; for forced it must be so long as a refusal of attendance would only bring along with it the odium of the poorer classes in the Districts to which they are severally attached, if not of the poorer classes of the Town generally.
   Independent of the time bestowed, I understand the regulations of the Board, if strictly enforced, would also, as in the case of attendance, oblige us to supply medicine gratuitously. This I have felt called upon to do myself and I happen to know others who have followed the same course.

Sir,
I am, your obedient Servant,
W.B. Stott.

12 Quay Street
September 14th 1832

To Mr. Walsh
Secretary
Board of Health.

Special Meeting
Board of Health, Manchester
September 21, 1832

Thomas Townend, Chairman
Drs. S.A. Bardsley, H. Gaulter; Revd. W. Marsden, W. Huntington, J. Crook;
Messrs. J. Barker, T. Potter

A public meeting having been called by the Boroughreeve and Constables of Manchester for the purpose of taking "into consideration the propriety of commencing a subscription for the relief of persons attacked with cholera; for the establishment of convalescent retreats, if necessary; for affording relief to convalescents, to their families, and to the destitute families of those who may sink under the disease; and for the general purposes of assisting to defray the expences of the Board of Health," it was

Moved by Dr. S. Bardsley. Seconded by Dr. H. Gaulter.

Resolved 1
That this Board deem it expedient to request the Churchwardens will postpone the call for a meeting of Leypayers, which was to take place on Wednesday next, to a more distant period – the date of which will be duly communicated to those officers.

Thomas Townend (signature)

Board of Health, Manchester
September 22, 1832

Lieutenant Colonel Shaw, Chairman
Dr. S.A. Bardsley; Messrs. H. Forth, Thomas Townend, W. Haynes

Resolved 1
That the proceedings of the Board on the 19th and 21st Instant be now confirmed.

Moved by Dr. S.A. Bardsley.   Seconded by Mr. T. Townend.

Resolved 2
That a special meeting of the Board be convened for Monday next at 11 o'clock for the purpose of taking into consideration the propriety of receiving the prisoners who may be seized with cholera in the New Bailey Prison into the Manchester hospitals and that Mr. Ollier the Surgeon of the prison be requested to attend.

Resolved 3
That a letter be immediately transmitted to the Chairman of the Liverpool Board of Health enquiring whether when the disease broke out in the prison at Kirkdale – the patients were treated in a hospital within the walls of the prison or whether they were removed to the hospitals of the Town.

Board of Health, Manchester
September 24, 1832

W. Haynes Esq., Chairman
Drs. S.A. Bardsley, J.L. Bardsley, E. Lyon, W. Johns; Revd. G. Dugard, J. Crook; Lieutenant Colonel Shaw; Messrs. G.W. Wood, Benjamin Braidley, T. Townend, O. Milne, J. Holford, W.R. Whatton, E.J. Lloyd, F. Foster, H. Ollier, T. Potter

Resolved 1
That the proceedings of the last meeting of this Board be now confirmed.

Resolved 2
That the letter from the Chairman of the Board of Health of Liverpool in reply to the communication of the 22nd Inst. be entered on the minutes. (See Appendix)

Moved by Mr. T. Potter.   Seconded by Dr. S.A. Bardsley.

Resolved 3
That a committee be appointed consisting of Dr. J.L. Bardsley, Dr. W. Johns, Mr. W.R. Whatton and Lieutenant Colonel Shaw accompanied by Mr. G. Shoreland to examine the two cholera hospitals and to report to the Board at its next meeting whether or not a Ward be provided in either of them which admits of complete seclusion from the other parts of the building, or whether one of the present cholera hospitals cannot be devoted exclusively to the admission of prisoners from the New Bailey.

Moved by Mr. Benjamin Braidley.

*Moved as an amendment by the Revd. J. Crook. Seconded by Mr. Townend.

That the Board strongly objects to the admission of prisoners from the New Bailey under the same roof as patients from among the virtuous and industrious poor. The amendment was negatived and the original motion carried.

Resolved 4

That a special meeting of the Board be convened for 11 o'clock tomorrow to receive the report of the sub-committee.

Appendix

Town Hall
Liverpool
September 23, 1832

Sir,

In reply to your letter of yesterday. I have to inform you, that no cholera patients were removed from Kirkdale to the cholera hospitals in Liverpool. But that an hospital was prepared for them in the Kirkdale Prison.

I am,
Sir,
your most Obedient Servant
(Signed) Samuel Sandbach

To
The Secretary of
The Board of Health
Manchester

**Special Meeting
Board of Health, Manchester
September 25, 1832**

Lieutenant Colonel Shaw, Chairman
Drs. H. Gaulter, J.L. Bardsley, W. Johns; Revd. W. Marsden, H. Fielding, J. White, J. Crook; Messrs. O. Milne, D. Dockray, W.R. Whatton, T. Townend, E. Evans, T. Potter, J. Holford

Resolved 1

That the report from the sub-committee be received and entered on the minutes. (See Appendix)

Appendix

The committee appointed by the Board to examine the two cholera hospitals, and to report whether or not a ward can be provided in either of them which admits of complete seclusion from the other parts of the building, beg to state that they have found that the Commercial Street Hospital does not admit of a separate

<u>entrance</u> for the patients; but that the new ward at the Shude Hill Hospital is now capable of receiving more than thirty patients; and that by making a new entrance from Cable Street and forming a porter's lodge and nurses' apartments, (all within that Ward) with the necessary divisions, ample accommodation from 20 to 25 patients may still be provided, and thus a complete separation from every other part of the Building effected.

The committee also beg to report, in reference to that portion of the resolution, whether one of the present hospitals cannot be devoted exclusively to the admission of prisoners from the New Bailey, that in their opinion there are several weighty objections to any such arrangement.

(Signed)
J.L. Bardsley
W.R. Whatton
W. Johns
J. Shaw

Board of Health, Manchester
September 26, 1832

Dr. S.A. Bardsley, Chairman

Drs. J.L. Bardsley, W. Johns; Revd. W. Marsden, J. White, J. Crook; Messrs. B. Braidley, W.R. Whatton, T. Townend, E. Evans, J. Holford, F. Fincham

Resolved 1

That the proceedings of the Board on the 25th and 26th Instant be now confirmed.

Moved by Dr. H. Gaulter.   Seconded by Revd. J. Crook.

Resolved 2

That the Board strongly objects to the admission of prisoners from the New Bailey under the same roof as patients from among the virtuous and industrious poor.

Moved as an Amendment by Mr. W.R. Whatton.   Seconded by Dr. W. Johns.

That such prisoners in the New Bailey as are affected with Spasmodic Cholera, be admitted in the proposed building in Cable Street, for treatment consistently with the report of the sub-committee and according to such regulations, with the view of completely indemnifying the Board against all expences as it may be thought expedient to adopt.

The amendment was negatived and the original motion carried.

Resolved 3
>   That a respectful communication be addressed to the Magistrates having them a copy of the above resolution in reply to their application to the Board.

Board of Health, Manchester
September 29, 1832

Lieutenant Colonel Shaw, Chairman
Drs. S.A. Bardsley, J.L. Bardsley, J.P. Kay; Messrs. Thomas Townend, D. Dockray

Resolved 1
>   That the proceedings of the last meeting of this Board be now confirmed.

Resolved 2
>   That the amendment proposed to the 3rd resolution on the 24th Instant be inserted on the minutes and that in future all amendments which have been seconded be entered on the minutes.

>   Moved by Dr. S.A. Bardsley.   Seconded by Mr. D. Dockray.

Resolved 3
>   That one Superintendant of Whitewashers being now sufficient for the purposes of the Board the services of Alfred Heslop be discontinued – a week's notice of the same being given to him and that it be left to the discretion of Mr. Walmsley to appoint the nights on which to burn bedding &c. as often he may consider requisite.

Memorandum
>   Read a letter from Mr. R.F. Spencer tendering his resignation as Medical Officer to No.1 District.

October 1, 1832

Revd. W. Marsden, Messrs. H. Forth, T. Townend, J. Holford

The attendance at half-past 11 o'clock being insufficient to form a quorum the meeting adjourned till Wednesday the 3rd Instant.

October 3, 1832

Dr S.A. Bardsley; Revd. J. Crook; Lieutenant Colonel Shaw

The attendance being insufficient to form a quorum the meeting adjourned till Saturday next the 6th Instant at 11 o'clock.

Board of Health, Manchester
October 6, 1832

Thomas Townend Esq., Chairman
Drs. S.A. Bardsley, J.P. Kay; Revd. J. Crook, W. Marsden; Messrs. B. Braidley,
E. Evans

Resolved 1
  That the proceedings of the Board at its last meeting be confirmed.

Resolved 2
  That Dr. S.A. Bardsley and Mr. E. Evans be requested to wait upon Mr. Loyd
  to enquire whether he will give the Board credit for a sum not exceeding two
  hundred pounds until another meeting of Leypayers can be held.

Memorandum 1
  Read a letter from Mr. R. Boyer tendering his resignation as Medical Officer
  to No.1 District.

Memorandum 2
  Read a letter from Mr. Stott tendering his resignation as Medical Officer for
  No.13 District and to the Commercial Street Hospital.

Resolved 3
  That it having been represented to the Board that Mr. Stott's services have
  been of the most valuable character the Secretary be directed to address a
  letter to him expressing the regret which the Board feels that he should
  have been obliged to resign and conveying to him their thanks for his past
  exertions.

Resolved 4
  That the Board until further notice meet on Monday, Wednesday and
  Friday at 11 o'clock and that the members of the Board be informed of this
  alteration.

Resolved 5
  That in consequence of the increased number of cases the services of Alfred
  Heslop, Superintendant of Whitewashers, be retained until further notice.

Board of Health, Manchester
October 8, 1832

Dr. S.A. Bardsley, Chairman
Revd. W. Marsden, H. Fielding, J. Crook; Messrs. T. Townend, G. Hall

Resolved
  That the proceedings of the meeting of the Board on the 6th Instant be now
  confirmed.

Board of Health, Manchester
October 10, 1832

Revd. J. Crook, Chairman
Drs. S.A. Bardsley, J.L. Bardsley, J.P. Kay; Revd. W. Huntington, G. Dugard;
Lieutenant Colonel Shaw; Mr. T. Townend

Resolved 1

> That Mr. Thorpe be requested to obtain from all persons canvassing for sub-
> scriptions an account of the amount of subscriptions obtained for the relief
> of cholera patients up to Thursday evening next in order that the same may
> be submitted to the Board of Health.

Resolved 2

> That a Special Meeting of the Board be convened for Friday next to take into
> consideration the necessity of requesting the Churchwardens to call an early
> meeting of the Leypayers for a further grant of money for the purposes of
> the Board.

Special Meeting
Board of Health, Manchester
October 12, 1832

Colonel Shaw, Chairman
Drs S.A. Bardsley, J.L. Bardsley, J. Hull, J.P. Kay; Revd. W. Marsden, G. Dugard;
Messrs. H. Forth, T. Townend, J. Heron, J. Woollam

Resolved 1

> That a requisition be made by the Secretary to the Churchwardens request-
> ing them to appoint a meeting of the Leypayers for Wednesday next the 17th
> Inst. at 11 o'clock and that the following gentlemen be appointed a commit-
> tee for drawing up resolutions and making such other arrangements as they
> shall think requisite and fit for bringing the necessary measures before the
> Leypayers – viz:

Lieutenant Colonel Shaw	Revd. W. Marsden
Drs. Bardsley	Messrs. Thomas Potter
Lyon	T. Townend
Kay	J. Woollam

Resolved 2

> That a letter be addressed by the Secretary to the members of the Finance
> Committee stating the necessity of the accounts of this Board being forth-
> with audited and examined & particularly requesting that the same may be
> immediately examined and made up to the present time that they may be sub-
> mitted to the Leypayers at the meeting to be called for Wednesday next.

Resolved 3

That the letter from the whitewashers be referred to Mr. Woollam and that he be authorized to use his own discretion in giving to the whitewashers such articles of clothing as he may think proper.

Resolved 4

That a letter be returned in answer to the one now read from the Secretary of the Board of Health at Darlaston stating that on reference to the reports of the Board there does not appear to have been any one of the name of Butler who has died of Asiatic Cholera.

Resolved 5

That the committee appointed to prepare resolutions for the meeting of Leypayers be summoned to meet on Monday after the meeting of the general Board.

Board of Health, Manchester
October 15, 1832

H. Forth Esq. Chairman
Drs. Bardsley, J.P. Kay; Revd. W. Marsden; Messrs. T. Townend, G. Hall

Resolved 1

That the proceedings of the Board of Health on the 12th Inst. be confirmed.

Resolved 2

That the proceedings of the Accounts Committee of the 13th Inst. be received and adopted.

Resolved 3

That a special meeting of the Board be convened for Wednesday next to take measures for reducing the establishments and expenditure of the Board.

Resolved 4

That the Board do not longer require the services of Messrs. Berry & Drew and that they be paid their salaries up to this date.

Special and General Meeting
Board of Health
October 17, 1832

Benjamin Braidley Esq., Chairman
Drs. S.A. Bardsley, C. Phillips, J.P. Kay; Revd. C.D. Wray, W. Huntington, W. Marsden; Lieutenant Colonel Shaw; Messrs. W.R. Whatton, H.H. Birley, J. Woollam, D. Dockray, E. Evans, T. Townend

Resolved 1

That the proceedings of the Board on the 15th Inst. be now confirmed.

Resolved 2

That Mr. D. Dockray be appointed a member of the Accounts Committee.

Resolved 3

That Mr. Townend be appointed a member of the Accounts Committee.

Resolved 4

That the requisite notices be given to the paid Medical Officers attached to the Commercial Street Hospital and that from this day forward all patients till further orders be taken to the hospital in Swan Street.

Resolved 5

That a communication be addressed to the Cholera Subscription Committee proposing to them to take the reception house under their charge and to defray the expences thereof.

October 19, 1832

Lieutenant Colonel Shaw, Messrs. T. Townend, J. Woollam

Attendance insufficient to form a quorum.

Board of Health, Manchester
October 22, 1832

Lieutenant Colonel Shaw, Chairman
Drs. S. A. Bardsley, W. Johns; Revd. W. Marsden, J. Crook, H. Fielding; Messrs. T. Townend, J. Woollam

Resolved 1

That the proceedings of the Board on the 17th Inst. be confirmed with the exception of the 4th resolution so far as it relates to the discontinuance of the services of Mr. Langford.

Resolved 2

That a Special Meeting of the Board be convened for 11 o'clock on Wednesday next to reconsider the resolution passed on the 17th Inst. giving Mr. Langford notice that his services would not be longer required.

Resolved 3

That the Cholera Subscription Committee be respectfully requested to place the sum of £100 to the credit of the Treasurer of the Clothing Fund, for the purchase of blankets, beds, shirts, shoes &c. &c., and that a letter be sent to the committee by Mr. Woollam explaining the cause of this application.

Resolved 4

That this Board until further notice meet only once a week viz on Wednesday at 11 o'clock – and that notice of this alteration be given to the members of the Board.

Resolved 5

That the services of the man and horse at the Knott Mill Hospital be discontinued as also of Alfred Heslop, Superintendant of Whitewashers, and John Shaw the porter at the Reception House.

Resolved 6

That in consequence of the very great decrease in deaths arising from cholera, the times of interment of persons dying of that complaint be limited to one hour in the day, viz: 5 o'clock in the afternoon, till Sunday the 28th Inst. and at 4 o'clock in the afternoon after that date and that the Secretary give notice to that effect to the Medical Officers of the hospitals and to the Boards of Health of Salford, Ardwick and Chorlton Row.

Special & General Meeting
Board of Health, Manchester
October 24, 1832

Lieutenant Colonel Shaw, Chairman
Drs. C. Phillips, W. Johns, J. P. Kay, E. Lyon; Revd. G. Dugard, W. Marsden, J. Crook; Messrs. H.H. Birley, G. Hall, J. Heron, P. Ewart junr., J. Woollam, T. Townend, F. Fincham, O. Milne

Resolved 1

That the proceedings of the Board on the 22nd Inst. be now confirmed.

Resolved 2

That the proceedings of the Public Vestry Meeting held on the 18th Inst. be entered amongst the minutes of the proceedings of this Board. (See Appendix)

Resolved 3

That the reports of the number of cholera cases &c. be in future made weekly only, viz: on the days fixed for the meetings of the Board.

Resolved 4

That the seven nurses dismissed from the Knott Mill Hospital be paid 30 shillings each as a compensation for one week's wages and on account of clothes.

Resolved 5

> That it appears to this Board that the two hospitals having district paid offi-
> cers subsidiary to their respective medical staff when one hospital is to be
> discontinued its officers will be removed of course unless the staff of the
> other hospital be dissatisfied with their officers, and that to dismiss an offi-
> cer from the hospital to be discontinued for the purpose of retaining the serv-
> ices of another would be to shew a preference which has not been done by
> the resolution of the Board on the 17th Inst.

Resolved 6

> That the resolution passed on the 17th Inst. directing the requisite notices to
> be given to the paid officers of the Commercial Street Hospital be confirmed.

Resolved 7

> That a copy of the two preceding resolutions be communicated to Mr.
> Langford with an assurance that the Board feels fully sensible of the value
> of his services.

Appendix

Town Hall, Manchester
October 18, 1832

At a Public Vestry Meeting of the inhabitants of Manchester, held here this day
"for the purpose of taking into consideration a proposal for a further grant of
money from the poors' rates for the purposes of the Board of Health," and to
receive a report of the proceedings already taken under the sanction of former
meetings.

Present – Revd. C.D. Wray, in the Chair

Messrs. J. Barker	Messrs. Rd. Potter
J.L. Bardsley, M.D.	G. Hall
R. Grundy	P. Eckersley
W. Haynes	S. Fletcher
E. Loyd	J. Wroe
J. Heron	J.P. Kay, M.D.
Benjamin Braidley	Revd. G. Dugard
H.H. Birley	S.A. Bardsley, M.D.
D. Dockray	E. Evans
J. Potter	J.F. Aspinwall
J.E. Taylor	Revd. Mr. Hearne
W.B. Stott	Revd. W. Huntington
J. Alexander, M.D.	P. Ewart junr.

After a statement made on the part of the Board of Health by Dr. James Lomax
Bardsley of the proceedings which had been adopted since the meeting of

Leypayers held on the 2nd August last and of the expences incurred in the execution thereof

1st It was moved by Mr. S. Fletcher, Seconded by Mr. E. Loyd and resolved unanimously,

That this meeting do now approve of the proceedings adopted by the Board of Health since the meeting of Leypayers held on the 2nd of August last.

2nd Moved by Mr. S. Phillips, Seconded by Mr. Newberry and resolved unanimously,

That a further sum of £2,500 be placed at the disposal of the Board of Health to defray the expences incurred in the support of Hospitals established for the reception of persons afflicted with cholera, and in the execution of the precautionary measures adopted to prevent the spread of the disease.

3rd Moved by Mr. Braidley, Boroughreeve, Seconded by Mr. E. Evans, and Resolved unanimously,

That the best thanks of this meeting be given to the Medical Gentlemen connected with the Board of Health for their kind, efficient, and laborious services.

(Signed) C.D. Wray, Chairman

4th Moved by the Boroughreeve, Seconded by Mr. T. Townend, and resolved unanimously,

That the thanks of this meeting be given to the Revd. C.D. Wray for his kindness in taking the chair and for the ability with which he has conducted the business of the meeting.

(Signed) James Wood

**Board of Health, Manchester
October 27, 1832**

Special Meeting, convened for the purpose of considering a communication from Messrs. Peel, Williams & Peel, requiring possession of the Swan Street Hospital in two months from the date of their notice: (October 23rd)

Mr. H.H. Birley, T. Townend, J. Heron, Dr. J.P. Kay

At a quarter past 11, the attendance being insufficient to form a quorum the meeting was adjourned till Wednesday the 31st Inst.

Board of Health, Manchester
October 31, 1832

Lieutenant Colonel Shaw, Chairman
Drs. S.A. Bardsley, E. Lyon, J.P. Kay; Revd. J. Crook, W. Huntington; Messrs.
F. Fincham, H.H. Birley, T. Townend, J. Barker

Resolved 1
  That the proceedings of the Board on the 24th Inst. be confirmed.

Resolved 2nd
  That the letter now read from Messrs. Peel, Williams & Peel be entered on
  the minutes. (See Appendix)

Resolved 3
  That the requisite notices be given to the two junior officers of the Swan
  Street Hospital for the termination of their engagement.

Resolved 4
  That a copy of the preceding resolution be communicated to the medical staff
  of the Swan Street Hospital with a request that if previous to the expiration
  of the month they see any reason for retaining the services of one or both of
  those gentlemen they will intimate the same to the Board.

Resolved 5
  That Dr. Kay be requested to communicate with his brethren composing the
  staff of the Commercial Street Hospital regarding the removal of the convalescents to the hospital in Swan Street and that if there be no objection such
  patients be removed.

Resolved 6
  That in the event of the removal of the patients taking place the nurses and
  other attendants at the Commercial Street Hospital be discontinued with the
  exception of one servant to be selected by the medical staff.

Resolved 7
  That the Secretary communicate with Mr. Thorpe and state his readiness to
  give every information in his power for the use of the Cholera Subscription
  Committee and that he be authorized to lend to the committee the daily reports
  and the Register Book of Cholera Cases.

Appendix

Soho Iron Works & Forge
Manchester,
October 23, 1832

Sir,

The period for which we let you a portion of our premises in Swan Street, for the purposes of a cholera hospital having expired on the 24th day of June last and the terms of our agreement with you requiring two months notice to be given by either party after that period, we now, agreeably with the terms of that contract, request that you will cause possession of the said premises to be given to us in two calendar months from the date hereof.

We remain
Sir
your very Obedient Servants.
(Signed) Peel, Williams & Peel.

Benjamin Braidley Esq.
Town Hall
Manchester

Board of Health, Manchester
November 7, 1832

Dr. S.A. Bardsley, Chairman
Dr. Hull; Revd. G. Dugard, J. Crook, W. Huntington; Messr. J. Woollam

Resolved 1

That the proceedings of the Board on the 31st of October, be now confirmed.

Resolved 2

That Mr. Crook be requested to arrange with Daniel Peeless the present porter at the Knott Mill Hospital to take charge of the Articles left at the hospital.

Resolved 3

That the 4 nurses dismissed from the Knott Mill Hospital on the 3rd Inst. be allowed 16 shillings each as a compensation for the clothing destroyed in their hospital duty.

Resolved 4

That the request of a Mr. Bennett to leave the service of the Board a fortnight before the expiration of the notice given to him be complied with.

Board of Health, Manchester
November 14, 1832

Lieutenant Colonel Shaw, Chairman
Dr. S.A. Bardsley; Revd. G. Dugard, W. Marsden; Messr. H. Forth

Resolved 1

That the proceedings of the Board on the 7th Inst. be confirmed.

Resolved 2

That notice be given to Mr. Lynch for the termination of his engagement with the Board at the time the notice for giving up the Swan Street Hospital expires viz: the 23rd of December next.

21st November 1832

Revd. J. Crook, W. Marsden; Messrs. G. Hall, J. Woollam

Adjourned for want of sufficient attendance.

Board of Health, Manchester
November 28, 1832

Dr. S.A. Bardsley, Chairman
Dr. J.P. Kay; Revd. J. Crook, G. Dugard, W. Marsden; Lieutenant Colonel Shaw;
Messrs B. Braidley, W. Haynes, G. Hall

Resolved 1

That the proceedings of the Board on the 14th Inst. be now confirmed.

Resolved 2

That the claim of Francis Morris for £2.16s.0d. as a balance of wages, be not allowed.

Memorandum

Read a communication from Mr. Thorpe stating that the Cholera Subscription Committee declined to allow a sum out of the Subscription Fund for the support of the Harrison Street Reception House.

Resolved 3

That the month's notices given by the Board to their Medical Officers for the expiration of their services be dated from the end of their monthly engagements and that their salaries be paid accordingly.

December 5, 1832

Revd. J. Crook; Mr. T. Townend

1/4 to 12 o'clock
Attendance insufficient to form a Quorum.

Board of Health, Manchester
December 19, 1832

H. Forth Esq. Chairman
Drs. S.A. Bardsley, E. Lyon; Revd. J. Crook, Messrs. T. Townend, J. Woollam

Resolved 1
That the proceedings of the Board on the 28th of November be now confirmed.

Resolved 2
That the following advertisement be inserted in the Manchester papers of Saturday next viz:
The Board of Health request that all accounts against them may be sent in for examination and payment to the Town Hall, King Street on or before the 31st of December.

Resolved 3
That notice be given to the clerk and porter of the Clothing Fund that their services will not be longer required – also to the person at present in charge of the Reception House.

Resolved 4
That four weeks notice dated from the 24th of December be given to the Medical Inspector and to the Secretary from the 22nd December for the termination of their engagements – also a week's notice to the Superintendant of Whitewashers.

Resolved 5
That notice be also given to the owner of the Reception House that the Board will not require the same after the 19th of January next.

Resolved 6
That Mr. Lynch be authorized to engage a man to assist in disinfecting the blankets &c.

Resolved 7
That the nurses discharged from the Swan Street Hospital be allowed 16 shillings each as compensation for clothing destroyed in their hospital duty.

Resolved 8
That the Accounts Committee be requested to convene a Special Meeting of the Board as soon as their report is completed.

Board of Health, Manchester
February 6, 1833

Lieutenant Colonel Shaw, Chairman
Drs. S.A. Bardsley, J. Hull, J.P. Kay; Revd. J. Crook, G. Dugard, W. Marsden; Messrs. D. Dockray, T. Townend, P. Ewart junr., J. Woollam, R.J.J. Norreys, F. Fincham, E. Evans, R. Addison

Resolved 1

That the proceedings of the Board on the 19th December last be now confirmed.

Resolved 2

That the reports of the expenditure of the Board of Health and of the Clothing Fund to the 19th of January 1833 now presented by the Accounts Committee be received and approved. (See Appendix)

Resolved 3

That the best thanks of the Board are justly due and are hereby given to the Accounts Committee for the great trouble they have taken and for their very satisfactory reports.

Resolved 4

That the reports now presented to the Board by the Accounts Committee of the Receipts and Disbursements of the Board from its constitution by the Privy Council to the 19th of January 1833 and of the receipts and expenditure of the Clothing Fund be advertised in the Manchester papers of Saturday next.

Resolved 5

That the proposition recommended in the proceedings of the Accounts Committee of the 31st January with respect to the accounts presented by Messrs. Peel & Williams be adopted and that Mr. Townend be requested to carry the same into effect.

Resolved 6

That the disinfecting apparatus be removed to the Poor-House on the understanding that the Churchwardens have the same erected in such situation as may be most likely to be serviceable to the Town of Manchester.

Resolved 7

That the blank form of Report (No.5*) transmitted by the Central Board be filled up by the Secretary and submitted to the Chairman of the Medical Committee previous to its being returned to the Central Board.

* See Appendix to Proceedings on March 31, 1832 in Vol.1.

Resolved 8

That the Board of Health have very great satisfaction in offering their unqualified testimony to and approbation of the uniform zeal, ability and attention evinced Mr. D. Lynch Junr. as Resident Medical Officer at the Swan Street Hospital during the prevalence of cholera in this Town.

Resolved 9

That the Board of Health being well satisfied with the diligence and talent of Mr. Walsh and with his very correct and judicious conduct during the performance of his duties as Secretary to this Board have much pleasure in giving him this public testimony thereof and in expressing their best wishes for his future prosperity.

Resolved 10

That in the opinion of this Board it is not expedient at the present moment to dispose of the furniture, bedding &c. now deposited in the Knott Mill Hospital and that the said hospital be retained and that the person now in charge be continued until the further decision of the Board. That Mr. Shoreland be requested to report from time to time to the Boroughreeve the state of the hospital and furniture.

Resolved 11

That the Board considers it unnecessary to publish the statement of the number of cases of cholera, attached to the report presented by the Accounts Committee.

Resolved 12

That Dr. Gaulter be allowed the use of the Register Book of Cases, the Classification Committee Tables No.2, Dr. Cleland's Report of Cholera in Glasgow and the coloured map showing the Hospital Districts.

Resolved 13

That the books and papers of the Board be deposited in the cupboard of the Boroughreeve's Room and that a key with a catalogue of the books be given into the care of the Boroughreeve.

Resolved 14

That the Secretary be requested to call upon the landlord of the Knott Mill Hospital and inform him of the foundation of part of the yard wall having given way from the recent floods and request that the same may be repaired without delay.

Appendix

Report of the RECEIPTS and DISBURSEMENTS of the MANCHESTER BOARD of HEALTH, from April 1st, 1832, to January 19th, 1833

Dr.	£	s.	d.	£	s.	d.
Amount granted by a Public Vestry Meeting on April 6th, 1832,	1000	0	0			
Do. do. do. August 2, 1832,	1000	0	0			
Do. do. do. October 18, 1832,	2500	0	0			
				4500	0	0
Donation presented by Dr. Henry for Disinfecting Apparatus				50	0	0
Amount recovered for Interment Expenses				18	12	0
Do. derived from Sale of Old Timber, &c.				40	0	0
Do. returned for Advertisements paid, also included in Churchwardens' Account				1	5	6
Discount allowed by Tradesmen				8	3	10½
Interest allowed by Messrs. Jones, Loyds and Co.				9	11	11
				£ 4627	13	3½

February 4th, 1833. – Audited and found correct:
 THOMAS TOWNEND
 PETER EWART Jun., Accounts Committee
 DAVID DOCKRAY,

             F.A. WALSH, Secretary.

HOSPITAL DEPARTMENT.	Swan-Street Hospital			Knott Mill Hospital			Cr.		
	£	s.	d.	£	s.	d.	£	s.	d.
Rent	51	5	0	86	2	0			
Salaries of Resident Medical Officers	344	2	6	292	15	0			
Wages of Nurses and other Attendants	147	2	4½	157	4	6			
Meat	24	8	9	33	5	10			
Potatoes, &c.	1	12	3½	1	17	6½			
Bread, Meal, &c.	20	18	5	22	15	5			
Groceries	13	3	2½	19	11	7			
Butter and Milk	11	5	1	16	10	5¾			
Porter and Spirits for the Servants	8	0	5½	13	4	3			
Candles, Soap, &c.	9	10	11	8	6	9½			
Coals	16	3	11¼	12	1	10¾			
Drugs	66	9	11½	41	3	0			
Spirits and Wine for the Patients	8	7	0	17	14	8			
Leeches	4	8	3	1	7	6			
Sundries	1	8	10	2	14	8			
	728	6	11¾	726	15	1½			
							1455	2	1¼

RECEPTION HOUSE DEPARTMENT.

				£	s.	d.	£	s.	d.
Rent				20	10	0			
Wages of Keeper and Assistant				30	4	0			
Meat				19	2	4½			
Potatoes &c.				5	11	2½			
Bread, Meal &c.				30	4	1½			
Groceries				6	10	11½			
Milk				10	0	5			
Candles, Soap &c.				3	19	6			
Coals				3	6	8			
Sundries				0	10	8			
							129	19	11

INTERMENT EXPENSES.

				£	s.	d.	£	s.	d.
Coffins, &c.				273	5	0			
Dues				109	18	0			
							383	3	0

WHITEWASHING AND FUMIGATING HOUSES, CLEANSING STREETS, &c.

	£	s.	d.			
Salary of Medical Inspector	66	0	0			
Whitewashing as a Contract	21	7	4½			
Wages of Whitewashers and Superintendents	213	17	7½			
Brushes, Buckets, Lime &c.	29	6	5½			
Vitriol, Salt, &c.	9	11	9½			
Scavenging and removal of Nuisances	45	8	1			
				385	11	4

OFFICE DEPARTMENT.

	£	s.	d.			
Salary of Secretary and Assistants	121	16	4			
Stationery, Printing and Bill Posting	124	14	11½			
Advertisements	29	18	0			
Postages	17	0	8½			
				293	10	0

MISCELLANEOUS EXPENSES

	£	s.	d.			
Medicines supplied to Out- Patients to the orders of the District Medical Officers	124	15	3½			
Instruments and Apparatus for the Treatment of Patients	35	15	0			
Scales, Bottles Phials, &c.	12	14	0½			
Furniture	178	13	6			
Bedding	215	16	4¼			
Flannel Gowns and Caps	15	1	8			
Ironmongery, Tinware, &c.	50	2	8			
Earthenware	11	18	1½			
Washing Utensils, Mops, Brooms, &c.	12	3	9			
Carriages, Repairing do., and Hire of Horse	211	3	11			
Cartage	4	1	6			
Law Expenses	14	6	6			
				887	2	3¾

Cost of disinfecting Apparatus, and Fixing and Supplying Water to do.	80	18	4

ALTERATIONS AND REPAIRS

	£	s.	d.
Sundry Alterations and Repairs at the Hospitals and Reception House	301	1	10
Building Apartments for the accommodation of the Nurses at the Knott Mill Hospital	134	14	1

Building New Ward at the Swan-Street Hospital - accommodation for 40 Patients	111	6	4			
				547	2	3
Sundries, not reducible under any particular head				11	14	11
Amount as per Voucher Book				4174	4	2
Commission paid to Messrs. Jones, Loyds and Co.				10	5	4
Cash in hand of the Secretary				1	15	3½
Balances in the hands of Messrs. Jones, Loyds and Co.				441	8	6
				4627	13	3½

REPORT OF THE RECEIPTS AND EXPENDITURE OF THE BOARD OF
HEALTH CLOTHING FUND,
FROM AUGUST 17th, 1832, TO JANUARY 19th, 1833

	£	s.	d.	£	s.	d.
To amount of Subscriptions received	271	10	0			
"　　" 　　of Donation from the Cholera Subscription Committee	100	0	0			
				371	10	0
" Discount allowed by Tradesmen				3	1	5
" Interest from Messrs. Jones, Loyds and Co.				1	19	3
February 4th, 1833. – Audited and found correct:				£376	10	8

　　THOMAS TOWNEND,
　　PETER EWART, Jun., Accounts Committee
　　DAVID DOCKRAY,

F.A. WALSH, Secretary

	£	s.	d.	£	s.	d.
By purchase of Bedding	155	7	7			
"　　" 　　of Clothing	65	4	2½			
				220	11	9½
ADVERTISEMENTS, PRINTING, &c.						
" Proprietors of the Guardian　Advertisements	5	8	6			
"　　"　　"　" 　Chronicle do.	5	9	6			
"　　"　　"　" 　Times 　do.	6	2	0			
"　　"　　"　" 　Courier 　do.	5	8	6			
"　　"　　"　" 　Advertiser do.	5	18	0			
" Printing and Stationery	3	10	3			
				31	16	9
" Painting and Fitting-up Store Rooms				6	12	6½
" Charges of Management				20	9	4
" Incidental Office Expenses				1	8	11½
" Amount as per Voucher Book				280	19	4½
" Commission paid to Messrs. Jones, Loyds and Co.					14	0
" Balance in hand				94	17	3½
				£376	10	8

Special Meeting of the Board of Health convened by the Boroughreeve for the purpose of taking into consideration the propriety of giving up the Knott Mill Hospital.

Manchester
May 8, 1833

Benjamin Braidley Esq., Chairman
Dr. E. Lyon; Revd. W. Huntington, J. Crook; Messrs. Addison, W. Haynes, T. Townend, G. Hall, P. Ewart junr.

> Moved by Mr. T. Townend.   Seconded by Revd. William Huntington and resolved unanimously,

1. That one month's notice be immediately given to quit the premises now in the occupation of the Board at Knott Mill but that if in the Interim any cases of cholera should occur in Manchester the Chairman of the Board upon the same being intimated to him be authorized to continue the engagement until the further decision of the Board.

> Moved by Mr. G. Hall.   Seconded by Dr. E. Lyon and resolved.

2. That the furniture now in the hospital at Knott Mill be transferred to the care of the Churchwardens with the condition that in case it should be again wanted before the 31st of October next by the Board, it be restored to them on an application to that effect signed by the Chairman.

> Moved by Revd. W. Huntington.   Seconded by Mr. W. Haynes and resolved.

3. That one month's notice to leave the service of the Board be given to Daniel Peeless now at the Knott Mill Hospital.

> Moved by Mr. T. Townend.   Seconded by Dr. E. Lyon and resolved,

4. That the Revd. James Crook, Mr. George Hall and Mr. P. Ewart junr. be requested to see to the proper removal of the furniture from the Knott Mill Hospital and of all the property therein belonging to the Board.

Adjourned.

Special Meeting of the Board of Health convened by the Boroughreeve for the purpose of taking into consideration the propriety of dissolving the Board.

**Manchester
October 14, 1833**

Benjamin Braidley, Chairman
Dr. S.A. Bardsley; Revd. James Crook, W. Marsden; Lieutenant Colonel Shaw; Messrs. George Hall, Thomas Townend, Henry Forth, William Haynes

Resolved 1
That the minutes of the last meeting be confirmed.

Moved by Dr. Bardsley.   Seconded by Mr. Townend.

Resolved 2
That the Chairman of the Medical Committee be requested to call a meeting of the members to make a report of the state of health of the Town and vicinity of Asiatic Cholera with the view of enabling the Board to ascertain the propriety of dissolving itself; and that the said committee be requested to report to the Board on or before the 23rd Inst.

Moved by Lieutenant Colonel Shaw.   Seconded by Revd. J. Crook.

Resolved 3
That this Board do at its rising adjourn to Wednesday the 23rd Instant at 11 o'clock for the purpose of receiving the report of the Medical Committee and for taking such measures as may be consequent thereon.

Special Meeting of the Board of Health adjourned to receive the Report of the Medical Committee on the State of Health of the Town and Vicinity.

**Town Hall, Manchester
October 23, 1833**

Benjamin Braidley, Chairman
Revd. James Crook; Messrs. Oswald Milne, Peter Ewart junr., Henry Forth, John Woollam

In consequence of the Medical Committee not having made a report to this board (for want of a quorum).

Resolved
That this Board be adjourned to Thursday the 31st October at 11 o'clock in the forenoon for the purpose of receiving a report from the Medical Committee and for such other measures as may be consequent thereon.

Resolved

That a copy of the above resolution be transmitted to the Chairman of the Medical Board.

Resolved

That a meeting of the subscribers to the Cholera Clothing Fund be called by advertisement for Thursday the 31st Inst. at 10 o'clock in the forenoon in the Boroughreeve's Room, Town Hall to determine as to the appropriation of £94 17s. 3½d., being the balance of monies in hand undisposed of, and also for the purpose of disposing such portions of clothing as may be yet undistributed.

Adjourned.

Special Meeting of the Board of Health held this day in the Boroughreeves room to consider the propriety of dissolving the Board.

Town Hall, Manchester
October 31, 1833.

Benjamin Braidley, Chairman
Drs. Bardsley, J.P. Kay, Lyon, Hull; Revd. Huntington, W. Marsden; Lieutenant Colonel Shaw; Messrs. T. Townend, J. Woollam, O. Milne

Resolved

That the proceedings of the Board on October 14th and 23rd be confirmed.

Resolved

That as several members of the Medical Committee are now present, and have, in absence of any formal report, stated their opinion that Asiatic Cholera does not exist in this District to any extent to require the continuance of this Board, the Board be dissolved at the rising of this day's meeting.

Resolved

That one month's notice to surrender the possession of the building at Knott Mill be given to the owner; and that a similar notice be given to Daniel Peelis, who has the care of the furniture there deposited, that his services will not be further required.

Resolved

That out of the balance of £275 19s. 0d. on hand all outstanding debts be discharged by the Chairman, and that the balance of all remaining furniture, be handed over to the Churchwardens and that the Books and Accounts of the Board be deposited with the Boroughreeve and Constables of Manchester.

Resolved

That the warmest thanks of this Board and of the community in general, are justly due to the Medical Committee and the medical practioners, who have given their services, for the most efficient and unwearied attention to the interests of the sufferers under this dreadful malady, which by the Blessing of Divine Providence has been most extraordinarily arrested in this district, and that these acknowledgements are hereby accordingly presented to each of them; and that a copy of this regulation be transmitted to the Chairman of the Medical Committee.

Resolved

That the best thanks of the Board are hereby presented to the members of the different committees appointed by the Board for the zealous and efficient manner in which they have discharged their respective trusts.

Resolved

That the thanks of the Board be presented to the clergy and ministers of all denominations who exerted themselves in mitigating the distresses of the poor sufferers during the existence of this malady.

Resolved

That the cordial thanks of the Board be presented to Benjamin Braidley Esq. for his able and unwearied exertions in promoting and carrying into effect the objects of the Board.

Resolved

That the most unfeigned gratitude of the Board is due to Lieutenant Colonel Shaw for his admirable arrangements in the origin of this Board, and his continued assistance in every stage of its proceedings.

Resolved

That these resolutions be advertised in all the Manchester newspapers.

CORRESPONDENCE WITH CENTRAL BOARD OF HEALTH

Council Office,
11 November 1831

Sir,

I am directed by the Lords of His Majesty's most Honorable Privy Council, to acquaint you that their Lordships have established a Board which will sit daily at this Office, for the purpose of co-operating with the Local Authorities of Districts, in precautionary measures against the introduction and extension of Cholera.

I have to call your attention to the Minute of Council of the 20 October, a Copy of which is enclosed, and to request that you will make known to me what steps have been taken within the Town of Manchester in compliance with the recommendations therein contained.

Their Lordships are desirous of establishing a general and combined system of sanative regulation, which in case of necessity may be acted upon throughout the Country, and it will be the duty of the Commissioners in London, to afford you in the first instance all the advice and information which their situation and their experience may place at their Command.

I am,
Sir,
Your obedient Servant
C. Greville

To the Chief Magistrate
at Manchester

Central Board of Health
Council Office, Whitehall
17 December 1831

Sir,
I have it in command to signify the request of the Board to be informed whether any and what measures have been adopted for the formation of a Board of Health at Manchester with reference to the Order in Council of the 20 October last, & the Circular of this Board of the 14 Ulto.

I have the honor to be
Sir
Your most obedient Servant
W. Maclean
Secretary

To the Boroughreeve
of Manchester

Answered 19 December 1831 BB [Benjamin Braidley].

Central Board of Health,
Council Office, Whitehall
27 December 1831

Sir,
   In reply to your letter to Mr. Bathurst of the 24th Inst. which has been laid before this Board, I am directed to transmit to you the enclosed Circular of the 29th Ulto.

I have the honor to be,
Sir,
Your obedient
humble Servant,
W. Maclean
Secretary

Benjamin Braidley Esq.
Board of Health
Manchester

Read 31 December 1831, BB

Extract of a letter from the Clerk of the Council in reply to Communications from Boards of Health requesting Information as to their Re-appointment under the Orders in Council of 21st November 1831, for the Purpose of obtaining accurate Returns of Disease, and for the Removal of Nuisances.

"I am directed to acquaint you that the Lords of His Majesty's Most Honorable Privy Council do not think it necessary that a new Board of Health should be appointed with the Powers mentioned in the Orders of 21st November 1831, except in the event of the cholera breaking out in your Town, or in the immediate Neighbourhood; or in the Event of some other Case of great Urgency occurring, the Circumstances of which will be taken into Consideration upon the same being specially represented to their Lordships.

The Order of the 21st of November was not intended to cancel the Boards of Health then in existence, nor to prevent the Formation of any others that might have been contemplated in consequence of the Order of 20th October; and their Lordships are of Opinion, that such Boards of Health may be very beneficially employed in discharging the Duties marked out in the Circular of the Central Board of Health of the 14th November 1831."

29 November 1831

Central Board of Health
Council Office, Whitehall
14 March 1832

Sir
In reply to your letter of the 7th Inst. to the Lords of the Council, which has been referred to this Board, stating the measures adopted by the Board of Health established at Manchester, & requesting the sanction of the Privy Council to the present constitution of the Board – also to the liquidation of all expences properly incurred in making the necessary arrangements for preventing the Introduction or spread of cholera, & to the monthly transmission of a statement of all expences so incurred to the Privy Council; I am directed to state to you with reference to the first point, that upon the List of names of the existing Board being transmitted to me, the same shall be submitted to the Lords of the Council for confirmation: at the same time it would be desirable that no more members should be placed upon the Board than may be considered absolutely necessary for the purposes required, & that the number should not exceed 50 or 60.

As to the second & third points of your letter I am to refer you to the Order in Council of the 6th Inst. relative to the mode of raising funds, in consequence of the passing of the Cholera Prevention Act.

I am further directed by the Board to express to you their approbation at the judicious arrangements which have been already adopted by the existing Board at Manchester.

I am,
Sir,
Your most Obedient Servant
W. Maclean
Secretary

Benjamin Braidley Esq.
President of the Board of Health
Manchester

Read 19 March BB

Central Board of Health,
Council Office, Whitehall,
23 March 1832

Sir,
   I am directed to transmit to you the enclosed Order of the Lords of the Council appointing a Board of Health in the Town of Manchester in conformity with the List of names transmitted in your Letter of the 20th Inst.

> *I am*
> *Sir*
> *Your most Obedient Servant*
> *W. Maclean*
> *Secretary*

W. Haynes Esq.
Board of Health
Manchester

At the Council Chamber Whitehall
the 23rd March 1832

By the Lords of His Majesty's Most
Honourable Privy Council.

It is this day Ordered by Their Lordships that a Board of Health be constituted in the Town of Manchester consisting of the following Members viz:

The Revd. Dr. Calvert	Drs. S.A. Bardsley
Revd. C.D. Wray	Jo. Mitchell
Revd. W. Marsden	E. Lyon
Revd. George Dugard	E. Carbutt
Revd. James Crook	James L. Bardsley
Revd. James White	J.D. Hulme
Revd. H. Fielding	William Henry
Revd. Huntington	W.C. Henry
	J.P. Kay Physicians
Messrs. J. Holford	H.J. Pendlebury
J. Kennedy	H. Gaulter
George Hall	E. Holme
R.J.J. Norreys	Jo. Hull
J. Bentley	William Johns
E. Connell	Charles Phillips

Jno. Barker
H. Houldsworth
T. Townend
D. Dockray
T. Weatherby
F. Fincham
Jos. Rooke
J. Woollam
P. Ewart junr.
Geo. Faulkner
John Potter
Thomas Potter
John Dalton

Messrs J. Thorpe
J.A. Ransome
J. Ainsworth
R. Thorpe   *Surgeons*
W.J. Wilson
T. Turner
R. Addison
W.R. Whatton

Lt. Col. Shaw
Messrs H.H. Birley
O. Milne
J. Heron (Hon. Sec.)

And the said Board are to proceed in the execution of the duties required of them accordingly.

C. Greville

Central Board of Health
Council Office Whitehall
30 March 1832

Sir
   I am directed to transmit to you the Enclosed order of the Lords of the Council adding the Boroughreeve, Constables and Churchwardens for the time being to the Board of Health, constituted at Manchester on the 23rd Inst.

I am
Sir
your most obedient Servant
W. Maclean
Secretary

J. Heron Esq.
Board of Health
Manchester

At the Council Chamber Whitehall
30 March 1832

By the Lords of His Majesty's
Most Honorable Privy Council

It is this day ordered by Their Lordships that the Boroughreeve, Constables and Churchwardens for the time being be added to the Board of Health constituted at Manchester on the 23rd Inst.

C. Greville

Central Board of Health,
Council Office, Whitehall
21st April 1832

Sir,
In reply to your Letter of the 19th Inst. which has been laid before this Board, I am directed to transmit to you the enclosed 30 Circular of the Copies of the Order in Council of the 6 March & to state that the Board have no means of supplying the act requested.

I have the honor to be,
Sir,
Your obedient
humble Servant,
W. Maclean,
Secretary

F.A. Walsh Esq.
Board of Health
Manchester

Council Office, Whitehall
May 12, 1832

Sir,
In reply to your Letter of the 8th Instant relative to the precautionary measures which in the opinion of the Board of Health at Manchester ought to be instituted against cholera at the different Ports on the River Dee; I am directed by the Lords of the Council to state to you for the information of the Board that Instructions

have already been issued to the Officers of Customs for the necessary inspection of the Crews of Vessels arriving from unhealthy Ports, and that Their Lordships have not interfered with the formation of Boards of Health in any Towns or Districts leaving them at all times to the spontaneous arrangements of the Local Authorities, and as a Board of Health was established at Chester under the auspices of the Mayor of that City in the Month of December last Their Lordships trust the Precautions against Disease are not altogether neglected.

> *I am*
> *Sir*
> *Your Obedient Servant*
> *William L. Bathurst*

Benjamin Braidley Esq.

> *Central Board of Health*
> *Council Office, Whitehall*
> *June 30, 1832*

Sir,
   I am directed to acknowledge the receipt of your Letter of the 28th Inst. & to acquaint you that it is not the intention of the Central Board to publish the cases of cholera at Manchester now reported, unless the disease should materially increase.

> *I am,*
> *Sir,*
> *your most Obedient Servant*
> *W. Maclean*
> *Secretary*

Benjamin Braidley Esq.
Boroughreeve
Chairman, Board of Health
Manchester

> *Central Board of Health*
> *Council Office, Whitehall*
> *July 21, 1832*

Sir,

   With reference to your letter of the 18th Inst. respecting the powers possessed by Boards of Health to compel the immediate interment of those who die of cholera, I am directed to transmit to you the enclosed order in Council of the 19th Inst.

> *I am,*
> *Sir,*
> *Your most Obedient Servant*
> *W. Maclean*
> *Secretary*

F.A. Walsh
Secretary, Board of Health
Town Hall
Manchester

> *Central Board of Health*
> *Council Office, Whitehall*
> *July 27, 1832*

Sir,

   I am directed to transmit to you the enclosed Copies [note in margin, 6 copies] of the order of the 19th Inst. & to state that the Board have no more at their disposal; – one copy only being forwarded to each Local Board.

> *I am,*
> *Sir,*
> *your most Obedient Servant*
> *W. Maclean*
> *Secretary*

J. Heron Esq.
Honorary Secretary, Board of Health
Town Hall
Manchester

Council Office, Whitehall
September 8, 1832

Sir,
  In reply to your letter of the 28th Ultimo, relative to the Burial ground for cholera patients at Manchester, I am directed by the Lords of the Council to state that the doubt in the minds of the Magistrates as to the power of conviction is not without foundation.
  It was not intended that the Establishment of separate Burying Grounds for the interment of persons dying of cholera should be compulsory, but it is made a condition precedent to the preventing bodies being interred in the Churches and Churchyards of the Town.
  If the Board of Health at Manchester are anxious for the Establishment of the proposed separate Burying Ground it will be proper that a certificate signed by two Medical men that no danger is to be apprehended to the neighbourhood from the Burial and that the situation is approved by the Members of the Board of Health be forwarded to the Clerk of the Council in Waiting, when their Lordships will issue an Order empowering the board to provide such burying ground.

I am,
Sir,
Your Obedient Servant
C. Greville

Joseph Heron Esq.
Honorary Secretary
The Board of Health
Manchester

Central Board of Health
Council Office
September 8, 1832

Sir,
  I am directed to acknowledge the receipt of your letter (with its enclosure) of the 4th Inst. and to state that the Central Bd. have caused the circumstances therein stated to be made known thro' the mediums of the London Newspapers as requested – and that an answer will be sent by this post from the Clerk of the Council to the communication alluded to in your Letter.

I am,
Sir,
your obedient Servant
W. Maclean
Secretary

Benjamin Braidley
Board of Health
Manchester

Council Office, Whitehall
3 January 1833

Sir,
   The Lords of the Council having Called upon the Central Board of Health to
make a Report of their Proceedings.

   I am directed to request that you will fill up and forward to me at your earliest convenience the Statistic Return No.5 a Blank form of which I enclose.

I am,
Sir,
your Obedient Servant
B. Harding
for Secretary

J. Heron Esq.
Board of Health
Manchester

A LIST
OF THE
MEMBERS OF THE BOARD OF HEALTH,
FOR MANCHESTER

BENJAMIN BRAIDLEY, ESQ., *19, Lever-street, Chairman.*

W. HAYNES, ESQ., *10, Cooper-street, Deputy Chairmen.*
H. FORTH, ESQ., *St. Peter's-square.*

The Very Rev. Dr. Calvert, *Mosley-street.*
Rev. C.D. Wray, *Strangeways.*
Rev. W. Marsden, *10 Ridge-field.*
Rev. George Dugard, *Grosvenor-Street, Oxford-Road.*
Rev. James Crook, *Granby Row.*
Rev. H: Fielding, *George-street.*
Rev. H. Huntington, *Great John-street.*

Churchwardens

Messrs. George Withington, *Pall-Mall.*
James Wood, *High-street.*
Evan Evans, *13, Cooper-street.*

Drs. S.A. Bardsley, *Ardwick-Green.*
John Mitchell, *Piccadilly.*
E. Lyon, *Princess-street.*
E. Carbutt, *Brazennose-street.*
J.L. Bardsley, *2, Chatham Street.*
J.D. Hulme, *Club House, Mosley-street.*
W. Henry, *East-Street.*
W.C. Henry, *Mosley-street.*
J.P. Kay, *Mosley-street.*
J. Pendlebury, *Piccadilly.*
Henry Gaulter, *72, George-street.*
Edward Holme, *King-street.*
John Hull, *Mosley-street.*
William Johns, *Oxford-street.*
Charles Phillips, *Piccadilly.*
Shaw, Dr., *32, Mosley Street.*

Messrs. John Thorpe, *King Street.*
J.A. Ransome, *St. Peter's-square.*
James Ainsworth, *King-street.*
Robert Thorpe, *Oldham-street.*
W.J. Wilson, *Mosley-street.*
T. Turner, *Mosley-street.*
R. Addison, *Ancoats-Crescent.*
W.R. Whatton, *5, Portland-Place.*

Lieutenant Colonel Shaw,
  51, Upper Brook-street.
Messrs. J. Holford, *King-street.*
John Kennedy, *Ardwick.*
George Hall, *Ancoats-Crescent.*
R.J.J. Norreys, *Davy-Hulme.*
J. Bentley, *Crescent, Salford.*
E. Connell, *Lloyd-street.*
John Barker, *Cannon-street.*
Henry Houldsworth, *Newton-street.*
T. Townend, *Market-street.*
D. Dockray, *Ardwick.*
F. Fincham, *19, Brown-street.*
J. Woollam, *Quay-street.*
George Faulkner, *New-High-street.*
Thomas Potter, *Cannon-street.*
H.H. Birley, *York-street.*
Thomas Weatherby, *Marshall-street.*
Joseph Rooke, *Horrox-Lane, Red-Bank.*
P. Ewart, Jun., *East-street.*
John Potter, *Pollard-street.*

John Dalton, *George-street.*
O. Milne, *St. James's-square.*
Joseph Heron, *Hon. Sec.,*
 Essex-street.
G.H. Wood, Somerset Street.

[Handwritten annotation following Weatherby states: left town]

LIST OF MEDICAL PERSONNEL IN MANCHESTER

Agnew, James	85 Piccadilly 1
Alexander, John	4 Princess Street 2
Bancks, John	23 Falkner Street 3
Carbutt, Edward	19 Brazennose Street 4
Fernely, John	11 Peter's Square 5
Freckleton, George	10 Mosley Street 6
~~Henry, William~~	~~East Street Lower Mosley St.~~
Holme, E.	96 King Street 7
Hull, John	37 Mosley Street 8
~~Hulme, James~~	~~Davenport Rd.~~
Hulme, J.D.	44 George Street 9
Jarrold, Thomas	37 Princess Street 10
Kay, James Phillips	35 Mosley Street
Lyon, Edmund	9 Princess Street 11
Mitchell, John	65 Piccadilly 12
Murray, Alexander	94 Oldham Street 13
Pendlebury, John	91 Piccadilly 14
Bardsley, S.A.	Ardwick Green 15
~~Kay, James Phillips~~	~~35 Mosley Street~~
Addison, Robert	7 Crescent, Ancoats 16
Anderson, Richard	121 Gt. Ancoats Street 17
Ashton, Thomas	4 Mosley Street. 18
Bamber, R.P.	95 Oldham Street. 19
~~Barber, Thomas~~	
~~Barker, W.~~	~~12 Paddington? Pendleton~~
Barlow, James	18 Young Street. 20
Barrow, Peter,	4 Dickinson Street 21
Barnett, William	2 Bridge Street 22
~~Billott, Thomas~~	~~4 New Richmond ? Pendleton~~
Blackmore, Edward	57 Piccadilly 23
~~Blease, John~~	~~42 Oxford Place in the Township~~
Blease, John	42 Oxford Place 24
~~Blundstone~~	~~19 Ridgefield~~
Brigham & Jeffs	28 Princess Street 25
Clarke, David	12 Oak Street 26
Cliffe, John Joseph	135 St. George's Road 27
~~Collinson, Joseph~~	~~380 Oldham Road~~
Collinson, Joseph	380 ~~Withington~~ Oldham Road
Crossdale, Edward	59 Portland Street 28
Crowther, Robert	2 Longworth Street 29
Dadley, Henry	6 Falkner Street 30
Fernely, George	St. Peter's Square 31

Fogg, Joseph	53 Oldham Street 32
Gaskell, Peter	33 King Street 33
Greswell, Charles	32 Gt. Ducie Street 34
Harper, William	14 Oxford Road 35
Harrison, J.G.	Manchester Workhouse
Huntley, Henry W.	103 Oldham Street 30
Halliwell, Richard	59 St George's Road
Howard, John	45 Oldham Street 37
Smith, Joshua	100 London Road
Hyde, John	46 Oldham Road 38
Holroyde, E.	20 Long Millgate
~~Ireland, Richard~~	~~6 Paddington~~
~~Johnston, Robert~~	~~228 Oxford Street, Chorlton Place~~
~~Kenworthy, John~~	~~15 Moreton Street ?~~
Lacy, Edward	88 King Street 39
Lamb, W. Hyde	10 Lower Mosley Street 40
Lewis, Francis Rudd	Ardwick & Ancoats Dispensary ~~140 Gt Ancoats Street~~ 41
Lewis, William	35 George Street 42
Lynum, Edward	28 Bridge Street 43
Lowe, James	33 Princess Street 44
Macgowan, Thomas	24 Dale Street 45
Nuttall, John	37 Oldham Street 46
O'Brien, Charles G.	17 London Road 47
~~Partington, James Edge~~	~~62 Oxford Street, Chorlton Row~~
Ransome, Jno. Atkinson	2 St. Peter's Square 48
Roberton, John	72 King Street 49
Robertson, J.J.	1 Falkner St.
Robinson, Thomas	25 Gt. Ancoats Street 50
Schofield, Robert	101 Piccadilly 51
~~Slack, James Hague~~	~~10 Downing Street~~
Stein, J.H.	26 Brazennose Street 52
Stewart, John	22 Oldham Street 53
Thornly, John	8 Green Street Oak Street 54
Walker, George	8 Dale Street 55
Walmsley, Francis	4 Dale Street 56
~~Winn, William~~	~~89 St. George's Place, Oxford Street~~ Chorlton Row
Wright, Thomas	33 Lower Byrom Street 57
Revd. J. Schofield	Every Street
Thompstone, P.	Deansgate
Radford, T.	64 King Street
Spencer, R.F.	103 Mill Street.

DISTRICT	NAME OF MEDICAL ATTENDANTS	RESIDENCE OF MEDICAL ATTENDANTS	NAME AND RESIDENCE OF DRUGGISTS
No.1	Boyer, Robert Catlow, Joseph P. Gordon, John C. Smith, Joseph	Pinmill Brow, Ashton Road 3, Russell-street, Chorlton Row 10, Charlotte-street 100, London Road	James Brereton, Great Ancoats Street, opposite Brown's Fields.
No.2	Bent, James Guest, Robert Phillips, C. M.D. Whitelegg, T.	39, York-street 19, Oldham-street 37, Piccadilly 43, York-street	Joseph McWilliams, 2, Angel-street, St. George's Road.
No.3	Haigh, George Holroyde, E. Joynson, J.N.	7, Hunt's Bank 20, Long Millgate 1, Princess-street	Thomas Pritchard, Old Millgate.
No.4	Braid, James Fawdington, Thomas Heath, A.M. Wood, Thomas	10, Piccadilly 6, Lever-street 101, Piccadilly 6, Downing-street, Ardwick	W. Smith, London Road.
No.5	Roberts, Benjamin Thorpe, Robert	7, Lever-street 21, Oldham-street	Gaulter, Piccadilly.
No.6	J.L. Bardsley, M.D. J. Sproat Windsor, John	2, Chatham-street 5, Portland Buildings 65, Piccadilly	Gaulter, Piccadilly.
No.7	Garside, Joseph Jesse, John Owen, John Whatton, W.R.	16, Piccadilly 7, Downing-street 14, David-street 5, Portland Place	Joseph A. Smith, 100, London Road.
No.8	Barton, Samuel Clough, C. Nathan, L.H. Wilson, W.J.	Mosley-street 32, York-street 36, George-street Mosley-street	R. Woodal, Piccadilly.
No.9	Ainsworth, James Miller - Radford, T. Thorpe, John Worthington, H.T.	King-street Brazennose-street 64, King Street 76, King-street 47, Princess-street	D. Bullock, King-street.

DISTRICT	NAME OF MEDICAL ATTENDANTS	RESIDENCE OF MEDICAL ATTENDANTS	NAME AND RESIDENCE OF DRUGGISTS
No.10	Gaulter, H., M.D. Greaves, George Henry, W.C., M.D. Kay, J.P., M.D. Turner, T.	72, George-street 18, Charlotte-street 9, Mosley-street 35, Mosley-street 33, Mosley-street	L. Simpson, 32, Princess-street.
No.11	Booth, B.W. Shaw, George, M.D. Tuer, T. Walker, John	1, Clarence-street 32, Mosley-street 9, Bond-street 29, Princess-street	J. Howard, 208, Deansgate.
No.12	Ollier, Henry Owen, William	44, Brazennose-street 38, Bridge-street	Robert Barker, Market Place.
No.13	Hunt, R.T. Jordan, Joseph Stephens, Edward Stott, W.B.	50, Gartside-street. 9, Bridge-street 11, Bridge-street 12, Quay-street	S. Thompstone, jun., 194 Deansgate.
No.14	Mann, Robert Sinclair, Martin White, W.	2, Great Bridgewater-street Lloyd-street, Hulme 12, St. John-street	S. Buckley, Deansgate.

NAME INDEX

Woolfenden, James, cholera victim 222
Woolfenden, Richard, cholera victim 222
Woollam, John, merchant 19 29 43 44 60
101 115 120 157 169 185 203 204 225
236 237 239 *17 18 28 28 31 31 32 34 35
35 43 59 84 86 88 91 95 99 130 132 147
158 163 164 164 166 167 170 178 197
201 204 205 206 207 209 212 212 213
217 236 237 238 238 239 241 243 244
245 246*

Worthington, Henry Thomas, surgeon 70
Worthington, John, manufacturer 69
Wray, Cecil Daniel, Fellow of the Collegiate
Church xvii 68 91 96 123 184 240 241 *28
91 95 137 155 225 237*
Wright, Thomas, surgeon 270
Wroe, James, bookseller 240

PLACE AND SUBJECT INDEX